Setting ~~~~

MARINA DE NADOUS

Matador
9 Priory Business Park
Kibworth Beauchamp
Leicester LE8 0RX, UK
Tel: (+44) 116 279 2299
Fax: (+44) 116 279 2277
Email: books@troubador.co.uk
Web: www.troubador.co.uk/matador

ISBN 978 1783064 922

British Library Cataloguing in Publication Data.
A catalogue record for this book is available from the British Library.

Typeset by Troubador Publishing Ltd, Leicester, UK

Matador is an imprint of Troubador Publishing Ltd

Dedicated to Little Arthur

The Celestial Sea Voyages

BUCKLES AND VELVET

The Leafy Glade beckons the Prince and his Lady,
As they play and they chase through the last dappled light,
Enticing with lips and hands they take flight,
Away from all eyes, save those of Angels and birds.
The Glade is a soft, quiet place,
Where small birds linger and drink in the light.
If you wait a while, you will find,
Buckles and velvet, breeches and lace,
Scattered about, discarded in haste,
For these Lovers' desire to entwine and unite,
Under moving green leaves, long into the night.

"Pray Sir, won't you follow?" She asks with a smile,
Adding shyly, "we may well be gone for some while,
I have secrets to tell you and truths that can't wait,
If you'll just step this way through The Green Garden Gate."
So, linking their hands they step into the light,
He's been holding The Key to The Gate all his life.
Buckles and velvet, breeches and lace,
Scattered about, discarded in haste,
For these Lovers' desire to entwine and unite,
Under moving green leaves, long into the night.

Now, many a month has gone by since that time,
And of the Prince and his Lady, there isn't a sign,
I think we all know where they are in their bliss,
Still behind The Green Gate, it's been sealed by a kiss.
But on warm summer nights carried in on the breeze,
You'll hear whispers and laughter and songs in the trees,
Buckles and velvet, breeches and lace,
Scattered about, discarded in haste,
For these Lovers' desire to entwine and unite,
Under moving green leaves, long into the night.

Prologue

Oh, for the interminable unknown to reach conclusion. The ambiguity is a place of stolen succour for The Celestial Sea, yet uncomfortable under its blanket of dull acceptance. She has her private world that exists in all reality, albeit denied in the physical, but it is a heavy load as well as a joy. A happy outcome is unlikely, whichever way the die is cast. She has risked everything for the chance to sail again. Her faith has never once deserted her. The golden light around her intention does not fade.

Sweet memory and hours of word-play keep her occupied. The storyline weaves naturally as if another guides her hand. The waiting game is perfect for reverie and fairy tale creation as she revisits the travel log entries. She is surprised by the quantity of script—an entire bookshelf in the galley is stacked with notebooks of every size and colour. She picks one with a floral pink cover and glances through the pages—why, even alighting upon the notes takes her sailing for a spell. The atmospheric detail is captured intact. She spends every available minute reliving the adventures of last year. She hopes nobody notices her constant absorption. She concentrates when few are about, although she suspects her friend in the orange worker's bib has spotted her distraction. She can't risk losing her creativity to The Marine Officials; that would be her undoing.

"Hey, Hon—something on your mind? You seem far away. Where do you go?" Her friend whispers as he passes; "do you sail again in your dreams?"

The friendly dockworker is increasingly drawn to the abandoned vessel. Last week he stayed late to scrape down the peeling paint on his charge's hull. Areas of the claret paintwork are flaky and weather-bleached. He likes to spend time caring for her. He needs to re-stow her sails too; has someone been on board? After half an hour he turns back towards the office, deciding to 'borrow' some of the flowers from the vase in the Boss' room. He will place them on her deck in the last of the evening light.

As he leaves the office a woman walking up and down outside The Marina's locked gates takes his attention. Does he recognize her? He hides in the office doorway with the flowers, watching. What is she doing? Maybe he should ask. Just as he decides to make a move she slides her slim frame between the gate and the Marina wall, running quickly to The Celestial Sea and ducking down behind her stern. A pile of metal sheets shields her easily. The dockworker is surprised; unsure what to do. The woman is trespassing;

he should haul her out and ask what she thinks she is up to. As he steps towards The Boat he notices someone else—a man—also approaching the Marina gates. He too is looking to gain entry. He tries the narrow opening beside the wall but can't fit through the gap.

The woman doesn't show herself. For many minutes the man gazes at The Boat with a softened eye. The dockworker knows he scans the vessel for any damage. Does The Boat belong to him? To her? Are they the distressed couple who crewed The Celestial Sea when she was first brought into dry-dock; the couple that was ordered to keep away?

The office doorway keeps the dockworker hidden. He intuitively knows not to interfere. Whoever the couple, they are integral to the mystery that surrounds The Boat; of that he is quite certain. Once they have left The Marina he places the flowers on The Celestial Sea's deck, as he had planned. Somehow, his gesture seems important.

Part One Echo Sounder

The padlock is rusty. A can of oil eases the unyielding lock; why such an old fashioned contraption? The metal bolts graze the dockworker's knuckles as he wrestles open the cumbersome barricade. Surely something more efficient could have been fitted when the heavy gates were installed. The man swears under his breath as his thumb gets pinched for a second time by the sliding metal.

"Leave the gates open from now on," The Harbour Master barks his order before leaving the office for the weekend. He is curt, declining any explanation as to why Marina security is suddenly dropped after four months strict surveillance. "A couple of heavy blocks should keep the gates in place once you have freed up the locks," he advises, walking away from The Marina for a pre-planned fishing trip. His step is noticeably lighter as he welcomes the long weekend. The dockworker finds two discarded blocks in a scrap heap alongside a mound of rope; they are heavy and he stumbles, ripping a hole in his grey combat trousers. A workmate hears the commotion—and the oaths. He volunteers his help but the fellow refuses. This is his remit. Anything linked with The Boat is his domain and he knows without having to ask that this latest development is indeed linked with The Celestial Sea and her future. He no longer hides his intrigue. Colleagues respect his inclination and leave him to the care of the stricken vessel.

"Well Hon; something's in the air, that's for sure," he says. "You seem brighter today. You're fizzing, I can tell. We'll call this your effervescent weekend, eh? I like that word; I heard it on the radio. I'll come back on Sunday afternoon and finish painting your hull. Best get you ready in case something happens. Funny time of year to be looking out through the gates, but heck, you go about things in a back-to-front way. We've several boats booked in to dry-dock next week. Winter's around the corner."

Removing the tattered plastic sheet he searches out damaged areas needing repair. Several mast rings need attention and a new coat of varnish wouldn't go amiss, but otherwise there is surprisingly little to do. For a moment he stands stock-still. Why, she really is beautiful; he hadn't realized until this moment. The plastic cover has been hiding her fine lines. A shaft of evening sun catches her central mast. The autumn glow brushes the polished wood. He watches the pretty fairy light for a while, mesmerized by the tangible magic that surrounds the vessel.

Six o'clock—he should be heading home to tea but can't tear himself away. Will the open gates bring the thwarted couple back to The Marina? He wonders if they know the barricade has been removed. He sends his family a text message on his new Vodafone mobile; explaining he will be late. What an ingenious piece of technology. He hasn't used it before. He wants to watch the open gates this evening. He needs to get to the bottom of the mystery that holds The Boat, The Man and The Woman in such profound and on-going quandary. He will replace the plastic sheet next week, but he won't secure it down. He hides in the office doorway again, enjoying the last of the evening sun. He is smiling. Meanwhile, The Craftsman nods with approval and re-lights his pipe.

Chapter 1 Effervescent

Sunday 8ᵗʰ April 2007 Easter Day
The pig has become a chicken slayer; eleven chicks down so far. "Oh no, Ma!" Rinky the Minx is beside herself; "Molly is murdering the babies! I can see their feet sticking out of her mouth!" The shout brings the outraged family running, including the Bog-Brush who charges the pig, barking madly while trying to bite the culprit's ears. The domestic chaos increases while The Laird brandishes a broom at the contented guzzler. Apparently it's quite normal for pigs to eat baby birds. Well, this is a new one on us, novice pioneers that we are. What an Easter afternoon awakening; a reality check on the fluffy chick and chocolate idyll.

P.m. Mouse: I sit in glorious sunshine in our Twealm Realm—The Castle Hound points and explores around the pond. A moment to relax after the fracas of discovering Molly eating the baby chicks! Did you know pigs had such unpleasant habits?

I wonder, did I understand your message correctly? The work we need to do—yes—and the writing. This is the beginning of the third Book. Over 200 pages of the first already completed and all the material collected and stored for the second. I want to work on it with you; it is our alchemy. Could you? Now that our acknowledgement is open, could we hold and complete this tale?

I will ask for three days away this week—to continue writing and to make decisions. Somewhere by the sea. Might you visit me while I work? We have been granted a meeting. I want you to know that although I am through The Castle Gates I would, at the point of crashing spume, have been unable to leave my responsibilities completely in the face of a choice over personal joy. I do possess some integrity. As an extra, our Go-Getter wondered if he could be part of the trolley-racing workshop. M—X

Re-running the Grand Finale of the Second Book, 'Dry Dock', I linger over Adrian's words. Is my intuition correct? Do I sense an opening or does my imagination continue to weave the storyline? What was it he said?

"As I write, a new idea comes to me. I cannot deny the pleasure and ease you bring into my life—to have a companion who understands my thoughts and ways is rare, and you do. I know I can

search my heart and write it and you will understand—a Companion of the Soul. So, my intention changes—softens—an idea springs. But first, the background. This was a message to invite you to a meeting; a meeting where I would tell you clearly that the maelstrom I would not meet. The calm contentment of my cud-chewing cows gives me a new steadiness and foundation for clarity—a measuring stick. I will protect their harmony for it is graced. So, no Tidal Wave will I call into the fields and folds of their farm. You must make your choice without me in the picture; your decision must be for you. I will not be a partner/husband to you. These were my thoughts and the ones I voiced to Simon who had suggested a facilitated meeting. But now— a new thought.

Clear, I stand by these words. "My cows are a symbol of God's grace; the hand of destiny and I trust them. Harsh this sounds. Hmm- you have your children and family to consider. I have my cows and community. They temper my desires and longings—elevating them to more refined forms; to service and to work; touchstones for steadiness. Pressing my head into a warm flank—breathing their warm goodness—herding them back to their field. Strong and steady I must be. And from here I say, "Dear Heart—my Soul's Companion— work we have to do together but run to me you may not—it will startle the cows."

What else is Adrian saying? He hints at a change of direction. Why did he use the present tense; 'it **will** startle the cows,' instead of saying; 'it **would** startle the cows'?

P.m. Mouse: *Dear Friend—I am heading for Tui Park alone, to walk the Bog-Brush. Come join me if you are able and willing. But perhaps you are away with family this fine Easter Day. Your Lady needs you to know she would never come 'running' to you; t'would be beneath her dignity and not what our bond is about. But, she would stroll with you hand-in-hand along the sands and even lay her head upon your chest if you felt clear in our intention—*

We are slow to activate ourselves today. The endless waiting is telling on my long-suffering Laird. He needs a firm decision and needs it soon. I take the day to think. Our 'bovine' message brings ambiguous indication; the way *we* prefer to leave things but impossible for everyone else in their need for clarity.

We join Andrew and Louise, this afternoon for an Easter 'tramp' through The Forest above The Mountain. The big children set out an Easter-egg hunt and we feast greedily under the towering Kiakatea trees. Silver paper-wrapped-goodies wink at us from fern nests while eager fingers steal into nooks and crannies before the spiders and bugs can reach the chocolate treasure. I am glad to see the teenage boys chatting comfortably; they haven't met before. I enjoy their company. We talk as we amble, trying not to stub our toes on the many raised and tangled roots. A basic picnic at the end of the trail sees us chatting to a friendly, older man—a local woodsman who guards the parking at weekends. A classic Kiwi, he tips his battered felt hat in greeting. His cotton plaid shirt has seen better days and I daresay his worn-in tramping boots have trekked many miles through the Native Bush. The commonly-worn shorts and leg protectors tell of hard labour and a pioneering lifestyle. He asks us to sign his visitor's book. "Yes, he knows our school; why, he had the pupils over to his place last year to learn about woodcraft. They explored his collection of antique saws and tools." The Go-Getter announces he had been part of the group outing. I remember them going. "That enthusiastic, male teacher had them all fired up. Do you know him?"

We had to leave the Bog-Brush in the car while we walked, another 'dogs prohibited' sign greeting us at The Forest entrance. "Sorry love," the fellow said; "can't have dogs with the protected, native species in The Bush. We have Kiwi Bird breeding programmes in place. There are possum traps throughout the Forest, as well as poisons that would harm a dog. Better shut her in the boot."

Our fellow trampers give us tea after our walk. We always enjoy visiting their luxury home. Andrew and Louise are the successful kiwi fruit growers I have mentioned before. They own a fine home with all the boy's toys; motorbikes, go-carts and a huge games room with a giant wide screen. Andrew's jovial, ruddy face glows with pride as he slides open a garage to reveal a powerful sports car. The male members of our party duly admire his pride and joy. I'm not sure what type of car it is, but I am informed it is 'rather special'. After our basic mountain cabins this is fun for my gang, along with all the girlie toys you could possibly dream of for Rinky the Minx.

In order to broaden their life and divert her husband from endless racing-car interests, Louise is planning an eight-week, European adventure this September. I sit on the spacious deck with her, drinking tea and drooling over brochures and guidebooks showing Tuscan farmhouses and fields of Provencal lavender. Louise's hands turn the pages eagerly; she wears several rings that sparkle in anticipation. The family is so excited about the trip and always open-mouthed at our numerous travel adventures and knowledge of life on the other side of the world.

Monday 9th April 2007 Rinky's Birthday
A.m. Mouse {Unsent}: Are we still silent, My Friend? Your continuing reluctance to enter into conversation with me is telling. Perhaps you can't let yourself go there? Even though you would like to? Tell me, what are your thoughts this morning? What do you think of my invitation of yesterday? Too much? Too close? You could not re-open our communication without being tempted? Or are you willing me to separate from The Laird and live alone, thus giving us the chance of a possible life together? I really don't know. I think you have probably moved on and I am not on your mind any more. That

is more likely. Other interests, other people now occupy you. I am not part of the equation. In true male focus you are filled by the tasks in hand and not by past or possible futures. Are you with your family in Auckland this weekend? If you are, who looks after the cows? I hear from Louise that you'll be un-chaperoned at the beginning of next term while Vonny is away in The U.K. Is that correct? Should we use that time to concentrate on The Book? Is our writing the work we have to do together? I think you told Simon you were definitely not harbouring any feelings for me—for us. From where I stand that makes me look rather foolish. I intimated to him that my gut sense told me things were not over; not really. I would like to send him the final chapter of 'Dry Dock', with your permission of course. I shall send it to you via The Internet. The Books intrigued him. Would you mind?

Today is Rinky's birthday. She was eight years old at 9.3**7** a.m. We stayed late in bed after yesterday's busy afternoon and evening. The Laird turned to me for some comfort before the children awoke. He lay still, making little effort, his hazel eyes blank and lost. He didn't even look at me, let alone say anything. I know he is feeling bad but honestly, his disinterest in me personally leaves me empty. I cannot conceive of this lack of connection for the rest of my life, knowing how it could be, how it is in the arms of my Lord Swallow; I really cannot. Yes, I know we can learn to love again but not without the vital ingredient, which I now know we don't possess. Perhaps I have knocked his hidden emotion into further hiding. I suppose I have damaged his masculine confidence. "I'm sorry; I never meant to hurt you," I whisper into the morning.

Today I need to move things on. No light shines from my phone screen; we are back to silence and minimal communication. Does Adrian want to hear from me? We *have* been granted a meeting. Until we can be close these questions remain unanswered. The Laird's mood is heavy with depressing, slob-out sport viewing. His heavy nature is weighing us all down. Even his footsteps are heavy as he thumps about the cabins cloaked in metaphorical chainmail. Yes, I shall write up all the past text messages that have led to the completion of 'Dry Dock' and present him with the final chapter. That way, nothing will be left out and hopefully he may glean the profundity and intrigue of our quandary. Uncertain myself, I also need to try and understand further.

Amidst birthday cake icing and present unwrapping I manage to tackle the enormous job of creating a twenty-three-page finish to this epic, four-month tale. I work late into the evening, {somehow managing a birthday hot-pool outing for The Minx while the boys play golf}. Eventually I hand the completed document to The Laird. A large part contains my talk with Simon, our Senior Marine Official, which he has been asking about. With cups of tea and ashen face my husband reads of my continuing love for another man and endeavours to get his logical head around the ambiguity. Paragraph after paragraph; I know he seeks the words of completion he so desperately needs to hear. The ending is a semi-ending, if that is possible. "Let's not speak about it now," I suggest. "Let's go up to bed and dream on the unknown outcome."

Tuesday 10ᵗʰ April 2007
 Early P.m. Adrian: Hi, My Friend. I'm rushing around getting ready for the trolley workshop. I have booked The Go-Getter in—is that right? Thursday, not Wednesday. I would like to meet with you—officially—with The Laird's agreement—to get clear on how we both stand in a way that those waiting can understand. What say you?

 Mouse: She decided to put The Laird out of his endless, waiting misery. She had to show him all the writing from the last couple of weeks—but not coldly—in story-format, as she is perfecting. It was Easter Monday yesterday and Rinky's birthday. For hour upon hour she worked; the family wondered if she was losing her head! At long last—late into the night—it was complete. She handed it over quietly. He was anxious and scoured the endless document for the definite ending he so needs; the ambiguity still there to soothe Lord Swallow and his Lady—but not what frightened Lairds are seeking. She continues to pray for his peaceful understanding and letting go of fear.
 This morning they were close and happy—a caring friendship—established and familiar. She sat on the bed—he stood beside it. She spoke of the bond she knows is true and rare between herself and Lord Swallow. She spoke clearly from her heart. She explained the essence of this new, yet old connection; the mutual nurture of a Lover's soul in longed for caress and challenge, working in perfect harmony and balance. And yes—she mentioned the presence of The Small One, at last. He raised his eyebrows at that but was accepting of her mysterious, extraordinary ways—understood by only one man, it seems. Hmm. Their Lady can feel a shift; The Laird is beginning to move the cumbersome rock. "I know this is of great importance and reality for you," he stated; "otherwise it couldn't have lasted so long and you would certainly not be considering breaking up the family unless it was true. But you are still in denial, even though Adrian says you may not go to him. You think he might come to you if you moved out?" I listened—not knowing—yet knowing—as I have always known. We calmly talk through the practicalities of a parting; he and the boys would probably return to The U.K while Rinky and I would remain here. Finance was discussed—all very practical. "And I would need to go home before making a final decision anyway," I said. "I would like to take 3 days away; beginning on the evening of the 12ᵗʰ April until the 15ᵗʰ. That way, I can make proper decisions—and write, of course. Our Editor has free time at the moment but may not have later in the year. I need to put The Books as top priority. They would pave many paths if successful."
 And what of him in all this? Lord Swallow—now a Gentleman Farmer on the edge of the Forest. Well, she does not know if he will really want to see her, but perhaps he may stroll along the beach with her one evening, to delight in the sea-birds and draw pictures in the sand with their toes. Maybe

they might be daring and dive into the crashing spume together—just for business, of course. What other reason could there possibly be?

The Laird and his Lady are close and cuddly today. There is comfort in having been through a big ordeal and come out alive; rattled, yes, but alive nonetheless. He is sad, almost accepting. She is excited, expectant and alert. They have talked through the possible outcomes with calm honesty. "I don't think things can move forward until you speak with Adrian and shake his hand to bury the negativity of your January outburst", I state. "How can you possibly ask me to shake his hand as he takes my wife from me?" He asks with unsure, raised shoulders. "I know it appears inconceivable but that is what needs to happen," I reply. I ask him, in all seriousness, if he really wants to spend the rest of his life with someone he is not deeply in tune with. I also tell him that every little remark of annoyance directed at me means I take longer and longer to climb back up to a position of total unity with him. I have found my reserves depleted in recent months; how else does he think I could have entered into such an intimate relationship with another man. "You know, Rinky is the person to ask about all this—she appears to have known all along. She seems to be in cahoots with The Angels. Why don't you ask her now?" I suggest.

"Rinky—can you come here please?" He calls with relief. His daughter is bound to prove his point. "If we could live anywhere, with other people, who would live with us?" Our youngest thinks for a short while before replying: "On a farm with some horses and all our family from England. I would like my best friend from school to live nearby—oh, yes, and Adrian of course"—

The Laird departs for a fishing trip, our final conversation ringing in his ears. "I think you need to go back home to live and work," I voiced. "Through my relationship with Adrian I am feeling very comfortable here. I have been given the chance to discover a new land through the eyes, the heart and the soul of the most beautiful man. From his school class to his family in Auckland, from his woodland knowledge to our epic creativity I am embracing New Zealand in deep contentment. But I think you need to be home; home with the familiarity of friends and family, seasons and held rhythm." "Yes, I think you are probably right," he replied. "Isn't that strange? We always thought it would be you who would miss home and need to return, not me."

Wednesday 11th April 2007
I am accompanied by a smoky, rainbow-halo around the moon as I stroll down the drive this morning. It is very early. I watch its momentary spotlight and wonder if the attention is welcome. I sense that it is. To be highlighted, even for a moment, is glorious. The ink-weed growing in profusion along our drive is producing its succulent, deep purple berries. I have been told they are poisonous; a tempting treat for small fingers. I must remember to warn

The Small One. How lovely to see their return this year. They protrude, phallic-like between the pretty leaves. I must be feeling at home; this seasonal return, so strong and definite in England, is less obvious in New Zealand's North Island. The heavy spider sacks are joined today by spider webs. As diamond covered trapeze baskets they quiver in the dew amongst the harsh pieces of cut gorse. Perhaps they wait for Bush Fairies and Cavern Gnomes to play amongst their intrigue.

A.m. Mouse: *My Love—can The Small One stay with me a while? I am missing his little hand in mine—his quiet, watching eyes and busy, bouncy legs in their leather boots jumping beside me as I take the Hound on her 6a.m stroll. We like to watch the moon in its final dawn glory and inspect the laden spider sacks that cling to the gorse bushes in ghostly pockets. The morning salute from the ducks and geese makes him laugh. I love to hear him laugh—*

I have time for some writing before the family and menagerie shout for fodder; again. My beautiful pig is defeating us. She continues to chase the poor little chicks, gobbling them down in a murderous frenzy. *"Murder on the Mountain, Murder on the Mountain!"* The cries go up from the distressed mothers, bringing The Laird running from the television with cries of disgust and a heavy boot at my porcine charge. We are all on the alert now, especially the Bog-Brush who darts out of the kitchen door to bite the pig at any opportunity. We can tolerate most chaos but murder is strictly prohibited. We have moved one vulnerable family to an enclosed pen but the others remain free-range. One first-time mother hen has lost ten chicks. The babes lining the Pig's rotund stomach now number fifteen. But, I *do* like to have them all around The Castle. It is a pleasure to watch their antics and funny behaviour; the children enjoy it especially. I am pleased to say that it is my big boy, he of the superior fashion sense and permanent grump, who is most involved in their welfare. We joke afterwards; "this Kiwi life is defeating us! Time to return home, most definitely, leaving mad dogs, murdering pigs and doolally wives behind in the gorse!"

I ponder on our strangely surreal situation as I write, The Laird's three a.m. chat still in my mind. "You know, Adrian told Simon that he won't take on your children. You have never had to live a normal life through your relationship. Whenever you are together you enjoy quality time, just for the two of you. How do you think he would cope with an everyday reality; the strains of family life? I have had years of coming second; second to the children, second to the many businesses you have run from home and second even to the animals. You have never been able to put time into 'us'; something has always prevented it." To prove a point our young cat climbed onto the bed with loud purrs and settled right in between our duvet-wrapped forms. "There, you see!" He exclaimed. "Things just don't change!" I heard his reasonable words; he is right, and I know why he is right. Because of our lack of deep connection and chemistry, our different rhythm, I do not enjoy his private company *enough* to put aside special time. He does not stimulate me. He never instigates a deep connection. Yes, he is steadfast and caring, a loyal husband and diligent provider. But he is not interested in finding the true depth of me. Twice now, I have asked him; "but do you *enjoy* my company?" He always answers; "oh yes, of course; so much." But he has not asked me, in return, if *I* enjoy *his* company. Thinking about it, we never really ask each other how we are *truly* feeling—not as Lord Swallow and I do.

"Things must be rough, to be awake at three in the morning," my perplexed Husband announced. "Hmm," I replied; "I am often awake at this hour; it's the best thinking time." "Don't I know it," I was told. "You are always asleep when I want you to be with me in the evening and awake when I don't want you to be!" "There you are, another instance of us not being in tune," I answered, my mind turning to Adrian and his instant recognition of my sleeping and waking movements. I have been honestly entranced by our perfect timing and shared response during the few nights we have spent together.

The Laird and I continued chatting. We talked about our working life and how we enjoy going out to others, providing an inspiring environment for family and friends. Oh yes, I could go there again, I suppose. But I think I have been there, done that. I need to go deeply into my private world now instead, tempered of course with going out to others, as at school. I know that our danger, Adrian and I, would be a sliding towards introspection and a narrow way of life. I would challenge Adrian on this and I think he would be open; reluctant at times, but open nonetheless. "You would miss the breadth of connection and opportunity you have always had at your fingertips. Your horizons would suddenly be very limited," The Laird remarked. I didn't say that I intended to swell our bank balance enough to allow regular trips across hemispheres with travel and adventure for us all. That would be classed as serious 'Pipe Dreaming.'

It was a good talk. We spoke honestly about our need to spend more quality time together if we were to stay married. "You have to dig the depth out of me," The Laird admitted. "It takes me quite a time to go there and you always interrupt and dash off to either a squawking child or animal. And I need you to dress up; make an effort to give me the right signals." Yes, I know, but at the end of the day our chemistry is not what it should be. I know that now because I have tasted the finest chemistry possible between a man and a woman. Can I let that go? Am I being asked to let it go?

A.m. Adrian: *He has read the story—applauds her skill—and courage—feels remorse over her heartache—worries over her stress—finds his own story in it. There is much to be said. A meeting, yes. Now, the Go-Getter—do I book him into The Workshop? And trolley modifications? Perhaps he needs to call me today. I'm at the farm until 10ish, then home woodworking. Text me first in case I'm out and about. X*

Mouse: *Hi Friend—yes, book him in. He keeps changing his mind. Should he just race? Should he modify his old trolley? Build a new one? I say—go for* *the day and do it all. Let's go with that unless I get him to phone you by 12 noon. Is that ok? Glad you liked the story, oh Gallant Hero—X*

Adrian: *Great. He needs a new trolley because his old one no longer exists. Her Majesty's Service' was executed and transformed into Racer no. 2. Want to do soup on the day?*

Mouse: *Yes, My Friend; can do soup; how many children? Can I use a cooker at school?*

Mouse: *Lady of the Castle calling Lord Swallow. The 'Go-Getter' inmate would like to make a new Forest Racer—might bring his old one too. Do you have enough materials? Let us know if you need anything brought from The Mountain—X*

The Laird stomps downstairs sporting fancy red boxer shorts and nothing else. He seats his heavy frame into the chair by the telephone and I kiss his neck in a friendly hello. "How can you kiss me while writing love passages about another? I really don't know how you can do that!" He is perplexed. "Well, I can and I will. There is plenty of me to go around. It is just your mind-set that says disaster is looming on the horizon. If you let me have my head you would be staggered at what I could achieve." "Hmm," the red underpants gentleman mumbles; "you know, Simon said after your meeting the other day that he hadn't realized how *infectious* you are. You have always been able to inspire people. I love hearing you talk; getting fired up. That is one of the main reasons I want you by my side." "*Infectious*?" I ask. "Well, I don't think I have ever been called that before." Reaching for the telephone The Laird suggests I leave the house for a while, as he needs to contact a close friend in The U.K about our predicament. I saunter outside, hoping to glean some of the content of his conversation. This is going to be hard for him, I fear.

There is a crop sprayer flying in constant zoom over our house this morning. I think it is dropping lime or fertilizer over the adjacent fields. It can't be too potent this time as the sheep are directly under the drop line. The noise blots out the conversation—obviously one The Angels don't wish me to hear. The only words I catch are: "very attractive fellow; pushes all her buttons." I sense it is a difficult conversation. Apparently The Laird was put on the line by his good friend Barnie. He had to answer questions about the actual state of *our* relationship—our heart and soul connection. I think it highlights how he really isn't as deeply in love with me as befits a husband. I see his watery eyes; he is hurting but coping; a much needed journey. Simon has told him that the prospects are not looking good for a happy outcome. The Laird suggests I shouldn't undertake the lunches for Adrian if I am trying to make unbiased choices. He is probably right.

Adrian: *Are you sure you want to do lunch? I have asked the children to bring their own—no pressure at all on you. Aren't you going away? If you do* *decide to cook there will only be 6 children and 2/3 adults. I have pumpkins here if you want.*

How does Adrian know The Laird questions the lunch thing? Uncanny. I reckon they are definitely tuned in.

Mouse: *Perhaps I won't then—yes, I am going away, but not until the Trolley-Making is over. Thanks—I'll busy elsewhere instead.*

Rinky is staying overnight with her best friend, Lucia, and the Go-Getter is restless. I walk the Bog-Brush to the top of the Pa site, to have a quiet word with The Angels and Ancestors. A vague circle of ridges with commanding views all around, The Pa Site is marked in the district maps as a Heritage Site. I send a golden ring of love around my dear Laird. I know he resides in bed with a distracting thriller and a puzzled frown. "Surely his wife isn't putting him through all this? He thought he knew her through and through; well, well." As I draw the circle of protection around him I remember the haloed moon this morning; a special image.

Meanwhile, my adorable young fellow is getting bored; nothing much to do today. His parents seem oddly engrossed with each other. He jumps in the car to accompany me to town, flicking his floppy fringe out of his eyes. We shop, we visit the library, we empty the recycling baskets and we stop in at a local holiday resort on the beach to book a space for my three nights away. There are some tempting villas right on the sea front but they are expensive. It is still 'high season'. I opt for using the car as a camper van so I can hook up to the electricity for my writing. I discuss the possibility of using our caravan lead to power the laptop I shall bring with me. Yes, this is the best spot I decide, strolling around the remaining sites. A quiet corner overlooking the sea and fairly near the amenities speaks loudest. I wander back to the desk, collecting the Go-Getter from a rather unusual, ground-level trampoline arrangement at the site's playground. He is enjoying the billowing, multi-coloured stripes; it reminds me of a large circus tent. I pay a deposit for the first night. Glancing at the map I ask the receptionist for the site number. She tells me it is number **7**—"Number **7**? Are you sure"? I ask. I suppose I should be getting used to these coincidences. I sense number **7** is linked with The Celestial Sea and her voyaging.

The Laird is unhappy about me staying in such basic accommodation. "Do you think you can decide about the course of our lives while sleeping in the back of a van?" I don't tell him that I have experienced a couple of nights sleeping in the van, with Adrian, and that it is very roomy and comfortable. "I dived in to see Justin and Freya on my way home from hockey," he continues. "They know about the situation. As Chairman of the second School Board, Simon needed to inform Justin." "Oh", I say. I have been worried about their reaction. "What do they think? Are they still speaking to me?" "Their comment was; "so, none of us old married couples are still in love, are we? That is only a temporary thing; something that brings us together in the first place. It tends not to last." The Laird looks at me in all seriousness. "Yes, I know," I reply. "But there is another ingredient behind it all for Adrian and me; something indescribably profound." "And we haven't really talked through the outcome for the children either; how they would be affected, have we?" "No," I respond. "We are not quite at that stage".

Chapter 2 Electricity

Thursday 12th April 2007

I am up later this morning. The dog has already taken herself for a mammoth, illegal walk; another lifeless Pukeko lies in a mangled heap on the floor. A real Kiwi symbol, the striking bird has long red legs, dark blue feathers and a white bob of a tail. A red beak makes it instantly paintable. We often see the birds depicted as a classic, Kiwi icon. Unfortunately they are easy prey. I glare at my wilful hound sitting in soggy splendour on the sofa. She eyes me with happy independence. I hope she hasn't been chasing sheep on the neighbour's land. She starts bouncing all over me; a game in which I sometimes participate. "That's enough—time to go out on the deck," I scold, grabbing her collar and dragging her outside. I stop dead in my tracks. In front of me, in a perfect, celestial arc, stands *the* most incredible, complete, double rainbow. "Oh my—oh my!" I gasp in total awe-struck wonder. The colours are intense. Our Mountain eyrie sits directly beneath the Heavenly brush strokes. I have never been so close to a rainbow. I dash inside to find a camera and grab the only child awake in the house to witness Mother Earth's Crown Jewels. The vibrant shades are clearly visible. Lucia and I name them in order with due reverence. This truly is the best rainbow display I have ever, ever seen, and today of all days. I wonder what it heralds.

Rinky is very excited when she wakes. Sitting on the floor beside her bed, reading a comic, is her best friend from school; Lucia. What a massive surprise! Freya and Justin asked The Laird to bring her home after The School Board Meeting last night. They have unexpected work commitments today. We make pancakes and I organize The Go-Getter for his day with Adrian. 'Sherwood Forest Workshops' beckon and we race down the hill to be on time. Unfortunately it starts to rain but that doesn't appear to dampen the happy faces gathered in the school's woodwork shed. I am so pleased for Adrian that his exciting plans are coming to fruition at last, and right here at school where he can share his gifts and creativity with all. I am proud to call him Friend.

Lord Swallow is calm and friendly this morning. He enfolds me in a glorious hug of easy greeting; at long last. We smile at each other. This is the start of our new story and we both know it. "I see you have brought our Go-Getter then," he states, grinning broadly. "And what are *you* up to today?" I tell him where I am heading, wondering if he will join me later. A new English parent arrives with a child for The Workshop session. Adrian extends a hand, welcoming Miles and his son Orlando and we introduce ourselves, discovering we both hail from the South West of England. I wonder if Miles thinks we are a couple. It feels good to stand beside my Man. I lend a hand with the preparations, working contentedly alongside Adrian. I have some black tape with me, which I bind around the rope ends; a length for each trolley. "Have you a can of oil in the van?" Adrian asks. "These wheels are stiff; they've been in my workshop too long. I don't suppose we'll have time to race the trolleys today. Perhaps we need another day to compete." "Last year it took us two whole days to make and race the trolleys," I remind him. "Did it really?" Adrian replies. "I don't remember."

The Go-Getter is especially chuffed—he has plans to design and make his own fiery seat along with a clever braking system. I thought there might be some strain, working alongside Adrian, but our usual harmony returns as naturally as the ocean greeting the shore.

Walking The Bog-Brush across the sands at Tui Park I find myself wondering about Adrian's lack of memory; had he really forgotten our Trolley Making Workshop last year? His total absorption in the present means he can walk away from the past without a backward glance. If he were to move away I suppose he might disengage entirely from our connection. I don't think I could trust him to stay true to 'us' if he were involved elsewhere. This 'Peter Pan' side to his character gets him into trouble time and again. He can be fickle. He can also gloss over important things; like the time we had a brief conversation in the staff room about our age difference; I had been surprised some months later that he hadn't remembered the details. Having said that, The King in the man usually wakes up, often after the event, but alert nonetheless. On the deepest level I know The King would not forget a bond as strong as ours. He is super-sensitive to the emotional undercurrents that wash his way, especially if they involve his good self.

It is colder today but the sun comes out eventually and the dog and I enjoy our playtime frolic. I stop at the chemist to buy The Laird a new gum-shield before driving home. He is playing hockey this evening in a staff/parent match. Adrian was meant to be playing but the organizers have been tactful with their choice of players. "Just as well," muttered my husband. "I don't know how safe I'd be on the pitch with a stick, a hard ball and 'your friend' on the opposite team."

I drive home to prepare for my evening trip. I make a large shepherd's pie to keep the family going while I am away. Then I pack my bags. I treated myself to some new toenail polish at the chemist earlier; a rich claret sheen—definitely suitable. I apply it with independent flourish and kitchen-sink liberation. "Do you know, I haven't bought nail varnish for about fifteen years! I was getting rather bored with the old one," I announce triumphantly. "Yes, and rather bored with your husband too," replies The Laird. He will be away at his hockey game when I return with my Trolley Racer. It is a poignant moment, more so for him than for me. I hand him a sandwich; "Last meal for a condemned man," he sighs. "Will I still have a wife when she returns home?" "My Love, it is going to be alright; we are being held. I am not going to disappear," I reply, knowing that until he views the new horizons with trust his fear will not abate. I have ever taken the lead and this is no exception.

I think back to our conversation of yesterday; "you never take the initiative on any outside projects," my husband accused me. "Look—no herb garden, no planting, no animal enclosures." "But hang on," I retaliated; "why does it always have to be *me* carrying the outside workload as well as everything else? Why can't it be *your* project with the rest of us helping when there is time?" I didn't add—"like Adrian"—but I certainly thought it. I don't have the knowledge or the time, and we certainly don't have the money, to really make a difference on the land. I think we need to realize that neither of us has the necessary impetus to be involved heavily in this way; in community, certainly, but not on our own. My dear Hubby cannot work happily alone; cannot do *anything* happily on his own, I realize. He looks to me for constant companionship and inspiration. I am so busy with everything else; children, guests, paperwork, house, shopping, cooking, washing, animals; the list is endless. Because he gives me so little, personally, I have run out of fuel. Something needs to change and I will have to make it happen.

With surprised expressions from the children I head out into the wet, black night of my rebellious adventure. I am leaving home—running away with my Lover, {in literary form}, and it feels marvellous! "We can come and visit you if we need to, can't we, Mummy?" I kiss my little Lady tenderly. She clings to me for a while. "Of course, Sweetie," I reply. "I just need time away to write my Book, that's all."

I think of the many times I have been left by The Laird for his increasing adventures away. This will be a good test. "You may prefer it without me," I suggested to him. I wonder how the family dynamic will work. The atmosphere might be freed up without our married frustration. We shall see. I clock in at the camp-ground reception. This is a well-run resort. My parking slot organized, I try in vain to hook up the electric caravan cable I have brought from home. Unfortunately it won't connect. I make up the undulating van bed, enjoy a light snack and decide I am too tired for much else. It is cold tonight. Wind and rain lash the vehicle and I pull the duvet up around my ears. My jumper remains firmly on and I wonder if I can be bothered to rummage under the bed for a pair of socks.

My thoughts turn to Lord Swallow. Should I let him know where I am? I am undecided. He knows I am on Pillans Beach, but not my exact whereabouts. I don't want to appear pushy. But, I did say I would inform him. We need to meet in order to gain clarity. That is decided. I take a Kiwi attitude and send him a text.

P.m. Mouse: *Pillans Beach Resort—Leafy Glade on wheels—wet, but okay for writing—any time. Thanks for today.*

My message is short and sweet; informative only. I am too tired for much else. I fall asleep relatively early. I snooze for an hour or so.

Late P.m. Adrian: *His finger throbs indignantly and he winces at the memory of the final axle-making strike that, unchecked, had slammed fingertips between steel vice and saw-handle. Milking is awkward, but the cows are patient and it is nearly done. But what is this? His Lady—well, his past Lady—freed from The Castle and skipping by most delightfully. How lovely she looks—perhaps he could accompany her tonight. He wonders if he could just relieve the cows; take a little of their milk to ease their discomfort—let them out to pasture early, then away. A damp tail across his cheek snaps him back—no, the milking would be done—his rhythm maintained. How easily he would throw it away for impulsive risk-taking. He presses his head back to the steaming flank and picks up the swishing beat again. Evenings are for Lovers and he has given his word not to be one. Daytime is for friends. Yes, perhaps a luncheon meeting. He has much to speak of—months of catching up. Tomorrow then. The pail fills—*

Mouse: *She slumbers, his text waking her in heart-thumping anxiety—alone on a distant shore—foolish or destiny-driven? The roaring sea, triumphant in its victory; a victim lured and held captive in crossroad quandary. The morning herald outside The Mountain deck across the immediate valley—outstanding rainbow splendour—the most vibrant and complete ever beheld in double arc; its pointer for today? His poor finger—she is sorry. His Lady—past—she is sorry. Please resend last message—only got as far as 'The Castle'.*

The completed message arrives, making remarkable passage through these wild conditions.

Mouse: *She thanks the bovine anchor—unsure of her desire for Lover or Friend. An Angel memory only, caught in photo-like pen stroke for all eternity—imagined? Perhaps, yet proof lies in the undeniable glory. The reason? The shared knowing? She slumbers on, content in his luncheon friendship.*

Adrian: *The outside bath is warm, but the rain is cold on his exposed legs and knees. He hunkers down and pulls the big piece of plywood right over the bath. It is like a womb—updrafts of hot water ripple up his back—almost uncomfortable—more cold. He basks contentedly, warm both inside and out, the golden glow of achievement—{some text missing.}*

Mouse: *The message from her Lord Swallow—her past Lord Swallow—is only half delivered. She enjoys his tale of hot, bathtub wallow. Please resend; the wind and rain defying this most delightful of language tools for Celestial Friends, or whatever it is they decide to call themselves.*

18

Adrian: {Message update}—*the golden glow of achievement radiates through him—another milestone—happy children and promises of more. His confidence expands. Thank-you Lord—closer I come to you.*

Mouse {unsent}: "*Come to me as sand upon the dune—come shift and rest in undecided quandary on the outer edges of my definition. Come shape my countenance into the unknown mystic of our home shoreline. Come to me," she sighs—"come home to me at last."*

Friday 13th April 2007

Mouse {Unsent}: She sleeps on and off—sometimes rest laps soothingly, but then it is snatched away in her constant search for his embrace. Longing subdued on one hand, but on another? She knows she will not rest until he comes to her. His evening messages tell how high his self-imposed barrier—the security he needs to keep steady. The strength he finds in continued denial; a drug he likes. He feels righteous in turning away. It feeds him with a certain fuel for self. She knows.

To the sound of the ever-rumbling sea she imagines they make love at last. Bowing to the greater force they relinquish their control and move together in right-placed union. A gentle urgency—in time with the early morning splatter of rain upon the roof—gasps and smiles—their four-month wait in easy surrender; their joint climax a blessed homecoming. And now at last they sleep; his head upon her breast; his open mouth resting on her as a feeding babe. She runs her hand up his long, lean back. He moves his limbs in sleepy recognition. The new day begins and they can go forward—together after all.

I sleep late for me. I must have been tired. This is a long and stressful journey. But, I would not have it taken from me. In the ebb of my imaginary love throes I relax at last, my Lover beside me still. I wonder, does he feel me when I take him like this? His presence is so strong. I can't help but think he does. Getting up at last, I stroll to the office to book my two extra nights and to request an electric lead. They produce one with ease—the sort used in tents. I chat to a friendly woman as I boil up some water in the new amenity block. Yes, she has come down from Whangamata for a two-day break. Why don't I borrow her saucepan instead of going back to my van? And wasn't the traffic *terrible* yesterday. Why was that?

Adrian: Hi Friend—no extra trolley racing today—too pooky. Are you still at the beach? Shall I bring some things for lunch? Can you tell The Laird that you are meeting me?

Mouse: Dear Friend—still on beach—trying to sort out power leads. Laird knows we will meet. We are past that stage anyway. What's pooky? Tired?

*Phone battery low—might cut out. Here at camping resort on the beach—site No.**7**, {of course}. Space for your car. Visitors welcome; ask at desk—X*

Mouse: *P.s—have got some fodder. Do bring extra if you have anything spare in the fridge. We shall be Fellow Noshers instead of Lovers—better be an interesting menu. Ho hum.*

P.p.s—just to warn you, Fine Sir, there is a mighty breeze down here on the water. Our Boat is raring to set sail. I can hardly hold her. It will take two of us to handle the rigging, platonically, of course. The sails are billowing. You had better hurry—not sure I can manage her alone. Bring diaries and laptop—power all sorted. Your Lady—your past Lady—is set and away. She will try and maintain a berthed stance until you get here—

I am very excited about my writing and settle down with relish. I enjoy the antics of two young boys who leap and shout outside my van, trying to catch the seagulls spinning and floating above their heads in the big winds. And now I really am set. Electrics sorted, cup of tea in hand, cushions to ease the tricky seating and our Lovers' story in bulging notebook form. What more could a bored housewife ask for? I am in Heaven. I start to log our messages from yesterday. I am surprised at how long it takes.

Midday, Adrian: *My Dear Friend. I am still 45 minutes away-ish—sorry to keep you waiting.*

Mouse: *Don't worry—you are with me anyway, our story taking off in leaps and bounds as I type away. Drive carefully in this wild wind. Might have to abandon the sailing—*

The unfamiliar vehicle pulls up next to mine; Adrian has lent the trusty 'Toolbox' to a friend and has brought Vonny's car. It is a dark blue saloon, or sedan as they call them in New Zealand. Estate cars are known as station wagons; the American terminology again. I'm not sure it suits him as much as his old steed. I am wind-swept and refreshed after a run for freedom through the waves in the teasing wind—*'Come dance and play with me; send sprays of sea-water dashing up my skirt; the sun is on my shoulders too. A warm patch shot through with the joy of imminent arrival.'* He is smiling broadly, his faithful dog beside him. Lord Swallow greets his Lady with a long, warm hug. The relief of being close—well—if they can never be Lovers again this would be enough.

They retire to the back of the Leafy Glade on wheels, the familiarity returning them to a place of comfort and ease. "Yes, he will have some tea, but let's not eat yet. He has serious thoughts in his mind that need addressing before he can relax—and then they will have the smoked fish he has brought. Her playful, suggestive texts worried him as he drove; she wasn't intimating sexual deviance? Well, he hadn't been too sure."

So, where to begin? There is a lot to say. Four months of harsh silence is a big deal. She is frivolous and giggly, her dance in the waves alight in her eyes. He is feeling too concerned for this and runs a hand through his wavy hair that stands to attention, meeting the intense moment with contained honour. Does she not sense his intention? *'For goodness sake, this is deathly important, Woman!'* He wishes he could pin her under him, make her connect and sober up in the way he knows works best. Hmm—and now he is feeling rattled, a wee smile playing at the corners of his mouth. *'Now, do I have your mature attention? We hold peoples' lives in our decision-making today.'* He does not say these words but on reflection she suspects they are in his mind. She enjoys having him beside her. He looks tired and somewhat dishevelled, in need of a woman's touch—his Lady's touch. They both know that she is still his Lady, and he, her gallant Lord Swallow.

"So, how are you, My Friend?" I ask. "I am really very well," Adrian replies. "I have been worried that you think I am being cowardly. I need you to know that I have felt it really important you give undisrupted attention to The Laird—and to your marriage. If I had given even the slightest indication that I still harbour feelings for you, on arriving here, at this point, I would be the target of The Laird's violent and angry accusation. You are not really through The Castle Gates, are you? The Laird will be watching like a hawk. I need you to tell him you are meeting me now; the official meeting we spoke about. Are we clear? I need you to tell me what I have said, so I know you are in agreement. We need to come to an arrangement that we both understand. I want to give Simon and The Laird something they can grasp. I am firm in my decision. I want us to be close friends—making music, daily texting and writing—all of our creativity in platonic harmony until such a time arrives when we can move to a new level. I miss our deep friendship. I want to open it again. After a year we might reach a point where we can move on another step. We are not there yet. I am really feeling for The Laird. I need to honour his journey and give him more time, otherwise I won't be able to meet him in The Light. As Big J. stated last week: Christ says; *'nothing can remain in the dark; all will be exposed'*. I will stand by that. I need strong sunshine in which to bathe my new-found strength."

I look into the eyes of the Man I love and hear what I have known all along. When he reads my writing in 'Dry Dock', he will find it there. We have so much to discuss. How can I tell him everything? I hold his gaze. "I love you. I have fallen into true, deep love for the first time in my life and I will not deny it. If we remain as platonic friends, {our only possible course at present}, then I will continue to claim our love as true but state that we are not taking it beyond the boundaries. If The Laird cannot accept that, then he will have to lose me. This is more of a journey for him than for me. I have long been in touch with this private side to my deeper person. Only now is it being aired. Never before has it been met by anyone, Lord Swallow. I could make love with you and still feel my integrity." I see him stilling. I sense a slight shift in his concentration. What thoughts traverse his beautiful mind?

Or should I say loins? Am I a naughty Angel, playing games with these two men? Am I being unfair, throwing them into deathly serious, life uncertainty?

I know that Adrian and I belong to each other in some way, even though Adrian says: "but I need you to know I am not waiting. If a lovely lady walked through the door tomorrow I would not turn her down." Fair enough. And that might very likely happen, I think to myself.

I feel a personal shift today. With our love confirmed, despite Adrian's physical distance, I can move on. In holding its 'right to life', {albeit it caged and compartmentalized in screen and logged message}, I know that it is safe, and ours. I need not visit our Kingdom of shared, sensual touch. My imagination can give me that quite easily. "Could you acknowledge our bond but internalise it?" I ask. "Knowing it is there; *our* knowing alone, giving us the extra spice in all that we do together?" "Do you mean in kissing you, in making love to you; in being a husband to you?" He asks. Well, I don't know how to answer. I brush past his statement, not knowing what he is indicating. "You missed what I said; what I meant. Did you hear me?" He asks." What?" I respond. "Your comments just now? Yes, I heard them." I sense this is important. What was I meant to hear? An invitation? A proposal even? He does not press me. I shall ask again when next we meet. I love the way he challenges me. He stimulates me in every way. Yes, The Laird is right. Adrian most certainly presses all my buttons.

"The thing is, I am bored by my marriage," I state as a single revelation. "Yes, that is it; I am bored. Can I really live with 'bored' for the rest of my life?" Adrian is thoughtful; pleased by my simple admittance. We talk about the transformation of our Love into vocational work and selfless action. The call to service and the priestly essence of his teaching is a strong pull for Adrian; refusing indulgence certainly feeds him. And me? Yes, I can go there. I can taste the riches. Have I not been there for sixteen years of motherhood already? "If you hadn't suggested this course of action as our only viable, present option then I would have done so," I state.

We are tired. A lot has been achieved. I look into the weary eyes of this man and know the stress of our predicament lies beneath the surface of his steadiness. We are managing admirably but this is a tough call for both Celestial Sea Sailors. I inform him of the other people who are aware of our relationship. We are blessed by their respect. Thank-you, dear Angels. And what is the intention behind bringing us to this point, for us to put up our hands and say; "It's alright, we are only friends after all?" Just food for thought while we tuck into our long-overdue lunch.

The fish is delicious; one of the great bonuses of living by the sea. A small business calling itself 'The Fish Guy' is often parked on the Waikite Bay road, providing passers-by with freshly caught and often-smoked, ocean bounty. We continue to chat as we eat. "I feel better, now I know where The Laird stands. I have been scared of his anger—oh yes. I am still feeling very delicate," Adrian tells me. "The need to tread gently around 'us' doesn't let up. I like the way you read more into my Easter message. I hoped you would see that it wasn't an ending." I smile knowingly and move on to ask about his lovely cows. "I am leasing the land from school. It is all going so well. I have moved my caravan up there too. I had to own up to Big J. that I had! I chickened out and asked Simon instead, knowing that he would be easier." I wipe my mouth with a tissue and mention the newly discovered, caravan origins. "Do you remember 'Yellow-Tooth Dave'—the strange bloke I did some painting for a while back?" I ask. "Well, he never paid me for my work and never paid Andy any commission either. Apparently the whole job went belly-up. Anyway, the only thing that Andy came away with was the caravan that he gave to you! How fitting is that? In effect, I worked for your new, Smoko Shed. {A 'Smoko' is a tea-break in Kiwi speak; with a cigarette I presume.}

Vonny has named the cows Daisy and Esmerelda. We talk about the milking; it takes about half an hour for each one. And then I talk about being a mother; feeling the milk let down; the extraordinary sensation and discomfort of being too full. "We shall get some pigs too," Adrian continues. "I'm going to build a sty with Class 3 for their building project." "Perhaps you can have my pig if we go back to The U.K?" I suggest. "Could we eat her?" he asks. "Oh, no! She is my friend," I state, horrified at the thought of dear Molly gracing someone's dinner table.

I ask Adrian how much Delphine knows about our relationship. "A lot," he explains. "She helped me stay silent. She was a buffer for me. And then things became flirty. I could tell she wanted our past relationship to resume. I let it happen, just once—yes, I slept with her again. But I knew as soon as it was over that I had lost interest. She is upset and a little cross. We have had a falling out. She knows that you are still my Lady. Her friend Susan also advised her that I wasn't over you. My family knows how things are progressing. They are being supportive. I told my Aunt Beryl recently; she understood immediately about a Soul-Companion. In fact, my Mother Jenny is coming to stay tomorrow."

So, My Lord Swallow has lain with another in the past four months. But then so have I. Our path continues to be set, even in the face of the largest obstacles. While we talk—endlessly talk—one of the resort owners wanders over to ask about the dog in Adrian's car. "Yes, only visiting and no, we won't walk the dog near the surf club." An instant, three hundred dollar fine is dished out to anyone overstepping the mark. Apparently some pit-bull terriers caused problems last year. One of the young 'Seagull Catchers' from earlier jumps up and down outside the van. He must have informed reception. "We find you far less tolerant of dogs, here in New Zealand compared to The UK," I comment. Most people keep their canine companions in spacious runs or loose on their land, so they are less used to behaving in public; something like that.

"I'd like to give you all my new music," Adrian announces. "Here, give me your flashdrive. I shall download it for you. I have been amazed at how many songs ring true for 'us;' I really want you to hear them. What do you think of this?" I listen with surprise and delight to a ballad of thwarted love, eventually honoured after twenty-one years. We smile at each other; a potential, future path shimmering unspoken in the time capsule of the cosy van. I speak of our likely return to England and my possible N.Z escape for part of the year. "I would like to get the family set up and established. We could communicate everyday by text and e-mail. I need to become more independent and encourage The Laird to do the same. Yes, this could be a way forward. Our writing is the key to it all. I really think it could go somewhere. I haven't sent Simon any of The Book. I wasn't sure it was the right thing to do."

The files are duly downloaded and resorted. I encourage Adrian to visit some of the chapters. I know he will find it a challenge. Yes, he has had a brief look at the files I gave him but he has been trying to get his head around our *present* relationship; trying to steady himself, rather than concentrate on the story. He reads. He is silent, a storm of uncertainty and discomfort knocking him from his steady perch. He will need to take this home and think about it. Feelings of horror at seeing himself so exposed, and yes, feelings of the same old guilt leap out of his psyche, just when he was getting stable. Suddenly he has new issues to address; several new and strong issues. A surprising level has been achieved today as the continuing adventure finds new horizons. "If I decided to commit I would be very firm and clear," Adrian states; "no matter whom I had to face. You do know that, don't you?" Yes, I know The King. But for now, seeing our present life and our past reality in vivid, literary detail, he is caught on the hop.

Again, I launch a mighty challenge at him. I speak of our alchemy; of my understanding about the feelings that refuse to subside. When he re-reads my printed words he will understand. "This could be the ultimate standing in the sunshine," I suggest. "Surely these blessed histories should be honoured and maintained; not in constant ritual but in recognition of where they have brought us." He thinks for a while before saying; "I may be like the actor who dislikes seeing himself perform—you know? And perhaps this *catching and immortalizing* is a chick thing?" Before leaving he holds me close for a long, long time. I am safe—cocooned in his love, I know. "Thank-you for holding it all so carefully," I say quietly, wishing I could kiss him tenderly with long, heart-felt blessing.

The chill night air increases as Adrian drives away. I pull on lots of layers, and yes, I find the socks at last. Bother, I've left my woolly hat behind. My folded skirt makes a suitable turban; that will have to do. Lord Swallow would approve, ever one to make sure of warm clothing upon his slender frame. Bother again, I feel the beginnings of a cold. I expect the recent adrenalin has kept it at bay. I grab the vitamin C. bottle, as well as my trusty box of homoeopathic remedies. Feelings of nausea overtake me as well. After our four-month ordeal my defences take a back seat and a normal pace resumes. We have agreed to write up an account of this long, long meeting; each of us recording our understanding of our current position. We will send them over the Internet, and yes, Adrian would like to write a synopsis for 'The Celestial Sea.' He likes my synopsis but it comes over as a touch 'sales pitched'. "Where is the Angel-held unfolding mentioned?" Yes, he will take it and have a go. After lunch he allowed me to massage his tired feet. He didn't offer to massage mine. I will have to teach him the ways of a gentleman. I love him, so much.

I write endlessly, before I forget any of this afternoon's life-changing conversation. This is the beginning of our Third Book, 'Setting Sail.' Will we continue to provide the necessary material for *another* volume in this epic tale? The pace and timing of the story continue to amaze us both. Nothing is added or taken away. We have no need to plan a storyline. Extraordinary.

I sleep eventually. It is after one-thirty. To the sound of the crashing waves I rest at last, held in Adrian's love, I know. Yes—at last I know.

Saturday 14th April 2007

It is a new morning and I wake early. I doze. All is calm in the campsite. I think of the family at home; my brief, monosyllabic chat with Cedric who sat in front of the eternal computer last night did not bode well for a stimulating home atmosphere. "Where is Daddy?" I asked. "Watching rugby, as usual." Oh, no changes in the bloto, uninspired state then.

I open the laptop. There is still so much to log. It takes hours to transcribe yesterday's conversation. I need to send it to Lord Swallow but that isn't possible from here. Maybe the library might take my flashdrive. I wonder if Adrian has put any thoughts down on paper. What does he make of my idea that he write the mythology of The Boat? And has he dared go into the files again? I don't know. I didn't put pressure on him. He doesn't respond to pressure from anyone; if anything he turns in the opposite direction. This tendency lies at odds with his desire to please others; another example of The Wild Man in the Pond tipping the scales. I have recently learnt to hold back, allowing him to make the first move. Any suggestion I make gives him an excuse to play the 'turning from indulgence' card; to tread the martyr's path. I find he takes a while to process new thoughts and challenges, and challenges don't come much bigger than those I am presenting him with. I sensed a new impetus as he left me yesterday. Was I right?

A.m. Mouse {unsent}: *We lay still in each other's arms—as unfolding husband and wife. A tentative step; a potential new horizon. Yes, we have agreed to platonic friendship. Yes, we will maintain a high level of contact and warmth while maintaining our private knowing; a silent, unspoken truth between us. I have submitted at last, as long as we quietly acknowledge our deeper bond. And with this acceptance a new impetus floods us both; a fresh wave of possibility. As you leave I realize we are both aware—aware of a pair of Copper Rings and a Life of Commitment; The Rainbow Herald making bold statement. The way is clearing.*

Our silent phones feel right-placed this morning. There is much to digest. My Lord Swallow is taken back into the realm he has pushed away; the realm he has blocked in order to cope with its forced loss. And now she asks him to bring it into his very centre, to continue as he has been doing but to acknowledge the reality of their Private Ocean in their minds only. Can he go there? Or is this the female way alone? The silence today is needed; the calm after a difficult birth. The newborn sleeps, relieved.

A conversation outside my window brings me back to the world of sun and sand. A holidaymaker from Durham chats away: "Well, although from The U.K I live in Canada. I come here to escape the cold winter," he tells my motor-home neighbour. Children dash past riding the pedal go-carts on hire from the office. My cold is present. A big cook-up is needed. I down a plateful of smoked fish and red cabbage with scrambled egg. A chunk of dark chocolate and I am ready to face the world; or my private world upon the waiting screen, I should say. Retrieving the telephone from the van's floor, I decide to put my poor husband out of some of his misery.

"Hello, how are you?" I ask. "Oh, dull and pointless," he says. "How are you? I am worried about you." "I'm well, except coldy; it was pretty chilly in here last night." "I'm not surprised," he retorts. "How is everything at home?" I continue. "Dull and pointless. It's horribly empty without you here," I am told. "Well, I need you to know that Adrian came over for his agreed meeting yesterday afternoon. You still have a wife. We have decided to remain as good friends. We haven't worked out the details yet." "So, what are your movements?" I am asked. "I'll stay here another night, as agreed, and meet you at church tomorrow, okay?" "I suppose we can survive another day," he sighs. "Take care. See you tomorrow then."

The continuing story claims my undivided attention for many hours. At long last I can leave the present 'Setting Sail' script and return to 'The Celestial Sea'. This is the story that needs to reach our willing editor before we lose her current time-slot. I will try to write the present story daily, as it unfolds, rather than reflectively. If I can make the time I'll work on both histories simultaneously. I stop at one point to take in the sunny scene outside my windows; perhaps I should climb out for some fresh air. I never make it. I never even get to the bathroom to wash and dress for the day. I must look a real mess but I am not seeing anyone so what the heck? The writing takes me to another sphere for ongoing hours. I do wonder if Adrian will come and see me again but he always texts first so I would have time to smarten up. And suddenly it is raining. Bother. I should have headed out after all.

I reach for my phone. I shall send Adrian a message; it is past three o'clock. We need to assimilate our decisions from yesterday so that we are clear in our agreement for the various waiting parties. I need him to read what I have written. Have I clearly understood our deliberated conversation and has he written anything yet? I tap in a few words and then I glance out of the van's windows. Oh, my goodness—standing outside, with his Mother Jenny, is Lord Swallow, come to seek out the hibernating Mrs. Mouse! Well, they will have to see me as I am; unwashed, pyjama-clad and absorbed in writer's creativity! I climb out, discarding my phone, laptop and various messy papers. I am somewhat thrown but greet my guests with a kiss each. It is good to see Jenny again. This is the third time we have met. They invite me to join them for a walk along the beach. We stroll in the semi-rain, trying to settle into this rather surreal and unexpected situation. "Goodness me," exclaims Lord Swallow, tongue-in-cheek. "Look at all these crumbling castles!" We pass five sandy creations in various stages of ruin, taking care not to hasten their demise. I want to take Adrian's hand but manage to behave decently. "Hey, would you like to come and have tea with us? We're having lamb chops followed by a trip to the Waikite Bay hot pools. How about it?" "Well, why not?" I respond without hesitation. "How lovely; Jenny, you can be our chaperone, can't you?"

I dash back along the beach to pack a simple bag and am ready by the time they drive down to collect me. Jenny takes us back to Adrian's lodgings. Vonny is still away so the house is available to our unusual little party. I take the opportunity of washing and making myself more presentable in the spacious bathroom. I enjoy viewing the abundant garden and Adrian's hot-tub creation. It sports a large garden umbrella, which lends a dash of sophistication. The organic garden is instantly recognizable; Adrian's trademark in circular paths and vegetable planting is creative. "You know, I didn't ask my mother to drive me to the camping-ground. She wanted to go to the sea and just drove. I was so surprised when she turned right, then left, then right again until we were at the resort. Can you believe that? I eventually told her you were here and we wandered along until we bumped into you. I have been feeling unsure again today, trying to get my head around what you *actually* mean to me. I have been thinking, perhaps I should just let you go; maybe I keep going out of obligation or something. And now this happens— my mother, of all people, brings me right to you without any indication from me." He shakes his head in disbelief and so do I.

The young rabbit residing in the hutch that I brought to the house at the beginning of term scrabbles for liberation. I help fashion a temporary run and watch the little creature stretch her legs. She jumps for joy in the delight of a new setting; rather like me. Adrian's mother is keen to try out Vonny's piano. Jenny straightens her skirt and seats herself on the music stool. She plays some delightful English hymns and then blesses our shared meal. I see touches of the mother in the son and feel honoured to be with them. Lamb chops and roasted vegetables make a good meal, followed by Adrian's homemade cake, of which he is rightly proud. "I invented the recipe: barley flour, sultanas and lots of cream from my cows instead of eggs." It is very good. I am impressed by the new skills acquired by Lord Swallow since we last spent time together. There are a couple of new fridges to hold the freshly-made cheese and large quantities of milk. The cheese stands ready to be wrapped in kitchen paper. I help store the new batch of Pecorino on the fridge shelves.

Once the washing-up is done we drive up to school in the dark as a threesome. Opening gates and following the car headlights we enter Lord Swallow's cherished world of gentle cow, milking pail and the starlit hillside. The quiet is beautiful. Daisy and Esmerelda are duly found and after a skittish escapade they follow their master with a swinging gait to their milking stalls at the top of the field. I have never been up this far before; the hill is higher than I had realized. A gentle calm descends. The twinkling of the now-distant town lights and the rhythmic chew of the cud makes blissful stopping. I watch as my beautiful friend washes the udders, and his hands, in well-practised rhythm. He wets his fingers with some of the waiting milk and then sets to, in fast motion; two teats at a time. The metal pail zings with the swishing, pure, white liquid—filling surprisingly quickly. "Would you like a go?" I am asked. "Here, sit on the stool and if she moves her weight, quickly grab the bucket before she puts her hoof in it, okay?"

The older couple that used to own the cows taught Adrian to milk. For several weeks during the summer he travelled forty minutes into the Kuwharu Hills to milk on their farm. He had been seeking a potential farming venue for his class; 'Farming' being one of the term's Main Lesson modules. He had found these two cows needing a home. For a while the commitment and work-load, along with financial strings, had put him off taking them on as a permanent responsibility; "but I came up daily to keep the milking going until school started and then brought the children to see them. The farmer didn't have the time or energy to keep up the work." A proposal to the school for the hire of the two fields was accepted and the 'Ladies' duly arrived with Adrian's agreement to indeed take on the full responsibility and ownership. He had fallen in love, twice in one year. Well, well! My Gentleman Farmer has only to saunter out of his lodgings every evening to find himself amongst the long grass, passing his woodwork shed on the way—perfect. While *my* summer past in an agony of not knowing, *he* had his bovine ladies to keep him sane and balanced; a whole new project; the timing and quality Heaven-sent—a truly blessed distraction in a period of frustration and uncertainty. I am so pleased he has them.

I try my hand at the rhythmic massage and pull action. "Why, you are a natural," exclaims the Farmer. "I expect you say that to all the girls," I laugh. "Have you tried this before?" I am asked. Well, I'm not sure what he will think of my reply, but he *is* a Kiwi, and they are pretty up-front, so I say; "actually, yes, I have. As a mother of three I have tried it on myself! Not with any great success I have to admit. I seem to remember a few hopeless attempts in the bath; trying to fill a bottle or two to share the endless feeding task." Adrian's Mother joins the conversation; "yes, my daughter finds an electric pump is the only satisfactory solution." While we talk, encouraged to keep our voices down by the Farmer, my eye travels to the adjoining hillside. A large subdivision project is underway. Apparently sections of **7** acres are up for sale. They will be very expensive in this sought-after end of town. An idea, revisited, pops up in my ever-idealistic mind; "you know, it would be madness for us, as a community, to let this opportunity go by without really looking into it. We could have a thriving small village up here; so perfect with the developing plans of the school and ideal with the new farm. A handful of people, clubbing together, could purchase the land and build their family homes, sharing in the daily workload on the farm and other projects. If handled properly it works well. We own a house in the U.K in just such a community." I ask Adrian's mother if she would be interested in moving down from Auckland to this region. "I have certainly considered moving here," she says, "but I'm not sure the spiritual philosophy of the school sits comfortably with my beliefs." We have an interesting chat after that statement where I tell her the 'inclusive' nature of the philosophy means many have their own take on religious understanding. It doesn't affect the abundant fruits shared by everyone.

The heavy milk container is lifted into the boot of the car, placed inside a dustbin with ice-blocks and roped securely. "Shouldn't you move it nearer the opening, to save your back?" Advice from both Adrian's mother and his Lady. Once the precious white liquid is stored in the creamery we head off to the Hot Pools. Strangely, I have never been here before. The pools are a hidden gem, just past school down a track beside kiwi and avocado orchards, they wait to greet those seeking relaxation at the end of a busy day. The business is run by a new family at school. I don't know them but Adrian does. Fin is a friendly man and charges us the child rate. He turns out to be an expert handyman with a wealth of knowledge about small farm machinery and animal husbandry. Like many Kiwis, the pioneer trait is ever-present. He and Adrian embark on a long conversation. I see a school farm advisor developing in his enthusiasm, especially as he lives across the road.

My Lord Swallow saunters out of the changing room, fastening the ties on a smart pair of board-shorts in chocolate brown. Goodness me—his beautiful poise fair takes my breath away. His Lady could only locate a standard pair of shorts and her vest top; not the best but never mind. A dignified, sliding water entry is soon replaced by the delights of underwater exploration and play; twisting, turning and revelling in the embrace of the watery bliss. And, guess what? Yes, My Fine Sir swims exactly as I do. What a surprise! Well, of course it is no surprise at all. We have never actually been *in* the water together; metaphorical sailing across it certainly, but this is our first discovery together in the slow motion of the buoyant element. We watch each other's underwater antics and then see if we can swim all the way to the end of the pool without coming up for air. We can! I enjoy being near Adrian, but we don't get close. The temptation to embrace each other would be too great. He looks very handsome as he leans back against the wall of the pool. He fingers his springy hair off his forehead, highlighting his fine-boned features and lean torso. I continue to swim a little way away, watching him watching me; the Underwater Sprites in growing enchantment under the mysterious ferns and rising steam of the geothermal water. Along with Adrian's mother we are alone in the peaceful moonlight; a perfect evening of chaperoned love.

Adrian decides to drive me straight back to the camp-ground after our swim. His mother has already gone to bed. "We won't feel like coming out again if we go home now," he suggests. My van is waiting for us beside the beach, greeting us with cosy duvets and snuggly cushions. I am so pleased that I brought the lamp. We are cocooned and comfortable; not hugging each other, but lying close with chastity pillows between us. We are safe with this control. We can manage; have been managing for months. We look deeply into each other; "let's just stay like this awhile." Our magical connection is alive and well, the caged sparks glowing brightly. We would only have to open the lids—but we don't. We are mature adults. Too much is at risk and we know it. I gently touch Adrian's cheek for a fleeting moment; he tells me that he loves me; that he can imagine me as his wife beside him. "All this time you kept faith, not letting go for a single day. I waited, trusting you, feeling sadness when you imagined my feelings for you were over, but then finding you always bounced back with the truth of me. I have been truly amazed by the accuracy of your intuition; time and again. Yes, I do love you. I cannot deny it any longer."

Sunday 15ᵗʰ April 2007
  A.m. Mouse: —Love you—X

I am going to be late for the eight o'clock church service, and The Laird is reading. I have promised to attend. The automatic gate at the camp ground won't let me out for some reason, probably because Adrian used the code to leave the resort last night but didn't return. The lady at the gatehouse eventually arrives. She doesn't ask about Adrian. I hand back the electric cable and dash to the centre of town. I am a few minutes late, but not enough to look bad. I sit in the pew behind The Laird; as a reader he is in the front row. Goodness, why are the readings always so relevant? Or is it just that one is more attentive when questions need answering? **"Write all you see down in a book, the disciples were told by Christ."** Today is **'Divine Mercy'** Sunday. The new French Priest is a softly-spoken man who smiles at his congregation with checked joy and strong conviction. I watch his sandaled feet as he preaches. They are quietly dancing. With a twinkle in my soul I recognize a fellow Free Spirit. I listen attentively. The boys have been left on The Mountain and Rinky is away with a friend. No children means that Mother can really pay attention. And what a sermon the Priest gives. With growing excitement he leads his congregation to the truth of unconditional love. His French accent makes it all the more memorable. **"You see, we have all these niggles and problems in our daily lives and we feel frustration. We need to move from getting bogged down in negativity and embrace deep communion with the Holy Spirit who resides within us all. This is the true meaning of linking Heaven and Earth."** Sitting behind my husband, I encourage him to move forward; to take that step into unconditional love; to forget his fear.

Mouse: *Dear Friend—in a café—just had the big chat—gulp. Laird just left—gave it to him straight—gulp. Think I left my wash-bag with you? Can I dive in now to collect?*

I step into the warmest hug. Lord Swallow is recently showered and dressed in my favourite shirt. Smelling fabulous, with toothbrush in-hand, he welcomes me so naturally. We are interrupted by Jenny who appears at the door in a colourful, church-going outfit. "You are looking very smart," I say, greeting her warmly. "Yes, well I am off to the Sunday service. I look forward to Adrian telling you what happened this morning," she adds, smiling conspiratorially while fixing the brooch on her silk scarf. I move my car to clear the drive and then return to be with Adrian. "You never guess what happened earlier," he continues. "Well, Jenny came in for breakfast, {she stayed the night in a cabin at the hot pools}. *'I had a strong dream last night,'* she announced. *'I have been given a message from Heaven that I am to anoint you with oil.'* I didn't know what to say! I laughed a little, but then said, *'okay, you had better do it then!'* My mother is a very religious lady and often has spiritual conversations. She reached for a dab of oil but I said, *'look, if you are going to anoint me, you might as well really anoint me; not with a dab but with a whole cup-full!'* So, she did! What an amazing thing to happen."

Adrian tells me about the Biblical reading they shared: 'The Lord is my Shepherd'. "And do you know the story of David?" He continues. "Apparently he was a musician and a harp player. He fell in love with another man's wife and begged for God's mercy on his predicament.

I have just realized that I have been fighting this Love of ours. Yes, really trying with all my might to put the spark out. Look, I even took your name out of my phone. But every time I have been brought back; every *single* time, and in extraordinary ways too. I hold up my hands in surrender. I cannot deny the truth of us any longer. I will not deny it. That does not mean I intend to act on it, but I will not be untrue to myself any more. There!"

Adrian's phone interrupts us, as if on cue. "Oops—it's Sasha—five urgent messages; she is waiting for me to open the farm gates. Her horses are coming to graze the land today. She is hoping to move nearer the school. Establishing the horses here is the first step. We have lots of exciting plans for the development of the farm. I'd better go;" he jumps up quickly, reaching for his warm, zippered jumper. "I'll head off then," I say. "I won't come up to the farm with you. I need to collect my little Lady." "Yes, do you mind?" My Farmer Friend is apologetic. I know that he needs to spend time with Sasha. They will be working closely together on the farm from now on. Should I be worried about their partnership? They have been friends and neighbours on and off over the past couple of years. Her daughter is at school. She is a single mum. He says that he finds her shy—she was his neighbour when he lived in the buses and I expect he tried to woo her. I imagine he can be a loose cannon around women. Delphine lives on the same property and they are friends. He won't want her knowing I am back on the scene, even platonically. Oh, well, these things are out of our hands. I drive away to the other side of town, secure in the knowledge that even in the face of other partners and life commitments, *nothing* on this Earth could possibly rival the profundity and joy of The Celestial Sea. I glow with the warmth of our extraordinary bond and with the freedom of unconditional love.

My happy blanket of acknowledgement takes me all the way to Mallory Falls; to a homestead behind the beautiful Reserve. My friend Sammy and her family live here. Rinky is considered part of the household these days. I count Sammy as one of my best Kiwi friends. Over large cups of tea I continue to tell her about my writing. "I am a rebel at heart. I've broken out and been staying at Pillans Beach resort for the past three nights to write; how wild is that?" Her eyes light up at the thought of letting one's hair down to that extent. We talk about the release from early childhood care once one's last baby turns **7**. We are both in that place. "I was *really* wild and bought myself some new nail polish!" I admit. Sammy laughs with genuine delight; endearing crinkles at the corners of her eyes always surprise me whenever she laughs. Maori by birth, but western in her outlook, she is a very attractive woman. Sammy is busy with many enterprising businesses, from property development to organic cookie baking. We tease each other about whose project will come off first—"my Book, or your Cookies?" I hint at the hidden ingredient in my diary tale. She smiles again. I wonder if she suspects. She was certainly one of the first to comment on the natural chemistry between Adrian and myself.

Our conversation drifts to the potential of developing a community village alongside school. Sammy is as excited as I am about the idea. "Perhaps we could form a charitable trust or something," I suggest. "I'll look into it." I cast my eye around the kitchen. A brand new industrial mixing machine is still to be unwrapped. It was here when I last visited. A collection of dogs, chickens, geese and goats wander past the open door. Carpenters tools and a pile of gumboots lie strewn about. I gather up my tired little Minx and we wave goodbye to the classic, Kiwi homestead.

I find the two boys alone when we arrive home. "He's playing tennis," Cedric informs me when I ask the whereabouts of their father. His warm hug surprises me; perhaps he *has* missed me, after all. I spend the rest of the day cleaning, cooking and writing. The Laird soaks in a hot bath when he returns. "Shut the bathroom door please. I need to ask you some questions, even though I don't want the answers." I am ready to stand up for my connection with Adrian. Despite our decision to remain as friends I cannot deny the truth. The steam rises from the cast iron bathtub. I watch it wander towards the wooden ceiling, waiting to receive my answers with the same reluctance as my husband. The larger the wedge forced between Adrian and me the more serious our bond becomes in our own minds and others. Why is that? I take a deep breath and respond honestly to the biggest question of them all.

P.m. Mouse: *She has had to admit to a breach of her marriage vows;* "*and* have you slept with him?" Her answer; "yes." "So—he is your husband now, not me." Hmm. She tried to explain their agreed standing—she cannot deny the truth of their love. She will not give up their platonic friendship. He is hurt; angry at her stubborn refusal to see things from his perspective. He talks about booking their passage home. The negativity is understandable. Her determination does not waver. She wonders if he is there; her Fine Sir. Are his feelings unchanged? She doesn't want to bother him. How was his day on the farm with Sasha? The horses settled in their new home?

Are you busy? I could telephone, although I understand if you would rather keep your distance. M—X

P.s Don't worry about the safety of texting. We are beyond that stage.

* * * * * * *

Late P.m. Mouse: The Laird—he sleeps at last—the stamping and crashing from the dungeon enough to rock the Castle foundations. An angry bull—hooves in pawing disbelief upon the stone floor, his massive neck thrashing from side to side. Yikes! In growing determination she grabs the washing-up brush to steady herself. He is hurt. She has blown his world apart, maintaining her insistence that things needed to change; that she doesn't regret anything—apart from his hurt of course. "So, you really think I need to be rocked to this extent to grow?" He roars; "that this peculiar journey is important for me? His furrowed brow reveals the consternation and incredulity of her cheek. "It takes a pretty huge explosion to shift the bull in you," she states. "Well, that is the strangest notion yet," he replies. She leaves him to his frenzy; a steady knowledge that this path has to be trodden. Hard-hearted? Perhaps. She will not back down. She knows he will quieten and follow her to bed; rather as the accepting cows follow the farmer to their milking stalls. She hears his footsteps and knows that the caring husband in him is greater than the thrashing bull. He takes her to him: "What are we going to do with you?" He asks gently. "Just let me use my sails," she sighs. "Please let me use my sails."

Later on he wakes and turns to her—a most unusual thing in itself, and demands to be shown this 'Gate' that she has mentioned. He pushes against it with his heavy feet, trying to wedge it open; to see into the beautiful garden beyond. He is frustrated by his blurred vision. She tries to still him, making clear eye contact in vain, despite the honest invitation. "But I just don't understand," he cries. "What is it, **exactly?** "It is knowledge," she replies. "A language—a connection with the Holy Spirit residing within us all. "And is this entry through The Gate exclusive?" His perplexed tone continues. Responding with tenderness she tells him; "no—The Gate is open to all, although we each possess a different dance step to take us across the threshold. You and I have different steps, that is all. I am willing to guide you but it may not be possible. Never in a thousand years did I imagine I would meet my Celestial Dance Partner. To step across the threshold in The Rhythmic Dance is the most beautiful experience.

"Does this knowledge need to be shared physically?" He asks. "No, it does not," she replies. "But if it **is** shared physically it becomes the ultimate, spiritual practice—possibly one of the most profound experiences open to human-kind. It exudes unconditional love—it knows no bounds—it knows not greed or selfishness. It can be elevated to higher intention." He closes his eyes. She prays that The Holy Spirit descend on them; all three. A tangible presence is felt—Holy—

Lord Swallow, comfortable in his Forest Retreat, hears the rumpus on The Mountain and sits up, alert. "For goodness sake, My Lady—don't contact me now—even though you need bovine advice! Please don't contact me now!" He checks that his door key is at hand, and his supply of arrows. Yes, he has enough. Perhaps he should build a hideout deeper in the woods? His Lady wishes she could reassure him. The Laird did not mention him as major enemy. She made sure he was aware of the honourable stand since December 2nd. It is this unknown wife who stands before him that worries him more. She is speaking a foreign language—that scares him. She wonders what the morning will bring. They are away to Hawkes Bay for a couple of days. She sends him her undying love. She cannot deny it—M—X

Chapter 3 Exactly

Monday 16ᵗʰ April 2007

A.m. Adrian: *Off in The Forest, making arrows is right—blimey! Had a major gut-clenching, fear attack. A little relieved by the end of your text though. Poor Laird. How you must know each other! Hawkes Bay, eh? I'm busy with Workshop preparations and attempting to get caravan paint. Brought the caravan question up with Big J. She was a little cool about that. We'll see if I can bring it to an acceptable arrangement. Lots of love to you both. I'm talking to Simon tonight. X*

Midday, Mouse: *My Love—how nice to receive your message. Sorry about the final shock. The Laird wasn't going to move in his mind without The Big Question being answered. Yes—we do know each other so well; hopefully well enough to recognize the need for change, whatever that might be. We have arrived in Napier. We are staying in a motel tonight before visiting farming friends further south tomorrow. The boys are keen to try out the skate-park on the sea front before we leave. Cedric is especially pleased because they have a foam-pit, which means he can perfect his mountain-board summersaults without fear of serious injury!*

I'm getting behind with the writing—so much is happening. I'm missing you. Need to look into your eyes. Need to be enfolded in my Angel's wings. Need to swim underwater for hours with you; moving in the ocean swell and laughing together over wrinkled fingers and toes, celebrating our compatibility with chocolate and lettuce. Loving you. My phone is safe. M—X

The town was virtually deserted when we walked into the centre to find somewhere to eat this evening. A Chinese restaurant with one other guest made us a good meal. The children enjoyed the treat. Red tasselled lampshades decorated the ceiling and an older, Chinese lady took our orders, bustling about as if the place was full. She had an especially large behind which surprised me. The set-up was very old-fashioned.

Tuesday 17ᵗʰ April 2007

A.m. Mouse: *The Laird and his Lady continue their discussions: "I need you to know that even in our closest moments integrity was never dropped. Adrian and I have never taken each other under lustful energy." "Oh—come on," he replies. "You can't expect me to believe **that**!" She ponders a while.*

How can she explain? *"Too many unusual things have happened—too many unexplained coincidences—too many perfect timings."* He is momentarily interested. Are his barriers down? Does she glimpse an opening? *"You know, Adrian has spent the last four months actively trying to extinguish our connection, but we have both had to admit that it, {whatever it might be}, is stronger than both of us. In acknowledging and accepting its truth we can free it; let it move to higher intention. I know you don't believe we can keep to the agreement we made in December, but we can. Adrian's self control is stronger than mine. He guides me."*

The Laird and his Lady are both tearful. He is accepting. They hold each other close. *"To deny this new, yet old connection is so hard,"* she continues, *"but neither of us is selfish enough to place our personal joy above the welfare of others. You have been loved and cared for throughout. You have never been pushed away. What Adrian desires more than anything is to shake your hand in genuine friendship. He wants to invite you to milk his cows with him. In fact—I feel certain there is something waiting for us, all three; some task. Hmm—why us? I know we are being held. Something Holy is happening."*

He is still—silent—accepting. A major shift? There is more work to be done, for sure, but something has moved. *"Hmm—I'd rather you **had** taken each other in a lustful fling,"* he mutters. She is pleased to see him set-to with gusto and a brush to clean out the car. The slob-out mood is left behind in the face of unconditional love. But it is short-lived. *"You don't love me—can't truly love me to be treating me like this,"* he says. *"You continue to be in that place with your writing; you never leave it."* *"I need you to grasp a new maturity,"* I say. *"In a way I am pushing you out of the nest—yes. I want you to take up your independence; become empowered in a measured way."* *"But that is why I got married—to be secure."* *"Well, well, Sir—that is not enough for me. I got married for spiritual adventure and learning. I am already secure."*

The long drive south takes us to a seriously large sheep station at the southern end of Hawkes Bay. The scenery is amazing. Fiona is a daughter of the family we visited in Taihape; the generous people with whom we stayed last year. They are close friends of Ricardo; The Laird's best friend in England. I always enjoy hearing the story of how the two families met. Ricardo's father was one of the Queen's Gentlemen at Arms and was on duty at a Buckingham Palace Garden Party several years ago. Always one to lark about he had struck up an amusing conversation with a Kiwi couple that waited with others for the Royal party; *"keep your toes behind the chalk line please, Madam. Her Majesty might tread on you otherwise!"* He supposedly joked. Anyway, they arranged to meet for supper that evening, enjoying the sociability over the summer weeks. They kept in touch after that, the younger generation from each family travelling hemispheres to stay with one another, hence the connection and our invitation to spend time with them.

Early P.m. Mouse: *Good evening, Fine Sir. How goes your day? How tranquil lays the meadow? How exciting the new plans and working team? I* *think of you as we savour the wonders of this new region through which we travel. The softly rolling hills, the autumn display from scattered clusters of deciduous tree; it is beautiful; different from the land further north. Somehow it is more feminine. The waving grass covering the hills is wispy, almost hairy in texture—like the hair on a giant's head. The giant is happy—carefree. A serious lack of rain highlights the revealed identity of the playful giant. His hair is sandy, not green. He thinks he remains invisible. We like this landscape and settle into its curve and hollow as we drive south.*

In many ways the scenery takes us home. There is something comforting about the falling leaves and established, farming contour. I catch the glitter of gum trees as we drive by; their twinkling dance stands out against the grey sky and empty hillside. The sun takes turns with the clouds and the gum trees flicker silvery in the golden light. Different types of tree line the route for miles and miles. Many are covered in ochre-tinted lichen. The light accentuates each trunk and branch. The trees call blatantly for recognition. Not a single car passes as we drive further south to the 2,000-acre farm behind Porangahau.

We are welcomed by another branch of the family we visited in Taihape; remember when we went there? Fiona is sparky—traditional—nicely irreverent and rebellious towards the very 'proper' upbringing she received. The rebel is displayed in the 'Kermit green' painted kitchen and a refusal to play any social games with other family members. She owns an up-market, cut-flower business. Mark is the son of a famous All Black Rugby player. We like their free spirit. They are keen marathon runners and are both well-travelled.

After lunch today we piled into Mark's mud-spattered Ute. With children hanging off the back, screaming and laughing, we were treated to a breathtaking, 2-hour tour of the enormous farm. The views were incredible, especially from the highest point on the land. We were blown away by the sheer size of the landscape. The vehicle defied impossible gradients as we checked livestock and water-levels in a newly developed, small reservoir. What an amazing place; the heart of Kiwi, sheep farming. As we travelled the bumpy tracks we acknowledged the hard work of the men-folk. Mark employs only one farm-hand.

We eventually returned to the rambling old villa for the evening. Ten dogs and two small boys make for a lively crew alongside ours. The Bog-Brush thinks she has died and gone to Doggie Heaven! It was lovely to watch her run beside the vehicle with canine companions. How she needs the space and freedom. We drive home tomorrow, stopping in Napier to re-visit the skate-park.

I hope The Workshop is everything you dream it can be. I love your writing—the expectant Teacher and Woodsman. I shall try and see you on our return—if you would like a visit from your Lady? X

Wednesday 18ᵗʰ April 2007

A.m. Adrian: He can almost hear the buzzing workshop—the thud and scrape of sharpened steel on wood—the calls and questions of the ten busy boys. He can hear the tug and jostle of the children, desperate to complete and fire their hand-made arrows through the blue sky into the target; that satisfying 'thwack'. Goodness, what a busy day lies before him. Late to bed, finishing a prototype—awake early with racing thoughts: the cows, the meetings, the lesson plan—

The guest bedroom in the rambling villa lies across a quiet deck at the back of the house. Like many older homes the ceilings are high. A faded chintz cushion on a wicker rocking chair waits for the evening. The antique furniture and family portraits speak of a strong link with tradition. The children sleep in one of the boys' bedrooms down a wide corridor decorated with wallpaper displaying an old fashioned hunting scene. I notice the faded, peeling edges. I could be in my grandparents' home; the Sussex farmhouse that I remember as a child. That house had such an exciting attic. Two cupboards followed the descent of the stairs and I was frightened of the consequences should I dare slide into one. My aunt's forgotten dolls house sat on a dusty floor beneath a dormer window.

I am awake before anyone; too much writing to address to stay abed. I look out of the window. An impressive Canadian Maple graces the front lawn. I miss the trees at home. We leave Porangahau after a good breakfast. I notice crimson algae on low-lying water, Tui and Bell Birds warbling, rows of Lombardy Poplars and Australian Plover—apparently they have barbs on their wings, {an unwelcome interloper from foreign shores, killing the native birds}. Cedric is delighted by his second visit to the skate-park in Napier. He manages a perfect back-flip into the foam pit. "Look, I could even come here by plane," he comments as we drive past the local airport.

The Laird and I continue our conversations: "I'll have to sort you out soon, woman, before you cause any more chaos." He is in a sullen, negative mood today. I cannot bear the heavy atmosphere. Well, I suppose I can but I really dislike the lack of joy. He won't stand for my writing either; "rubbing my nose in it."

P.m. Mouse: Hi there, Lovely Friend. We are home. Full of fast food and amazing scenery. A successful trip except for The Laird who blows hot and cold; slothful then angry. I continue to apologize for hurting him, although I am still unable to move from my position. Oh well, all part of life's rich lesson. Hmm—he hates not knowing where he is heading, so this is a really tough call. A serious lesson in 'letting go.' Anyway, My Friend—how was your Workshop day? I have been thinking of you. T.V is on in the top cabin—X

Adrian: The milk lies warm and white in the pail—steaming lightly. The tired milker rests beside it, listening to the crunching munch of the milk-givers nearby, stealing a supper from the horse paddock. His mind drifts over the busy day—the highlights—the disasters—the proud showing of a successfully fletched arrow—the hidden tears of the child holding a broken bow—the crows of delight at the far-reaching arc of a well-shot shaft—the fascinated horror of the long-dead hawk, which gave its feathers to the endeavour. Indeed a rich day; incredibly rich—such a thing to do. And at last he can relax. Music comes flooding back to him and the desire to dance rises. He feels elated—and liberated—a big thing to carry alone. So, now his holiday begins; everything falls into place beside these biggies—mmm. Sweet life. And his Lady? He is beginning to trust again. Maybe things are in order.

He has spoken warmly and clearly with Simon. He has been through the fire of guilt and fear. What comes next? How does it work from here? His integrity is clear; his past misdeeds that have caught and choked him with anxiety have been exposed and discussed candidly. Goodness me! What more can hit him? His intentions have been clearly laid out—now just to keep the lid on the growing excitement at the wafts of possibility that emanate. She feels it too, he knows. This is where the goods battle begins; to keep humble and let things unfold, expecting nothing, expressing gratitude for all that happens; the milk, the grass, the grazing, the shed—grounding responsibilities. He looks up and thanks God for such a life. Oh, Healing Spirit, bringer of wonder—praise your Holy name—whatever that may be—X

Mouse: She reads his messages with love and the growing knowledge that something is happening. She realizes that the more restrictions they self-impose, the more serious their liaison becomes. Has he noticed? A catch-up session is needed. Had an honest talk just now with The Laird. He outlined the Earthly reality of her vision. She continued to justify her position. No, he will not let her see Adrian. He won't stand by and let him enter their lives. She has to decide between them. "You are my wife," he says.

She needs to see her Friend. Are you about tomorrow morning? The Laird has a meeting at school; the phone is safe. I love my underwater companion. Sleep well—X

Chapter 4 Expecting

Thursday 19ᵗʰ April 2007

A.m. Mouse: Their perfect partnership lies as waiting 'clip art' for the story. His knowing—her knowing; a shared magic in The Rhythmic Dance. But—it is no 'clip art'—and they both sense its reality. A button to download and print? They understand now—they are not in charge of the keyboard; not entirely. The persistent possibilities grow stronger. Daily they light up the screen. So, My Fine Lord Swallow—do we dance off the pages or not?

*P.s: Put this date in your diary: **7.07a.m and 7.07p.m on 07.07 2007**- just one of those recurring reminders. Are you home, My Love? —X*

Adrian: Just getting up. Away to a meeting with Sienna at Midday, then back for enrolment at 2p.m—new pupils. Then free. Free now for a short while—

Mouse: Am leaving Mountain now—few errands—no children. Will you still be home if I come straight over? X

Adrian: Sure. Come for a cup of tea.

Mouse: On my way. A bit grotty—need a bath, but never mind. I'll bring my flashdrive to download more of The Book—X

I arrive to find Vonny and Thomasina enjoying the sun with friends on the front deck, sorting through a basket of laundry as they chat. They have just returned from their long holiday in England. "He's waiting for you around the back," Vonny tells me. I walk into Adrian's room, happy and excited at the prospect of spending time together. Lord Swallow is on his knees, sorting papers. He doesn't get up, acknowledging me with a casual grin. He is a Kiwi and doesn't stand on any ceremony. Hmm—I might have to teach him some gentleman's manners. What is he wearing? A rainbow, tie-dye T-shirt? Hmm again. His room is chaotic; the pre-term clear-up begins. I lend a hand and make the bed, perching on the edge of the duvet while he sits at his desk. We chat about this and that. The atmosphere is slightly dull. As always we need time to come together.

"I don't want to hear about all that," his dismissive tone stops me from chatting too much. He isn't interested in hearing about the people we spent time with in Hawkes Bay. I am stung by his disinterest, realizing this side to his character would probably appear more often if we were a permanent couple. How would he cope with my English world? Have my recent texts been too friendly? I need him to hold me. We head outside to talk some more; the ice breaks at last. "How are you, really?" I am asked. "My bridges are being burnt," I say. "But I'm okay. I suppose I am fairly self-sufficient. I am content with the small things in life. The Laird and I have been talking—a lot. He doesn't think it possible for you and me to work together platonically without reigniting the spark; 'a time-bomb waiting to go off,' he said." "I suppose he's right," Adrian replies. "I need to make decisions," I continue. "I am feeling humble and guided."

"I get the feeling that it is down to you to help The Laird find forgiveness; to move beyond resentment," my platonic Lover suggests. "Simon and I agreed that there are two issues here; your married relationship and the growing partnership between you and me. I really love you. Simon and I had a good talk. He is pleased to hear about our platonic stance—our intention. He can see what we are trying to achieve. He imagined you might be 'dizzy with love' but found you to be surprisingly level-headed when you met before Easter. He could feel the same respect that I have for you. He is pleased to be a character in The Book—'it's really very good,' I told him. So, I think you need to give The Laird lots of time. Don't jump too quickly into any decision-making.

The sun is lovely this afternoon. We chat for many minutes. Vonny's guests have departed and she is busy inside. We discuss Sasha's horses and the farm projects they are designing together. "I find it difficult to share the planning and vision," he says. As Adrian admits his concerns I begin to realize he is a controlling character; like me in many ways, although thank-goodness I don't have to deal with the constant disruption of a 'Wild Woman in the Pond!' I have my pride, which is stubborn and deep-seated. Perhaps my pride is my own, personal challenge. I am unsettled by the thought that I could annoy Adrian. Would I feel his hard edge more often if we were a permanent couple? Whereas The Laird has a vulnerable, soft centre, Adrian has a steely, detached core, which is less comforting but certainly stronger. Part of me knows it might be more positive to remain as forbidden lovers; unobtainable yet belonging. I come away, resigned to the fact that we need to return home to England. I share my 'returning home' thoughts with The Laird and begin to sort out the caravan and the house. There is a lot to address.

P.m. Mouse: *Thank-you, My Friend; sage advice-as always. I will try to give it time. I hope the school meeting and enrolment went well? The sun shines and your Lady is feeling humbled. We are being held. My Lord swallow was firm and distant at the start of their meeting today, unnerving his Lady for a while. Perhaps they should begin their meetings with a silent hug—so much to say, and sometimes no need to speak at all; the quiet, shared knowing, enough. X*

P.s: Do you have the phone number of the parent who is involved in Real Estate? The Laird is away playing hockey this evening. The kinder are in bed. Hope you are okay? M—X

The Laird returns home late with an injury. I help him inside and administer first aid and care. "I twisted and fell on my right ankle," he tells me. "I think it might be broken; it's very painful." My poor hubby; how low is he meant to stoop? He stretches out on the sofa with his leg supported by cushions. I cannot continue with my writing; the computer is in the same room.

P.m. Mouse {Unsent}: *She saw a harder-edge to him today; the controlling, determined edge that tells it straight. He ended her waffly conversation—his lack of interest in a less immediate world a potential stumbling block in their togetherness; in her upbringing and home life. You see, she is also a controlling person, although she is surprised that she often lets him lead her. She adores him. She respects him. That is all she needs. He fills her—totally. She aches for his gentle touch. The very fact that that they have caged their flame instead of extinguishing it points to a potential future. Does she need to get the family home? Does her husband's sanity depend on known structures and institution? Their marriage appears to work positively amongst friends and family only. It is not strong enough on its own. Lord Swallow's revealed harder edge today makes her announcement to The Laird easier; "we should think about going home; perhaps by the end of the year."*

Friday 20th April 2007

Midday, Adrian: *The first staff meeting of the year went screamingly well; all the teachers present—bright—willing. And The Master of Ceremonies—who incidentally had been up til 1.30 a.m making cheese—negotiated the herd through the many gateways to rich, new grazing, even receiving a compliment from Martha on his herding. Not only that, his Workshop endeavour received the stamp of approval from Big J—even a 'thank-you'! The anointing begins to show its effectiveness.*

Mouse: *The King, his reign in full, unfolding glory—his Lady smiles for him, and bows her head. She sends him humility. She is in 'Accident and Emergency' with The Laird—a bad ankle injury at hockey; not sure of damage yet. Another lesson in submittance? And the King's Lady? She is missing his tenderness—his touch upon her brow—X*

* * * * * * *

P.m. Mouse: *The Castle Inmates are home—badly torn ligaments—no weight to be applied for **7** days. Leaning heavily on crutches he tackles the* steep incline to The Castle Infirmary, which is made ready. Perhaps a padded throne in every room might be required? Sinking into forced inertia—ever a safe place for a bewildered Laird—he laps up the attention. The red underpants and the T.V. 'slob-out' indulged. "The Good Lord appears to be dishing it out to you at the moment," his abominable wife remarks. "Hmm— I'm being punished for keeping my wife from her ecstasy," he replies! A stop at the Dairy on the way home sees him mollified with a hot pie—the children running out with packets of jelly too—"might he like them as well?" At this point the Lady of the Castle gets a fit of infectious giggles; the whole car rocks with mirth. "What's so funny?" The next page of the story is written; the irony of it all with Lord Swallow's message of minutes before, in sharp contrast with the crumbling Castle—memories of a beach walk.

So, how come one Lord is raised so high and one Laird taken so low? Stripped in fact. Is it her doing? Does she really wield that much power? She tries to stifle her naughty mirth. Please Angels, surely this isn't my doing, entirely. She brews a cup of tea and makes a dash for the infirmary. She will look serious—X

Adrian: the flashdrive protrudes from the end of his computer, both cursed and cherished. When will she claim it?

Mouse: My Friend, how remiss. Not intentional. Cursed? I hope not. I am on my way to swim and walk the dog. What are your movements?

Adrian: I am on the farm, moving the caravan. You could—hmm—good idea? Want to come up? Simon is here. Big J. maybe here too. Is it time or not? To awaken public wondering? Or risk it at least. Angels appear to be smiling. But the measure is The Laird. Could you ask him? What say you? He would need to know. No secrets will we hold. Otherwise, just drop in at home and collect it—

Mouse: Darling Friend, too early to invite questions—I think. I won't come up to School, even though The Angels are with us. I am leaving for Tui Park for my dash with the Castle Hound—then on to the indoor pool to swim. I'll dive into your Forest Den on my way home to collect the flashdrive. Might or might not see you? X

Thank goodness for the dog—and routines. I thrive on routine and I love my swimming. I'll call into Vonny's later on; I am out and about later than usual. The pool feels different. I don't like it as much. There are too many people in the water.

Early evening, Adrian: I've been home; now heading back to the farm. 10 minutes. Isn't your family missing you?

Mouse: They have cooked themselves supper—excellent phone directions.

Laird watching rugby. Hau about to join him. I was told to go out for my usual swim and dog duty. Boys putting Rinky to bed; very good for them! I can't be too long; okay for a short visit. Is that all right with you? Should I park at school? I just need to collect the flashdrive. Alternatively you could put it in an envelope sticking out of your post-box.

Adrian: *I have the flashdrive up at the farm.*

Mouse: *Nearly there.*

We meet in the evening dark. I find Adrian by the farm gate above the school playing-field. He is looking the part in his farm waterproofs and woolly hat. It is raining. "Shall we have a catch-up?" He asks, handing me the precious flashdrive. "We can sit in your van." We climb into my spacious vehicle where Lord Swallow is engulfed by one exuberant, hairy hound, beside herself with joy at being reunited with her second master. "I haven't seen you for ages. I need to spend more time working with you, don't I, girl?" Adrian fondles his excited friend, his strong hands and warm eyes all hers for a precious moment. "The Laird doesn't really like his dog. She is afraid of him," I say. "You have her respect and love. I reckon she's your dog really." "Yes," Adrian agrees. "I think she is. I'm sure I could get through to her given more time."

Lord Swallow and his Lady sink into their familiar place of sharing news and feelings. I hear all about the good resolutions of various issues with school and with Vonny. The kitchen counter has been taken out and the room is bigger. The staff meeting had been so useful; those present were open to reaching deeper levels of trust and sharing. We laugh over The Castle antics and the irony of The Laird's troubles. Adrian had enjoyed my recent, tongue-in-cheek texts. We both continue to shake our heads over the unfolding events. Oh, how lovely to be together again, even platonically. Our togetherness is natural and right-placed. Nothing can steal away our love that we hold as a golden secret between each others' soul.

Late P.m. Adrian: *So—peacetime. The war is over. There are perhaps some sporadic battles to be fought, but overall, much of the danger has passed. What is to take place now? An air of rich possibility is present. What will emerge? What will come to form? How should we be? And what is to be learned now? Perhaps a time of plateau; solidifying the new strengths gained—learning—stars—animals—pasture—building—relationships—dragons—music—writing. Aha—writing and cheese.*

Mouse: *They come together in such easy sharing, like an old married couple who are past the first flush of love and passion. How good to speak together of their daily happenings. She has so missed their beautiful friendship; their togetherness. Yes, it is ever-present. She likes his message. A stilling—a peaceful plateau—leading to what? They continue to trust that* *the way will be shown. What are they to become? Passionate Lovers in ink and paper? Or more? Time will tell. The Angels will protect. So, a solidifying of all their laboured groundwork. And proudly they can hold their heads up high, raising autumnal swords as guardians over precious goods—richer than gold. They have a child. They have a farm. And now they own a dog! A grand day all told. She will answer The Laird's expected question, once Hau has left. She will speak to her Fine Sir in the morning. For now she bids him goodnight—X*

Saturday 21st April 2007

A.m. Adrian: *The great bull is tethered—brought down at last—a resting time for him. No stamping and charging for a whole week and then careful steps for a while longer. This is angelic; the possibility for inner growth opens. What if that box of illusion was broken too? Reliant on his companion's care— listening—a rich time if distraction is kept to a minimum—strengthening —softening time; perfect. Oh Christ, may peace descend upon this home— wisdom clear—X— {7u7}?*

{This **7u7** appeared from nowhere—on the 14th March 2009, two years later, as I worked on this text. I had put the computer aside to make the children breakfast.}

Late morning, Adrian: *Another fruitful morning, dream-planning session—a rearranged dairy, an advertisement in the newsletter, a streamlined bottling system, a califont for water heating, a new sink and cupboards—yes—the creative force is strong and deep, and it flows boldly, though it knows not where.*

Yes, they were like an old married couple last night, he agrees—deep and steady—back to that place so quickly. He watches himself grow—larger than life? He wonders—what will bring him down? What is—

Midday, Mouse: *She is thinking of him—lots to say—love the messages. Away at the rock-climbing wall with 2 friends for Rinky's birthday. A delayed celebration. Laird alone at home. Heard him in long phone discussion last night—more questions about 'being in love;' couldn't catch much. I told him we had spent a short time together. He wasn't too sure how to take it. Pretty cold with me today. Hobbled bull is right. Poor man—what a dreadful wife I am. Out of time now—phone later.*

Early P.m. Mouse: *Hi there, My Friend—are you doing a stint at the Home Show next weekend? If so, when? I have to organize the parent roster. Hope all is well—sounds like you are on a productive roll. I'm not quite there yet! In The Warehouse—school shopping. Wish I were with you—X*

Adrian: *I'm doing Sunday last session and then the 'take down'. Looking for someone to take the caravan. Know of anyone?*

Mouse: *Would say we'd take it if we weren't in limbo. Would be good to keep hold of—writer's den? Not too sure where we could put it. Something might become clear. Could you store it somewhere if no takers? —X*

P.m. Mouse: *Darling Friend—pray for us right now* **777777777777777777 77777777777777777777777777777777777777777777777777777777 77777777777777777777777777777777777777777777777777777777 77777777777777777777777777777777777777777777777777777777 77777777777777777777777777777777777777777777777777777777 77777777777777777777777777777777777777777777777777777777 7777777**

{This is very strange. Typing this set of messages on 16th March 2009, after a weekend full of magic and 'signs,' especially **'7 signs,'** I come back to the laptop to find 65 pages of **7's**—as above. I have left a few in place. Hmm. Perhaps the computer lid compressed the spine of my diary onto the **7** key? It could have done. Why number **7**—again? The last interruption also coincided with a prayerful text passage.} To continue:

Pray for us right now. The Laird is speaking to The Abbott of the Sussex Monastery as I text—about us—gulp. One of the leading, Catholic monks in The U.K. Hold me—X

Late P.m. Mouse: *Dear Angels, the waves loom high and impossible above our heads. There is talk of a return to a job in Sussex. The Laird would love the security; he is unhappy without the familiar backbone of religious institution. I don't want to leave, but perhaps I have to. Please continue to guide us all. Look after my beautiful Lord Swallow. He knows how much I love him—M—X*

Sunday 22ⁿᵈ April 2007

A.m. Mouse: *She slept with tears in her eyes—fully clad—ready to run to him in her dreams. Did he hold her as she slept? She thinks so. She is writing—a little time at last; the family calls her constantly and The Laird frowns whenever he sees her working. The Book will take ten years to complete at this rate! She will have to stop soon—and take him a cup of tea. Her sentence awaits The Laird's decision. Will she have to choose?*

Later, Mouse: *Yes. She is right—a decision she has to make. They are calm—subdued—a candle is lit—their wedding rings are removed and placed over the candle flame. They pray that The Holy Spirit descend upon them. This is their church service today. They stand around the kitchen table. The children are elsewhere—quiet. Stillness envelops them—a solemnity. The different paths lie ahead in stark reality. They watch the rings sink into the wax. "Mine is submerged—has disappeared," he notices. They read the verse from Michael B's book—the relevant prayer for the week:* **'Refreshed, renewed, replenished, I am standing within this world of golden,**

autumn light. A mighty, wondrous sword the Gods are handing, to those whose souls with fire of love burn bright. This flashing sword like sunrays streaming, searing in darkness shines and makes me firm and sure. No dragons on my path need I be fearing, I'm armed with light, God-given, sun-forged, pure!'

As I send this message to Adrian the telephone rings with uncanny timing. It is Simon—The Chief Marine Official and, I suspect, another of our Guardian Angels. Yes, he can meet with The Laird tomorrow; Lord Swallow's birthday— of all the days to choose. Our unusual Sunday continues. Warmth and friendship abound. "I am surprised that you are so calm and steady," The Abbott apparently remarked. "We shall pray for you. There is a job here if you would like it." The pasta is cooked. I had better dish up. Our rings remain embedded in the candle.

Midday, Mouse: *He is waiting—she must decide soon. She is scared. Can she really throw a lifetime's work away in an afternoon? And would Lord Swallow really want her to anyway? The Laird questions her Lover's ability to remain faithful, but that is a different issue. Her choice has nothing to do with their future—her Lover has said so. Hmm—X*

Monday 23rd April 2007 Adrian's Birthday

A.m. Mouse: *The morning arrives—she reaches for him—HAPPY BIRTHDAY, My Darling Adrian. I am with you now. A busy morning, I am sure, as you prepare for the new term. Are you free at any time? I have a little something for you and I would like to spend some time with you today. I shall tell The Laird. I will be at school early this morning. I am on traffic duty by the top classrooms. Still unclear—perhaps an idea forming.*

Adrian: *Free at 11.30—quick visit?*

Mouse: *Yes, My Friend. I can be free after 11.30. Shall I come to you at home? A quick Birthday visit—*
P.s-you had better be careful what you wish for this year! M—X

I tell The Laird I will be seeing Adrian for his birthday. "Well—I can't stop you," he retorts. I am chatting to Stephanie in the car park when My Fine Sir walks past. He looks fresh and smart for the beginning of term. The jumper I found him looks as if it's come from an upmarket catalogue rather than the municipal recycling bin. It suits him. His short hair-cut completes the new look. I want to say 'Happy Birthday' but the moment passes. Stephanie and I are busy discussing the potential land opportunity. She is interested and excited, both. Simon walks out of the office as I leave school. "I'm seeing The Laird later on," he tells me.

Lord Swallow—how I long for your arms around me today, even for a short while. The Bog-Brush and I pass a happy half hour dashing over oozing mud and sharp shells in Tui Park. The tide is coming in. It is exciting to go right around the headland. We disturb a group of small sea birds with red beaks and dark top feathers; I think they are oystercatchers. A lone heron sits on a sandbank, watching our clumsy progress. I stop to gather some exotic seedpods at the edge of the shore where the trees provide shelter from the sun. We linger awhile to dry off. The wattle is in bloom; surprisingly late this year, and the honey bees are droning above our heads, feasting on the rich blossom. 'Google' informs me that Wattle is another name for the Acacia tree, also known as The Thorn Tree. The lightly scented honey is often chosen to sweeten tea without stealing its flavour.

Tui birds hop from branch to branch as we stroll, calling to one another with their throaty cronk/warble. Everything is still, and waiting; like me. It doesn't really feel like autumn. I have only seen a few deciduous trees; two trees on the Waikite Bay road are magnificent in their autumn robes. Their colourful display begins as green, graduating up through pink and bright yellow to meet the sky. Do the October trees really look as splendid at home?

Yes, I am waiting. "I need a decision by the end of the week," The Laird has told me. "The job at the Monastery school in Sussex won't hold beyond that." I shop. I wait to visit the man I love. I wait to hear his true desire. What a quandary; a romantic adventure of rapidly expanding proportion. Who would have thought I would be walking a road like this? What is going to happen? I can't imagine not being with the family, but as we discussed yesterday, I don't have a strong need for security and stability. I am blessed with a generous helping of both. But The Laird? He needs security. This morning I found a piece of Adrian's painted paper; the one depicting St. Michael with a raised sword came to hand; a good choice for today. I wondered which of my pieces of prose I should write upon the paper; 'He to Me?' 'Intensely Alive?' Eventually I decided upon 'Will You?' I chose one of my white camisole tops that Adrian likes so much and wrapped them together in a birthday parcel.

WILL YOU?

Will you—
Go beyond with me?
Will you—
Go deeper with me?
Bypass all conquest, surrender to vulnerability,
Forget passing encounter.

Will you—
Be my fellow sailor for always,
No matter where we are,
No matter to whom we are attached?

Will you—
Keep The Boat afloat
In your heart and soul with me?

I wondered if the piece sounded like a proposal when I had finished writing. In a way, I suppose that it is.

Midday, Adrian: *Just coming home now. Where are you?*

Mouse: *Just leaving Waikite Bay shops.*

The Bog-Brush is snarly and snappy with Vonny's dog when I arrive, so I leave her in the car. She is in season, which makes her even more unsociable. The Birthday Lord comes out to greet his Lady and we hug each other closely. I can tell he is out of sorts. He is on edge and leads me outside to sit in the open. He places two cups of tea and his homemade cake between us. "The topping is made from my own cream cheese," he announces, offering me a generous slice. "Last time we met you said you felt distant to begin with;" Lord Swallow dives in at the deep end. "Let's start with some stillness. You must be stressed with all that's going on." "I'm okay," I reply. "Really—I am not too fazed by recent events." We sit quietly for a while. Adrian breaks the silence, saying; "that was quite a day you had yesterday with the rings and the candle." "Yes," I reply. "It certainly was." "I'm sorry," he shakes his head; "I haven't much to give you today. I've had a few knocks at school. I haven't completed the work on the car-park signs and Martini is disappointed with me. There are a few other things too—annoying really. My need for approval is so strong, I'm sorry. Sometimes everything is held in the sun, and then at other times, like now, everything is in the mud. Sometimes I can stand up straight and say what I feel without worrying about others' opinions, but at other times I push myself to please."

I tell Adrian of my dilemma; my indecision. And yes—I admit that of course, in truth, it is him I have to decide about. Our relationship is central to whether my marriage continues or not, even though we try to persuade ourselves otherwise. If Adrian was out of the picture; off with another, {a likely scenario}, then I would not consider leaving The Laird. That is the bottom line. "So," Lord Swallow states—"I *am* in the picture then." "Yes. I will be honest and say that you are."

I give Adrian the grey jumper I found recently. It has a Guernsey neckline. "Happy birthday, My Friend." I also give him the pumice heart I found in Napier. It has a copper arrow through the middle and fits comfortably in the hand. I have written our initials on the back. We speak about the potential Community Village. We chat about his class and his cows. "A Monarch Butterfly hatched in the garden yesterday evening;" Adrian points to the delicate creature absorbing the sunshine on the leaves above our heads. I reach out for a seedpod from the Swan Plant and surprisingly the butterfly alights upon my forearm. We are both surprised and watch the

50

beautiful creature as it unfurls its wings for the first time. Lord Swallow seems to have this effect on the ladies! We watch with amazement as the creature tastes the wondrous world for the first time. The brown and orange markings are vibrant and shiny.

Adrian takes me to his room before I leave. I hand him the special parcel I prepared this morning. "Open it later, when you are alone," I advise. He takes my hand before I leave him to rest. I am left feeling a little flat but I know he will text me before long with his processed thoughts.

* * * * * * *

Early evening, Adrian: *She comes with kind wishes and gifts. He feels undeserving—plagued by mind-talk about his lack of worth after letting down colleagues. He goes to bed and sleeps. Where is that clarity? He feels that the decision is now his too, for without him she would not make these family-breaking moves. Smaller pushes, yes—to give herself more room—but not leaving; journeying. He struggles with this. So—back to your husband my Lady. Throw it not away, for I am fickle and not to be relied upon—one part of him says. The other would say something quite different if he could just find it beneath the weight on his Solar Plexus. Which to trust? Certainly the way of courage has been their course to date. He takes it seriously and makes a vow. He will make this decision with her. Seek his heart deep—and get clear and real. Strip away the false. I am with you—*

Mouse: *The screen lights up. She knew—she knows. The man she loves is tired. They have been through weeks of stress and honest toil. They are being directed. And now—they arrive—'Alighting upon shores of a beloved, known land.' Their defences are down. Yes, the war is over. The air is calm—flat—edged in golden promise as they rest. Their passion is at bay; for the time being. They are waiting. They need to pray. They need to look honestly at the feelings that run so deep, but not out of a sense of obligation. She would be strong about that. Acknowledging their bond as something stronger than, 'nothing else has come along.' {Oh, she knows that he doesn't mean it like that—more that no other distraction has come his way}.*

She sends him a butterfly kiss—a new life taking tentative steps into a world full of snares and surprises. His Birthday; joint love-journey a full year to the day. Thank-you, Fine Sir. Thank-you for taking my hand. I need your Spirit with mine as we tread this virgin territory—with swords held high and a butterfly guide. Courage will show us the truth; the path to tread. Two heads are better than one in this; our crossroad quandary. I am with you—X

The Laird is ensconced in the top cabin with a plateful of food; the distraction tool I recognize all too well. I join him and we continue to talk; for a long time. We highlight our negatives and positives. We discuss the option of moving to another home here, in New Zealand, or returning to The U.K.

together. Perhaps he might return on his own as a trial separation? Can we work on our marriage? Do I want to? I insist that I have done no wrong to myself, although perhaps I have to others. "A relationship that causes pain to your family is not God-given," I am told in no uncertain terms. I question my husband's reliance on our marriage for personal security; "is that healthy? You take but can't give me any nourishment in return. I need nourishment of a different kind. We don't share the same love-language. Our marriage only works in a community setting where we work with others; where you can feel a sense of worth within a wider circle. I cannot supply your constant need for admiration." The Laird is thoughtful. He will make some notes on the things we have discussed.

P.m. Mouse: Lovely Friend, I hope The Birthday Boy is feeling better? Are you doing anything tonight? Going out—or visitors? The Laird presumed I was going out with you this evening. He seemed surprised when I said I had already seen you. Please text any time—my phone is totally private. My thoughts are with you. I expect I'll hear about The Laird's meeting with Simon before long. Cooking first—ever the cooking! Take care—X

Adrian: Help—floundering—feel the tidal wave growing—could simply be a guilty conscience and paranoia; coolness from Hau, letting down Martini, the possibility that I might have poisoned the teachers with my cake and cheese icing, but maybe just my own fear. Hope so. Very good lesson with the children today, though. Sometimes things get so overwhelming that finding myself seems impossible. Waves of fear sweep me away; doubt. But the cows, I'm thinking they will be cross and resentful of my neglect but there they are, placidly chewing the cud—and the wide-open space relaxes me. Distance. Safety in the silent darkness. The lights are on at School for The Board of Trustees Meeting, but here I won't be touched. I lean against a fence post. I need to focus on the children; term time is busy like that. My wobbliness today makes me pause. Has it arisen to show me areas I need to improve? Or is it flaws in my character that will continue to trouble me? How can I stand up and contemplate taking another man's wife—breaking up a family? Now that it has come to this threshold—where The Laird stands, saying; "choose!" It is not easy. I had made my stand that I loved you, but would not act on that without complete resolution. But now it has changed—you are being asked to choose and in that I have to state my place. Fair enough too. This is my turn. How strong are my feelings for you? Would I put it all on the line for you? Is this the question being asked of me? I don't know. Lots of me says "no," but another part says; "wait—don't cut it off yet—there is another way." But if I was asked to make a decision right now—feeling that tidal wave looming I would say; "no more contact. I cannot be part of your separation; cannot be the reason you break up."
    This is coming from my settled place here at School. Maybe this is time to change. Maybe it's time to—no—I just can't see it. You can't run off anyway. No, it cannot work. This ultimatum beats me. I can't see a way forward, yet

it doesn't feel like the end. I will end it though—if necessary. The only way I stay involved is with The Laird's blessing, unless I get some mighty guidance to take you as wife; to face the tidal wave and step up as man. Maybe, but it would have to be a strong sign. So, until then I bow—

Mouse: *We have had another frank discussion—more about our married relationship; the positives and the negatives. The Laird's long talk with Simon had been good for reflection; more about **our** marriage than about you and me. The Laird mentioned your ability to stick to your word. My Darling, I hate to think of you in turmoil. I am of the same mind as you. If I had to choose— right now, no going back—I could not take a step into the unknown. But—like you—I know that is not the end. We haven't come all this way for nothing, surely? What are we meant to be? It is so strong. The Laird is busy typing up a list of our strengths and weaknesses; our different options. So, this really has more to do with our married future than you and me. Our love has highlighted a lack in my marriage.*

My Lovely Friend, please don't fret. Imagine we are holding each other close on our Celestial Sea. We are being held and rocked with such care——

Part Two Atrip

The Celestial Sea wakes abruptly in the blustery dawn. Something is happening; at last. Her dockworker friend is nervous and excited. The vessel is to be manoeuvred back to the forecourt. She is to be overhauled and prepared for—what? Is she to sail again? Nobody seems able to tell him. The loosened plastic sheet escapes its bounds, freed by a cheeky gust. Whirling and dancing across the yard it leaps at the high fence, testing the patience of those who struggle to keep order. Chains are unlocked, freedom scaring the bound vessel. Is she to be reunited with the ocean? Will she remember how to sail? She sings to herself; sweet words of encouragement before she loses confidence. Is she strong enough?

'With exquisite, Angel-laser light I am crafted. I am long and sleek. The plane and lathe have fashioned me for the tides and ocean swell of many lifetimes. I have lain under The Craftsman's hands for a long, long time. Every angle, every joint is a fine-honed work of art. I have a knife-edged keel. I am built to find smooth, swift passage where others may fail. My central mast is tall and strong. I sense a growing excitement at the dignity I possess. My sheets and cleats are aligned; the sheets a magical twine; a thousand strands of unspoken mystery make up the whole. My fittings are of the highest quality—Eleven. I shiver with anticipation, even when night-time deepens.'

The man and the woman stroll, hand-in-hand, down to the boatyard. They only take a few minutes to get there; Lord Swallow's new lodgings are close by and his Landlady is away for a month. No questions dog their steps. The gates stand wide open—they can't believe it! Approaching their beloved Boat with confidence they are surprised to find she has been moved. She is sound, showing no sign of any rust. Lord Swallow lowers the gangplank. He gallantly extends his hand to his Lady. She accepts with a homecoming smile and climbs aboard. They have arrived.

The quiet Marina feels odd. They remark upon the open, ambivalent manner of The Marine Officials. A workman in an orange bib appears to watch them closely, but he is smiling. They are slightly stunned. After an arduous five months they can relax. Inspecting their vessel close up they are a little dismayed by the neglect. In places the polish is worn thin and the brassware dulled. Some areas they hardly recognize as belonging to their beautiful Boat. And has someone retouched the paintwork? But of course, they mustn't forget the harsh conditions of the past months. She is a little changed—a little older.

The couple holds each other long and close. "So, My Lady has walked out of The Castle Gates—bold and strong, eh?" Lord Swallow kisses her gently. "Yes, she surely has." A time of maintenance and repair is needed, and then they will discover if The Celestial Sea is seaworthy for long distance voyages or local, day trips only. They will be patient. Perhaps The Harbour Master might relocate the entire boatyard; who knows? They have done all they can.

Running their hands along her familiar lines Lord Swallow and his Lady smile in anticipation. The Craftsman watches the activity in the boat-yard and reaches for his notebook; where is his little blue pencil? He checks the pages of script; the destiny story is on track. The Boat is strengthening herself. He needn't intervene—for now.

Chapter 1 Activity

Tuesday 24th April 2007

A.m. Mouse: The cost is too great. The Laird in late night discussion with another close friend in The U.K; she hears all—his choice of action—her unbelievable action. And yet, he explained some of its truth. But the cost is too steep. Both her fine men are reduced to turmoil and distress. She should step off the tidal wave; find the calmer waters and keep everyone happy—be untrue to herself and their love. Her morning amble takes place in the dark. The Morepork owl calls in The Bush above her, accompanied by a ruffle of feathers—friendly and hidden; 'more pork.' The morning is slow to rise in this exotic land. The dog halts for medicinal grass. She is in season—on edge—snappy with other dogs and anyone approaching the car. The neighbour's house is lit up; the most life she has seen all year; every room is glowing. Her footsteps are soft on the gravel. Her thoughts are with the man she loves. The Laird wants her to return to their marriage; "of your own free will." On the level they have always shared, she could—it would be easier—it would be 'right' in many ways. Yet, she would have to lie about her deeper, true self. She would have to shut it away again, as they have discussed.

To wait—now is not the time? She bows her head—not knowing; open and waiting; half expecting Lord Swallow to walk down the drive to meet her this cold dawn. And what should she make of a strong vision in her waking eye this morning? The vision of a small figure in white looking down on them from a high, dark balcony. At first she was a little disquieted. A ghostly element was present. The figure disappeared but then returned. She could just make out the smiling countenance of a child, delighted that he/she had been noticed. Is this just mind-play? Pretty dramatic if so—hmm. She bows her head again, in prayer. The cupboards smell of mice. She had better get to work. She wraps herself around him in love—X

Adrian: His last message seemed to be eaten—no record of it. Strange? Perhaps it was too inflammatory. Oh Sweetheart—thank-you for your tender gift. "Yes—and yes—and yes," 'cos you've got a friend; aint it good to know you've got a friend.' Our friendship is the buoy. I will support you to find the life of respect.

Mouse: My Darling, only part of your lovely, lovely message came through just now. Can you send it again? Lots of love—yes—'you've got a friend'—wherever you are—loving you. X

I take the children to school. I dash with the dog through the glassy stillness of the bay at Tui Park. The water is sun-filled, reflecting my strange life-turn. The dull sound of distant traffic reminds me of the different roads ahead, soon replaced by the noisy hound as she leaps through the water, chasing the seabirds. A Black-Backed seagull with her large chick brings to mind Adrian's remark about The Laird treating me as a chick would its mother; head down, calling and circling. And in the small trees on the shore three Tui birds sing and hop about in the branches. We walk around the headland again. I find the Taniwha breathing hole. I even place my foot in the disappearing sand and *think* I touch the bottom. How brave is that?!

The Laird needs collecting from College at lunchtime and I take him to the surgery, lending a shoulder to lean on as he hobbles along. His ankle is to be bandaged in plaster. We come straight home afterwards, settling the patient in the top cabin. "Lots of R&R," instructed the nurse. Now the television can blare constantly without his wife complaining. Is he smirking? Hmm—-

Midday, Mouse: She is amazed by the waves of unconditional love for all, ignited by Lord Swallow's tender message of this morning. She realizes they are the first intimate words she has received during the past 4 months. He need not fear their intimacy—if anything it frees her. Secure in the knowledge of their love she can move forward; a surprise to feel herself basking in such heavenly truth. And then—another thought strikes home. They are in love with The Higher Body; in love with each other too, but as fellow Celestial Sea Sailors in pursuit of deep communion with the very essence of God. This is why they can move beyond. This is why they can share. This is what she tries, unsuccessfully, to explain. How can anyone be jealous of a Heavenly Love Rival? But—The Laird is jealous. The physical gets in the way, even though they have proved they can refrain. "In sickness and in health;" The Angels make sure she remembers. The look on The Laird's face was almost gleeful when the surgery phoned to say they suspected a fracture! His wife will need to be in constant attendance; 4 weeks in solid plaster—he has just had it done. A box of sushi comfort food on the way home completed the attention.

He was harsh with her this morning, threatening to make life difficult if she didn't back down. She overheard his phone call last night: "Yes, she is being extraordinarily clear in her thinking and discussion." Hmm—love you, My Friend. Can you resend your morning text? Also, can you e-mail me your synopsis? There is a pressing need to get The Book done. Thank-you—X

Midday, Adrian: He finishes his work. A dragonhead lies quietly outside the classroom. He checks the cows and moves them to new grazing. He wonders if his Lady got his morning messages. Warm-hearted—loving—appreciative of her care and thoughtfulness; her wit and warmth. "Yes," he answers as he unwraps her present—such a gift. A blood-surging gift. How—he cannot see—but his willingness is strong. Vonny's easy acceptance of his tale and keen observations still lie like—

Mouse: Lovely Friend, I am at home until 2p.m. The Laird is here but not straying from the top cabin. Do phone if you are free. I keep receiving unfinished texts. Was the last one meant to finish; 'still lie like?' And I only received a short text this morning—X

I take The Laird more food. The pig follows close behind, the tasty morsel tempting her porcine greed. Goodness—she's chasing me! She'll be big enough to run me down before long. I visualize us barricading ourselves in the top cabin, shouting; "Pig Attack! Quick—out of the back door before she barges her way inside;" The Castle Inmates dispersing hilariously, clutching tea and toast.

It is time for the school run; baby chick down my shirtfront—another Mountain rescue. The latest bantam family has made its home in Adrian's Gorse Garden. I have fenced them off from the pig by blocking the gate. Is it pig-proof? I make sure they have adequate food and water before I leave. I think the wobbly chicks must be late hatchers. They aren't ready to hop along after their heartless mother. I deliver some papers at College for The Laird before I arrive at School. My Lord Swallow looks dashing in his orange shirt; the vibrancy suits his character. I overhear him inviting Freya to try her hand at milking. The community is beginning to enjoy the unprocessed milk. I stand with them for a while, contributing to the conversation. Is it strange to be there, knowing that Freya is aware of our relationship? Not really. It feels natural. Freya takes Rinky home with Lucia for a sleepover while I chat to the lovely Louise. She is on traffic duty this afternoon.

P.m. Adrian: It was enough. I had finished. Out in the woodwork shed— fatigued—thinking about The Laird's hurt attempt at control. It is very easy for me to be shunted out of the picture. Simply by letting out a rumour—if he wanted, he could easily stop me. I almost get paranoid. Hau's daughter looked at me strangely today—could be my imagination. Good luck to you, My Love. May you be blessed as you strive to find the right action. Heading home now. Food desperately needed—

Mouse: Thank-you, My Friend. The shirt is lovely on you. Wish I could see you—talk to you—lie in your strong arms to know what we are again. There are too many unknowns. I don't want you to feel paranoid and anxious all the time. What did you say to Vonny? The Laird has outlined various choices, which is helpful. One of them sees me staying here for a month on my own in July. He would take all the children back to The U.K. for a holiday. I would have time to feel the reality of an empty house. I would understand the full implication of a family split. I'm not sure. How can I make such huge choices when we are not able to spend proper time with each other?
Keep texting—it really helps. Thank-you—X

The Go-Getter and I cook together in the kitchen this evening. He is intent on a garlic, onion and fresh ginger concoction, lightly fried together in olive oil. He devours it before anyone else gets a look-in, completing his aperitif with a big swig of fruit juice. "I suppose it might make some people vomit," he says. "Not the Africans and Indians though—they are so hungry, they would eat anything! I think I'll make some more. I'll write down the recipe. Can I borrow your little blue pencil?"

I am tired. It's that time of the month again. At least I am not pregnant—no opportunity for that! The only child I would consider bearing is Lord Swallow's Little Arthur. Our own family is complete and quite enough of a handful.

Late P.m. Mouse: *Sleep well, My Love—X—*

Wednesday 25th April 2007 Anzac,(Australian & NZ Army), Remembrance Day

A.m. Adrian: *Restored—his singing voice returned. Clear and straight with Big J. Honest, good friendship with Vonny. Easy with guitar students. Something has passed. The tummy eased though tender. He has just eaten a strip of dark, mocha chocolate and is sitting in bed with his laptop, about to start the synopsis—wondering about the discussions—how his Lacy Lady fares—loving her, {but not encouraging her!} Care is needed that he can stand by as supportive friend. X*

Mouse: *Good morning, Lord Swallow. How does the morning find you? Replenished? Relaxed? Busy or a quiet day ahead? Your Lady walks under a welcoming sky. She has lain with you as the dawn broke—her womanhood pains upon her again, eased by your soothing hands. She stops—your signal lighting up her phone. She hears you; home—settled—replenished, yes. Perhaps you feel the lull? They did not talk last night. She ponders The Laird's options upon the screen. She needs to write down her own possibilities. Thank-you for being there—without encouraging me!*

Did you tell Big J. where we stand? Did she ask? Thank-you for thinking about The Book. In a strange way, I think it may be the key to everything. My intuition tells me so, but perhaps my optimistic self is unrealistic. All I know is that I would be a freer woman if we could bring it to birth.

I love you. A quiet day lies ahead with shopping and writing—X

Adrian: *It is Anzac Day. Somewhere, people will be gathering—shivering in the dawn, sending plumes of steamy breath into the whispering crowd, waiting for the first strains of that haunting bugle call; The Last Post. But he is not there, choosing instead to send his thoughts and keep his body within the warmth of his bed. Somewhere is his Love, his Sweetheart, his Friend—maybe writing, maybe troubled, maybe clear in mind and heart. His phone has had no reception all night—no contact have they had. He wonders what has taken place; things are moving at such a pace. He is clear. Some* breakthrough took place yesterday afternoon—he is not even sure what—perhaps it was dietary; no cream and a short fast. Hmm—he was over doing it on the cream front; yum yum. But he is back in the saddle. He spoke confidently with Big J, asking to catch up on missed planning check and Play discussion. She is friendly and he tells her about his successful lessons; stroppy Class 6 was so responsive! Class 3's model house projects are coming in; it feels complete. Nothing needs hiding or skirting—his life may lie open—all parts. The sun shines and there are no shadows.

He thinks of her. Will it be tough for her right now? The Laird is acting out the resentment and hurt that he feels. Can she rise through it? He sees himself as a friend, reaching out a steadying hand from his snugly, blanket stronghold. He pictures his ideal: she gets fed up with her husband's chauvinism—figures out their separation—either returning home to settle them in and coming back, or—his words falter—she is right there—on the brink of these realities—the splitting of their family; how can she choose? She doesn't know. There are so many unknowns. Will her Lover be there for her? He comes and goes. She cannot rely on him. She cannot make her decision based on him, but she cannot leave him out of the picture either. He must be part of her decision. He must commit with her, but he will not do so unless he receives a sign; a clear signal that says; 'go boldly, this is your wife; this is your son—your daughter—stand up and proclaim your love and intention. Face the fury and be strong—trust; it is my will.' Until then he stands behind, not encouraging, but supporting.

If you and The Laird could work things out and fall in love again I would support you both wholeheartedly. I would still ask to be a creative friend, but free I would set you. If you cannot do this, then I would support you to free yourself—not for my own need, but to see you maintaining your integrity and self-truth. But then I may miss out—you would return to England, surely? I don't want to set myself up as the one to blame—but maybe this is—

Mouse: Thank-you, My Darling. Thank-you for being there. Just received your recent updates; it is such a relief to talk like this. I see my bridges being burnt around me, but I am strangely unfazed. Even with my reputation in ruins at home I could return with my head held high. What I have gained are Heavenly riches beyond judgement. And if I stayed? Yes, I could do that too—as long as I could afford regular flights home.

P.s—I have just changed you to Adrian on my phone—might you change me to Mouse? It feels right. Big, wrap-around hug. I won't tell you how we were this morning—mmm—

Adrian: Name changed, My Love. Maybe that is it. Nothing changes in your life with The Laird, but he gives you permission to work on The Book. No choices to make until that is finished and we see what emerges. What is incredible is how transparent everything is now. The Laird knows the content of it all—our love—

Mouse: Here's some food for thought: The Benedictine Abbott asked The Laird what the esoteric, artistic philosophy we know and love would have to say about the situation. Ekhart Tolle says that if something isn't working then you should change it—carefully.

Oh no—pig and baby chick alert! Help! New clutch just hatched! Back soon.

Mouse: All clear—murdering pig distracted with compost bin. Lady of The Castle hopes her little cheeping charge from yesterday is still alive. A day spent down the Mistress's cleavage is the answer for saving lives—if you are of a feathered nature of course—swallows included. Well, I had better stop bothering the gifted wordsmith. The kitchen floor looks as if a dog on heat, a rampaging pig, a flock of chickens, 3 children and a Laird on crutches have just been through the place! Better get to. Wet socks from the emergency chick rescue don't help. Bother. Look what I'd be giving up! X

* * * * * * *

Later, Mouse: Your last text about The Book didn't come through entirely. Can you resend? Another pig alert—your gorse garden is shored up with a piece of wood to try and prevent the chick scoffing. It has become the nursery. You should see the tomato plants; a veritable jungle! Don't you just love the smell of tomato plants? I do. No socks this time—pig pooh between my toes. Expect you're glad to be away from the chaos. Your Lady isn't at her best.

P.s. Mouse: The Mistress tried her best. The sad, desperate cries of the mother hen—not a single babe was spared. The Mistress has a gorse-spiked rear from leaping over the hedge to save the vulnerable family. The accusatory glare from the chief chicken carer hasn't left his face; his mother didn't do enough. She takes The Laird his breakfast in bed; "why have you got mud on your nose? What have you been up to now? For goodness sake, woman!" Ah, one chick is found, alive. We have moved him to a safe cage.

The Laird is cross. He is threatening. She has walked the dog in the open field—the sunshine on her face. A decision at last; a way forward. She asks for a creative separation—for him to go back to The U.K. with Cedric. She will write—and work out her relationship with the man she loves. The Laird will be amongst friends and family while he works on the new school idea. After a few months they will all know how they feel. She takes a deep breath and gives it to him.

"So, what you are saying is that you don't want to be married to me at the moment; that you will pursue your own ends above your duty to others?" The Laird demands an answer. "If I were to tell you I could walk away from Adrian that would be a lie," she answers. "Our journey, wherever it may lead us, is not over yet. Perhaps it might end in a few months, or perhaps not.

Who knows? Maybe it is just a Book. But I am not ready to finish it now. I have to be honest." "Please write it all down," he asks. "This is a major decision. You don't know what I might do. You might regret this for all time. I am aware that we don't nourish each other at a personal level; that something needs to change—so, yes, for a trial period I am prepared to take a risk." She feels sure—gently sure, knowing the boil has to burst.

Thank-you for resending the message; a bit more came through. Can you send it again; in case I've missed anything? I love you. I will spend the day looking at my decision and decide if it feels right—X

* * * * * * *

Early P.m. Mouse: Hello, My Friend. I have had a cleaning, tidying frenzy. The house is more presentable. I still haven't written up my decision. I'll get there. I go from hot to cold over my choice. Any esoteric advice? Freya is about to deliver Rinky back home after a forest walk. Did you notice how fine it felt to be together with her yesterday? Knowing that she knows about us? Perhaps she felt odd but I didn't. The two boys are enjoying each other today. Could I part them? But it wouldn't be forever—just for a trial period. We shall see. Once it is typed up I might be clearer. I shall e-mail you the finished piece. And how are you, My Love? Nothing like a spanking pace to follow. Hope you are finding some quiet waters in these giant swells. I am so glad you are an experienced sailor. Tell me about your day—your heart—your cows. Loving you—X

Adrian: The messages tend to update automatically, but I'll send them again. I'm not even sure which ones—there have been so many. Vonny and I are cheering for you. Now we get to see true colours; now it really is a choice of love over personal need for security. Why be cruel? Is it another's happiness we truly seek, or do we protect our own picture of how things could be—what we would like? The affect on the children could be the lash. God bless both of you. Light on your home.

P.s Just on my way to the 'More to Life' course. I'm late because I had Cordelia and Joni at the farm, milking. Relief milkers? Could be good. Finished spreading some special Preparation 500 on the fields. More to make up.

Better go—I'm here for you—Adrian—X

Mouse: My Darling Friend, thank-you for the support. Freya and gang ended up staying for roast lamb. Great to see them and excellent for The Laird; boosting his mood. I just heard him on the telephone; another serious conversation with a friend at home. He was talking about the various choices we have already outlined. He is making noises about taking all the children; more of a threat I think. We shall see. Hope the course is good. I keep feeling wobbly. Will need your arms before long—M—X

Thursday 26ᵗʰ April 2007

A.m. Adrian: The morning finds a cat under his covers—Miffy—in complete trust, snuggled up, even with his nightly movements. His belly is gurgly but he feels clear; a little distant from his class, but coming in fast. The meeting last night; a good break from the usual—new people with whom to interact; people not used to carrying roles of responsibility. Life-shocks for them all. He sees that his work has given him skills. He had completed the majority of his commitments and felt most virtuous. He did some nice things for Big J yesterday and feels clear with his work place and colleagues. Just want to complete planning—this morning's work.

He loves her. He wonders without undue anxiety whether the tidal wave will hit today. Somehow this doesn't faze him. He reasons it like this: "My Lady is not leaving The Laird for me. She is leaving for herself. We had a nice friendship that crossed boundaries but was stopped. I have not coveted her for my own in a way that has influenced her choice. Simon stands as guardian at one end of The School—Big J at the other. My Lady stands on one wall and I on another—held and protective; I can stand. Rumour and gossip may fly. Your choice relates to me, but is not because of me."

And how is The Fine Lady herself? And her Good Man and Kinder? How have they fared? Angelic wings surround you—God's hand within reach. He is with her—very much, however—

Mouse: He is the first to grace the paper with his quill this morn. She has been sleepy in his arms, waking slowly—only just rising. She takes him down the drive; that's where they are now with the sound of the mumbling brook, a handful of bird chatter and the Bog-Brush halting in Pointer-mode. "There is something there, Mistress—listen—use your ears; be alert to the tune." The hound chooses to be still for several minutes at a time.

Her heart this morning? How can she possibly consider disrupting their lives to this extent? The selfish action of even dreaming to go there. The Laird has to decide about The U.K. job tomorrow. She must let him know her definite decision. Her family is appalled that she is capable of such disloyalty. She feels flat; unsure. What will the day bring? Thank-you for your message. I like the picture of the guardians and the held honour—the gentle care and respect as the wave reaches the shore—a warm comfort. Something has led us to this point—has brought me to you from across the world. These loving guardians have been primed. Yes—we are ready—X

The morning is busy. The Laird is cross and unhappy. Somehow we manage to arrive at College on time. I watch my sad, hobbling husband climb out of the car and head away, into the building. Should I feel awful? Sorry? Maybe I do a little. But not guilty, no—never guilty.

We pass three hawks on the road home. The Bog-Brush is so excited. One bird doesn't even bother removing itself from the road-kill as we drive past; a regal creature under these blue skies today. I write. We walk in the big field next to our land where the bubbling stream reminds me of Scotland.

64

Midday, Mouse: *Hi—at home—writing and trying to assimilate thoughts. How is my Fine Sir? Love you—X*

Adrian: *Your Fine Sir is brimming. The School is a loving place to be. Big J greeted him so warmly this morning—children happy and interested—usual funny little greeting from The Go-Getter—smile and wave from Rinky. No sense of any Tidal Wave. To come? Maybe not. Wondering how you are feeling?*

Mouse: *But it must be with The Laird's blessing, with the knowledge that he is held in love and security too; that we can make it work if we so choose. His grim morning countenance—his fierce determination that the state of marriage is what matters most leaves no room for growth. She watches as he ruthlessly hacks away at the candle, digging out their rings and forcing his back on his finger. Her ring, he leaves buried in the vandalized wax. Her heart goes out to him. She hates to see him suffer. Need it be like this? Luckily the children don't ask what he is doing. She is saddened by his action— understandable, of course. His beloved companion of twenty-five years is profoundly in love with another man.*

She sighs, her hopes for some ceremony with the retrieval of the rings dashed. She needs to write him a letter today. Perhaps a call for humble surrender. She will not act without his blessing. He can hold her captive if that is his top priority. She had hoped he could see beyond, but that is asking too much. So, a missive she must write, but she won't deny her Lover's presence in her heart and soul. She has room for all.

My Darling Adrian, I will send you a copy of the letter. You know I am still with you, but perhaps we have to play the game their way for a while longer. And—we have to decide what and how we should be together. I refuse to disappear. Please hold me. Please love me—X

Adrian sends me an e-mail this afternoon. He has been working on The Book. Great—this is just what I need; something positive that doesn't ruffle feathers and lives. At least we can be together in the story. Nobody can steal that away. I shall send him a bedtime text message followed by my reply to his e-mail.

Early P.m. Mouse: *She should be writing, but instead she sleeps on the sofa with the Bog-Brush. She imagines her Lover is with her. He is kissing her. Her breath leaves her body as their lips meet in the most tender, checked passion. They cannot wait any longer—flushed faces—exploring fingers— months of intoxicating longing in this knife-edged moment. They smile at each other. They know each other. Their bodies pick up the beloved Rhythmic Dance with graceful ease. She reaches for him; he finds her soft curves; 'buckles and velvet, breeches and lace'—X*

E-mail to Lord Swallow:

Darling Friend, thank-you for spending time on the synopsis for Dry Dock. I have edited it, added a few things and taken out a couple of words when it didn't run as smoothly as it could. It is beautiful; my heart is yours. I shall send it back. Let me know what you think and I can e-mail it to our waiting editor. I wondered whether we should write the mystical element of The Boat and its creation in text form—each adding a piece to the story. How about The Boat actually speaking? I shall send you a text with a beginning idea and if you like the concept, you could run with it. We could work on it together that way—especially as you don't have much time otherwise. What say you, my fellow adventurer?

Later, Mouse: We are wearing the same colours today—caught a glimpse of you through the school railings on our way home. Neutrals—browns and beiges—gentle background tones, perfectly blended for waiting on our opposite walls. You must wonder what your Lady is playing at—messages of surrender one minute—passionate sofa episodes the next. At least she knows you will be able to follow her bouncing mind. We always 'bounce' in tune, unlike The Laird who seriously dislikes any unfocused 'bouncing'! Anyway, I have sent him a text message today. I shall send it on to you now. Darling Friend—how are you? Well, I hope. I Love you—X

Lady to the Laird: I cannot put my own joy and longing before my duty to others. The fondness I have for my husband remains unchanged. The communion I share with another is not a selfish, exclusive union. It is centred in the very essence of unconditional love and delight in sharing. Do with me as you will, but know that I cannot deny the reality of this bond. It enriches me; I want it to enrich others, not cause anguish. I am truly sorry for any hurt I may have caused. Just believe—just believe. So, I will not take a creative sabbatical without my husband's love and blessing. I will obey him. I will do my duty.

Adrian: Goodnight, Dear Friend—Lion, not Mouse. Sleep well, My Dear. I'm pooped—nodded off with phone in hand.

Mouse: Goodnight, My Darling. Sleep well. We are having a quiet evening. The Laird ponders his wife's submittance, knowing it is a negative—a missed potential and a dead end for her. "So, will I have a sad wife for ever more?" He asked. "Yes," she replied. "What am I to do with you? With these other, mystery parts of you?" She was downcast. "You decide," she answered. "I have been honest with you, but you cannot accept the truth. You decide now." She is making them a pot of tea. A mouse runs across the floor. The cupboards still need sorting—and mousetraps setting. Hmm—mousetraps, eh?

She sends him her love. She will be with him tonight. Blessings and Angel spray as the wave hits the shore, My Beautiful Lord Swallow. X

The Laird and I lie on the bed, watching television. I am uncommunicative. I can do the duty thing if that is what he truly wants, but I cannot commit to our marriage. At this moment I cannot say that I want it to last. "Can you look me in the eye and tell me you want to work on our relationship?" "No, I cannot," I admit. "That would be a lie. Adrian and I have unfinished work. We need time to be creative together. I cannot say if it will last or not. I just know that I have to go with my intuition. Why don't you try it my way for a while? I know I could make it work—give you love, if I am allowed to see Adrian."

"WHAT?" —

No—sorry—of course I can't ask my husband to share me with another. What can I be thinking? "I am prepared to try hard; to provide the things you need," my long-suffering husband offers. "But you can't be someone you are not," I reply, thanking him for his generosity, adding that as individuals neither of us possesses the ingredients we need to truly fulfil one another. We talk about the children. I suggest that I hold our N.Z life while he holds the English side. "But then the children would be without a father for much of the time, and I won't do anything to hurt them." He sends me up to the top cabin for the night—"more fitting for the moment." Yes, I agree. With liberation and growing excitement I take ownership of our smaller cabin. It is after midnight. It is the **27**th —just begun. Why do our important days always include a number **7**? What a strange accent.

Chapter 2 Accent

Friday 27th April 2007

A.m. very early, Mouse: It is just after midnight. They have had the serious talk. She has looked him in the eye and told him she cannot commit to their marriage at present—not without Lord Swallow in the picture. The Laird is cross. He cannot believe she is no longer in love with her husband. He cannot accept that she has another man in her life. He sends her out of the house—away to the top cabin, saying: "You have my love but not my affection."

She is a free woman. He will make plans for a separation; gulp. Goodnight, My Dearest Friend. I know you are sleeping. I hope this doesn't wake you—X

A.m. Adrian: How will it be for The Laird today? Blown apart by a bombshell—or not? Will he turn with anger and tear me down? A formal complaint and down I fall; the farm proposals nothing more than pieces of paper blown away by the storm. Or what? How can The Laird sit with this? He has nowhere to go with it—he is stuck. His own College career is no longer important; he cannot hope to win you back. What is left for him? He is backed into a corner. Does he give up? What is he living for now that his family is breaking apart? There is only one chink of light; to trust that she knows what she is doing; that what she has been saying all along may be true—that there is more for them all. But that step—that step of giving in—of trusting in such an absolutely unconventional idea as sharing his wife with another; his mind balks. It is repulsive. How could he stand up amongst other married men and admit that? That he cannot satisfy his wife's needs. He could not. How could he possibly step to that new tune? She asks the impossible. But what is the alternative? Destruction—disaster—everyone suffering. Could he? How could he? "What are we to do with you, Mrs. Mouse?" And there she is completely guilt-free, not at all troubled by her actions—only by the hurt they cause him.

"And that Teacher—that sneaky little teacher—the cause of it all—bet he is smirking somewhere; laughing at my ignorance and blundering, having won." No, it is not like that. I do not want to win. I am not out to take her away. "Then what do you want?" I want you two to be fulfilled. If she turned back to you Sir, and worked at restoring what you had, I would be gone—pursuing my own life—looking for my own wife. And I have tried to turn her to you many times. But until she does I am standing by to offer her support and in a crazy way, you too. Were you to work it out I would back out—

reluctantly because I now love her—but to honour the family I would. However, she speaks of a hope she has that is so different, radical, and maybe possible. It requires stepping out of worldly law—and I can see it sometimes—see what she is driving at; this floating idea where everyone seems to win, but then I get scared and guilty and smashed by worldly law and lose that vision. Could it work? It is only her hope that keeps it afloat. But look at her—she is the only sane one between us—consistently steady—positive and energised, whereas both of us are a bit wobbly and one-sided. It racks me with guilt sometimes but I have learnt to trust.

I pray about it and ask for signs about the rightness—if I should set a boundary and say 'No' for my sense of honour, but I keep being drawn back into her vision. It is so beautiful. And not only that—doors keep opening—we are put together in class—the pig needs a home—festival meetings—we both have free periods at the same time—not conclusive reasons but not thwarting either. After my prayer for a sign I expect a slam—something difficult—a question—a judgemental comment or a scornful look from someone who knows; Bernard, Hau, Simon. It is all it would take to stop me dead in my tracks—but instead nothing—clear road—only my own sense of honour to put the brakes on. And is this it, I wonder? A test? Conscience training?

But then we are together and it is so rich and natural and life-giving and I give up. I don't know and I'm tired of trying to figure it out. I'll put God in charge and when he says it's time to stop he'll let me know like he did the last time. And I'll face it—if it comes—could mean ruin—condemnation—a tidal wave of accusation—maybe even publicity. But I'll face it if it comes. X

Flip, the pace slackens not. Have I really chosen this roller-coaster of a life? There is no turning back now. I have written my letter to The Laird:

Mistress to the Laird: My Darling, you ask me what I want—what I ask of you? That I should even be putting you through this fills me with concern—and yet—the beautiful picture and the Angel-held path shine stronger everyday and I know we are being called to take on something quite extraordinary for some purpose. I do not see this as the 'end' of you and I, rather as an emergence; a moving forward to become the best versions of ourselves. I may be proven wrong; I am not so arrogant as to assume 100% knowledge, but the constant joy and unconditional love that shower over this entire happening continue to take my breath away and call me to step into unknown waters. I am unable, at the moment, to turn away.

In practical terms, what do I see? This is the picture that comes to me:

We maintain our N.Z residency and acquire property and perhaps a rental/property development small business to keep afloat.

I continue to spearhead the new developments at school and community, perhaps owning land or a building on site. Maybe even a salaried position.

I spend time with Adrian as I do now; when there is free time or everyone is out at the weekends. I would like to ask for a night a week to be away from home. Adrian wants to be our back-up—caring for property, animals, tenants etc. He would never dare to call himself replacement Father—just a really close, family friend and special support.

I would like to see you giving yourself a sabbatical, both here and at home. I would ask you to take on a craft—join a monastery for a while—research the new school idea. If we were self-sufficient in N.Z then this would give you the free time you richly deserve and need. You have worked such hard, long years for us all that now is the time to gain something deepening for yourself. Perhaps even write your book, it would probably hit the bookshelves ahead of mine.

I would like to continue with my writing—and with my involvement with the community village idea. I see your/our school dovetailing beautifully with the plans we are working on at present. I see myself spending time between N.Z and home, perhaps using some of our U.K house sale money to convert the garage at Ma and Pa's into a two-bedroomed home base for us. This could be used by all the family and be useful when M & D need looking after in years to come.

I see us making money—from writing—from the school.

I would like to be a strong part of your/our school back-up team; but from a point of 'holding the fort' and to have Adrian alongside while you are away would give me the completeness I need.

Our journey is not exclusive; it is more about pooling our joint strengths and giving something really quite extraordinary back into the communities we live in and establish. Our combined force is something quite remarkable. I could even see us hitting the headlines with it.

What would you say to others? You could say in all honesty that your wife has found an extraordinary, life-changing bond in her friendship with Adrian and that you have decided to work with it, rather than against it. The positive balance it brings to our lives may be most unconventional, but in a wonderful way, it works.

I would suggest a leap of faith to begin in September when you go to Europe. I would like you to trust us, your loving family, to Adrian's care—as a trial time perhaps. No, I would not hold his hand or jump into bed with him when the children were with us. We would maintain a dignity.

I want you to be free and happy, My Darling. I ask you to let go of fear and to trust. I love you. Thank-you for even considering listening to my vision for our future.

{I do not include the following suggestion in my message to The Laird.}

"And what if you conceive a child?" Ah, yes—'The Child'. There is

a Child—perhaps the impetus behind this whole event. A Child who waits; who hopes. A Child who has chosen two Fathers; two fine men. I know not why. A Child who is destined to unite Northern and Southern Hemispheres, with strengths in both Heavenly intuition and Earthly Holiness—-who chooses the media to herald his/her birth through the medium of a mystical storybook. And The Child's name? The Child's name is Arthur.

Later, Mouse: With piercing, Angel-laser light I am crafted. I am long and sleek. The plane and lathe have fashioned me for the tides and ocean swell of many lifetimes. I have lain under The Craftsman's hands for a long, long time. Every angle, every joint is a fine-honed work of art. I have a knife-edged keel. I am built to find smooth, swift passage where others may fail. My central mast stands strong and tall. I sense a growing excitement at the dignity I possess. The sheets and cleats are aligned. The ropes a magical twine—a thousand strands of unspoken mystery make up the whole. My fittings are of the highest quality—Eleven. I shiver with anticipation, even when night time deepens.

Lord Swallow: He wonders—if his Lady and her Husband have built a ship of their own? A relation-ship? What is happening to it now? Perhaps it is a grand and heavy vessel that doesn't go anywhere, or a higgledy-piggledy one with wild and fantastic sails, but poorly designed. Or maybe it is a powerboat and she is putting up a sail. Is it a catamaran trying to go in different directions? Perhaps it is a beautiful boat, but moored in a harbour all the time, with The Laird on-shore a lot. He suspects that a picture of their situation could be helpful to objectify things a little more, and give the heart more breathing space. All this close-up work is taxing. As for this teacher, he feels himself only lightly around his class—just enough he hopes. His thoughts are sometimes ones of desire—fewer of fear; hope and excitement growing, but held back. He strives to keep his wants and hopes warm, but without energy—transferred to good wishes.

He decides his life is like a ship on the sea—it must roll with the waves. Sailors would give up their activities while the ship righted herself; an easy flow with what we do and what we hold. Sometimes the roll is towards School, and he attends to this—leaving farm developments and home duties until the wave has passed, for his craft has wisdom and he can trust her. Sometimes, waves can overwhelm a ship and break her apart—then the survivors must scramble out and find another one—nervous breakdown.

These are the thoughts he woke with. He bids his Lady a restrained good morning, hoping the new day finds her and her husband restored and clear. Blessings on you both. Loving arms around you—X

Mouse: Yes, a nautical picture of our situation would help, perhaps The Laird would understand more easily. Thank you.

Our marriage boat—our 'relation-ship': To begin with, The Laird has never believed our craft could actually sail at sea. It has ever been anchored in the harbour—for sure—The Harbour Master content on dry land for most of the time; yes. His Galley Slave has been pre-occupied with the care of the crew and general ship maintenance that have left her tired and over-stretched. The Harbour Master, a splendid figure of a man, is really a 'man's man'—a difficult mother, and an all-male boarding school, have put him off the intrigues of the female psyche. Oh, but of course, he is generosity itself; a diligent husband and adoring father at all times—patient in waiting so long for her to regain her stamina. Their boat is full of loving commitment and friendship at all times. However, to keep himself from boredom within the endless domesticity, he gets busier and busier on dry land, neglecting his wife and resenting her domestic routines.

Their vessel is incredibly solid. For a quarter of a century it has withstood many storms and gales—never moving an inch from its mooring. The Laird likes to use the motor on the odd occasion they head out to sea. His Lady would prefer to travel under sail, but he does not understand the difference. He moves to a different rhythm to his sailing companion. His Lady realizes this more and more with each passing year. In fact, she longs for the joy of sailing under the fine, billowing sails she has stored away so carefully. She often gazes on them—they are her private Heaven. She needs them, imagining she will have to wait for another lifetime to unfurl their potential. The Laird knows of their existence. In a way, it was because of them that he was drawn to her in the first place. But he has no desire to see them, let alone use them. They do not ignite his imagination—he does not possess the knowhow to unlock their finery. They block his peaceful sanctuary. His is a simple life; no time or interest in the mystical unknowns these sails represent. In a way, he rather wishes they would disappear. She has tried to engage him with their majesty, but deep down, they both know that is not possible. They do not share any artistic chemistry. In their place he assumes a short-tempered, controlling stance over her, which increases each year. And to compensate, they fill their solid boat with crowds of people, lots of action and many grand plans—several of which come to fruition. They are a successful working team.

And so the day arrives when they are offered the opportunity of a lifetime; to sail away to the other side of the world and start a new life! They both know that something needs to change, so they say 'yes' to the offer. To be sure, their vessel is strong enough for the voyage. They pack up and leave—a long and arduous task indeed, made possible by the constant help and love of their immediate family. Eventually, they arrive in the stunning land of New Zealand. They quickly find a berth—everything they have ever dreamed of. Yes, they have arrived. They moor up alongside some other interesting boats and return to the way their lives have always worked; lots of action, socializing and community building, and to replace her need for her beloved sails, she starts the small enterprises that have always sustained her in the past.

But—the wilder winds and smaller foundations of The Marina in this new land start to take their toll after a year of being away from home. Their vessel *is rocked violently; the absence of a solid framework made up of family and friends, structure and culture unseating him, more than her. They discover their boat has been reliant on outside elements to give it its ballast; something she has suspected for a while. And then, to unseat them further, The Lady at the helm moors up alongside a fellow Sailor. She notices him immediately; his magnificent sails are in full use—his passionate skill and mastery with them, a joy to behold. They are identical to hers. She cannot believe it. His name is Lord Swallow—*

Adrian: *And he—he will not rush in—nor will he sneak. His steps take the sunlit path now. So he watches, from a distance—reined soul—patient for the first time—accepting what will come—unattached to the outcome—extending a helpful hand. Is he really that clear? What keeps him grounded? This is a noble but difficult stance that needs maturity. Does he really possess it? What else lives in him? Where is his selfish and greedy side? What is he hiding? Let's see—*

Mouse: *"The spotlight! For pity's sake, My Lady—turn off the spotlight! It is blinding me. I cannot think straight. Too many thoughts and reasonable words create barriers to simple processing. Please turn it off, or down, at least. I was expecting The Tidal Wave, but not accompanied by a spotlight!"*
She smiles—mirth hovers, despite the serious nature of the material. Don't worry, Lord Swallow. I am not shining the light on you, personally. I shall turn it off if you prefer. Please don't be afraid.

I walk on the low tide sands at Tui Park. I feel bloated again; too much food recently. I only seem able to diet when I am sad. And I am tired—too little sleep. Am I surprised by Lord Swallow's reaction to this fast-paced week? No, not really. This is a Tidal Wave, for sure. He never wanted to break up a family, or to take on the complicated baggage of another man's life. It will take a lot of courage to climb back on board our precious Boat. We shall see. The Laird asked me how my conscience was last night. I told him that I felt calm.

I have parked in a different area of the park today. Classical music and a full bottle of Supergreens make for something different. I need to drive home; I can't stay here all morning. I have work to complete on the college project I am handling. Perhaps I will feel better being freed up around The Laird. Perhaps we will have more fun. Strange that it begins now—of all days, the 27th. Yes, this is how I wish we could be: a healthy, working relationship between The Laird and me and a hallowed, sacred partnership between Lord Swallow and his Lady. Hmm—The Laird will not countenance it, and I cannot have it any other way. I like Adrian's passage about the boat The Laird and I sail together—or don't.

Midday, Mouse: *Yes, there is a glorious Light. It glows from a sky of possibility. Her wings have been returned. They love The Light—the beautiful,* dancing Light. She flexes them. This is what he senses; the breeze and reflected dazzle. She prays for The Light to enfold them all. This is about sharing and freeing up. She smiles at him, blowing him a kiss full of promise.

I pass Vonny walking to School in the sun at pick-up time. She waves at me exultantly with her homemade, flax hat! I bow and blow her a kiss; the joy on my face complete.

Midday Update, Adrian: *And what of this man she has chosen over you? What does he think about all this? He considers the raised eyebrow question from the family. He answers slowly—watching the unfolding drama with compassionate interest. He keeps his own hopes and desires reined. He wishes not for their separation but for their truthful selves to have freedom of expression. There is always compromise but this must not hinder truth. His opinion is that this courageous step will release the greater benefit to the world. Short-term pain—the painful acceptance of failings—areas of denial and ignorance desperately needing the light of acknowledgement for long-term gain. Far greater mobility of soul—less need for supportive structures—more power—less clutching—of benefit to them both, and in the long-run the children too; they who have been the before and the after—they who have witnessed courage and truth.*

Mouse: *My clear thinking, wise friend. Thank-you for your beautiful message that eventually arrived after five attempts. The last part came just now; profound food for thought. I have been at the park all morning—writing. The Second Book is gaining form. I have been with The Laird this afternoon. He is at home, resting his ankle; still sad and disbelieving. "If I return to The U.K. there will be no chance of mending our marriage." I speak of allowing us our creative bond—again—that we could make it work. He always asks me to imagine my feelings if he was the one with a lover. How would I feel? Hmm; "You are asking me to adjust my entire belief system." Anyway, My Darling Friend, I don't think he could tear us all apart. You and I can both see the potential, but it is unorthodox. Just a lovers' pipe dream?*
The little mouse is watching me from under the fridge. I—need you. X

Adrian: *Even the weather seems to be waiting—holding its breath; these still, still days. He has just dropped Vonny at the airport for her month away. It is Friday; fire bath night and maybe band practise. The supplies are in. The dogs run and bark on the beach. The setting sun is wide and free—huge and open—a big out-breath that feels like a holiday. He is reading her updates with interest; dialogue giving such an immediate picture. She sure knows how to write.*

P.m. Mouse: *Are you home, My Friend? I imagine you playing on the sands with the dogs. Nice. I came home to a ransacked kitchen. The crutched Laird left the kitchen door open by mistake. The pig—oh my—the pig! A sea* of cornflakes, sugar, jam—everywhere. The mice will be thrilled. I am tired; the strains of the day telling. Even The Inmates' trainers have received a dusting of breakfast debris. And where is the expensive new bag of dried dog food? Surely Molly hasn't polished off that as well? Including the bag?

I have the house to myself for once. The Laird is in the top cabin with the children. Cedric is away for the night. Would you like a phone call? Only if you feel like it—no obligation, please. Your Lady is pooped; worn thin by all the extra dashing about and general life crises—X

Adrian: He sends her love and strength and courage. Sleep my Love—anywhere—as much as you can; the great restorer. Spend time with The Angels if you can't be with me. I can hear your ache. Bear up, sweet craft. Somewhere ahead lies a safe harbour. There is more journey yet. Maintain the watch. Keep the crew in good spirits. Rest and play any way you can. Take comfort any way you can. Take comfort in each other even now. Remember your love—it has not gone but is being stretched and tested. Slacken it now.

Mouse: The Laird goes from hot to cold about his idea to leave the country—or not. He cannot abide the lack of direction. He feels trapped; standing still in the same area as his wife and her lover. He could remain here and trust again if she relinquished their association. But she will not renounce her intention to remain in touch with Lord Swallow—she says they can be platonic friends. It is unreasonable of her to ask that of him. His forced inertia is making him think long and hard. Will he step over the humble shadow? Or does he have to leave in order to free things up? A time of waiting—yes—of Angel-held waiting. She would come and visit him tonight—in secret—but she knows that would be unwise. He would send her away. She is tired; running low on energy and impetus. She needs him. X

Saturday 28ᵗʰ April 2007
A.m. Mouse: Hi—mmm—ah—X—X—You feel good this morning, My Fine Sir. Hello—mm—X

Adrian: What are you up to, I wonder? X

Mouse: She sits at the kitchen table, the sound of rain on the roof a comfort—a dripping percussion outside the windows. Soggy fowl and resigned dog—her morning walk abrupt. The Little Princess plays quietly upstairs; "Where's Daddy?" The Laird is sleeping in the top cabin. The lure of late night rugby providing the perfect escape from his perplexing wife. "I don't know whether to hit you, or hug you," he said as she boldly snuggled under his duvet last night to watch a romantic film. They are close—but as friends, not lovers. Strange not to feel those stirrings of intimacy during a love-story. She felt his matched thoughts. As she headed for bed in the main house, he said: "Yes—I could see myself returning to The U.K." She is unsure about his statement. Is it a threat? Does his intention include his wife, or not? She decides it is the beginning of his acceptance of the possibility. She will read to the Little Princess—then take The Laird his tea. She has told him that she won't return with him to the Sussex Monastery. She would only consider a new area—with a steady job to provide the stability she knows works for them. "But, I would only come if I could maintain contact with Adrian; our literary dialogue allowed to continue. "Well," he replied; "It wouldn't matter so much. You couldn't do anything about it, and he will shack up with someone else soon enough. I know what he is like. He is a man. He will forget you." She is slightly stung by his words—knowing he is probably right in an earthly way. But—theirs is not an earthly way. Lord Swallow knows it—and his Lady knows it. The Angels will direct. Whatever is meant to be will be. She loves Lord Swallow—she is with him—snuggling under his cosy blanket, wrapped around him. She will keep him informed today. She might even pay a brief visit if it feels right—and in The Light.

I love you—X

Adrian: The weather has broken; in great sobbing breaths her held grief and tears pour out. She breathes again—new life flooding in. Seeds, lying dormant in the pastures are awakened. Quivering, they swell to bursting with The Mother's nourishing tears; sparks of life tearing through them. Other grasses almost rustle in their growth-rush; autumn flush. In the shady places the drops and torrents disturb spores, whose white, orange and red caps soon cover every rotting log and leaf. The animals are washed clean in the long awaited shower—warm and steaming like a freshly washed maiden stepping from a bathing place.

The farmer listens with pleasure to the drum of the heavy drops, knowing that this tattoo heralds a fine flush to take his stock far into winter; healthy and strong. It helps his decision to take the offered calf—abandoned at birth by a belligerent mother—kicked away—damaged by her. Yes, there would definitely be enough food for all the animals.

His bed is hot—his body a little stiff and not quite right—belly unsettled from slightly forced, late night conversations with band members and eating chocolate biscuits. His joints feel a little swollen from too much something; maybe dairy—maybe porridge, an old allergen for him as a youth. But his mind is clear—ish. Actually, it could be clearer. He checks his heart for self-love and humour. He remembers his dreams—fighting a polluting factory—dangerous detective work; confrontation—lots of confrontation—shouting—exposing baddies—following clues in cars and on water—probing —one step ahead—just. Probably related to conversations of gloom last night that he felt compelled to raise higher. He raved at length on The School's philosophy and reincarnation, coming at last to the stand of Guardian Of The School in service to The World. Phew!

Mouse: Longing surges through her—so strong today. She wants him. She needs him. She wonders—does he feel the same? The Laird is deciding *his course of action. She is in half a mind to tell him she will go to her Lover. She wonders about his thoughts—what is he doing?*

Adrian: *On his computer, studying the constellations—making a booklet for the night sky observations. If you are allowed.*

* * * * * * *

Midday, Mouse: *I'm so tired—reaching the crossroads with no future route. "No, I most certainly won't let you see Adrian. How can you imagine I would ever allow you to visit your Lover?!" Even my suggesting it knocks The Laird—brings the reality of the situation to the fore; again. Unmentioned, the focus diminishes. In a strange way, life works better if he just doesn't know. I suppose I have always realized this—why it worked before when hidden. I need to be close with you, soon. I may have to choose; 'all or nothing.' I cannot do that if I am unable to see you—to talk—to feel—to be clear. Does that make sense, My Friend? X*

Adrian: *So much work—a full morning. He emerges, blinking into the midday sun—neglected animals call his attention. The newly captured hen— Susie-Rose's from Class 2—still sits in the box with the plant on top, quite content after the blood curdling cries of murder during last night's capture. The white bunny hops hopefully around its cage—desperately trying to catch his attention. He takes a shower and the computer headache begins to fade. What was his intense drive to learn the constellations and their stories? He is not sure, but trusts it in the same way he has trusted his woodwork impulses now bearing fruit. He now has a splendid resource for The Greek Legends; the artists' impressions and the star charts for the entire Zodiac and a couple of other significant ones. Class **7** astronomy lessons? Adult Workshops one day? He had an idea yesterday on driving past the sweet little dairy farm on the Waikite Bay road—ever seen 'Babe'?*

For The Laird: It's denial we're talking about here. Poor man. Constant life-shocks waking him up to it, when all he wants is to put it to sleep. Stay soft with him—and insistent. Help him to accept there are changes taking place—by—um—doing a process is the best way, although that's not going to be possible. Maybe—could you ask him to check what happened when you asked him that question? What were his feelings? Then gently probe the mind-talk. What led to that feeling? Because moving through will be painful and difficult with an uncorrected mind-talk going on and resentment clouding the love; anger and separation knocking back any progress. Get down to the bottom of all that. "What do you think about me, Laird? I really want to hear it." Stick to one moment though. Write it down and at the end, ask if it is a truth. A fundamental truth. "Am I like that all the time?" Ask about him too. Who else will help him through? Most would escalate the blame and self-righteousness; it's uphill otherwise. Find a way to bring movement—be creative and wild, if you can muster the energy. Keep it active. Your ship needs careful piloting to stop it floundering; so heavy and difficult to steer. You need to work hard with your pull and push away from obstacles—leaping from one side to the other. You're the only hope. Or are you? Can you call in some assistance? Do you have a fairy godmother anywhere?

P.m. Mouse: Thanks Darling. I could try, but the belligerent teacher/ psychologist always shouts me down. "Choose me, woman. Why can't you choose me?" Exasperated, he waves his invalid's crutch in my face. "Because you don't voyage under sail," I reply, having shown him my recent nautical missive. Ho hum—loving you—X

Adrian: It is a sulk. A hurt-feeling grump. By not taking your question seriously—by not hearing you—he forces you to a choice: either to obey him— or disobey him. Child stuff. And if you choose to disobey him, then your choices are to do so in open defiance or in secret defiance. Maybe he is unaware that this is what a lack of acknowledgement does. Call on the adult in him, or else you are both playing games.

He reclines lazily on the couch, casting out these gems.

Mouse: Yes—you are right on many levels. We had a more real talk just now. "Are you still in love with him? He gives you things I don't? On a heart level it feels all wrong—despite convention. You should be exclusively mine. I can learn about these 'deeper' things." She senses some lowered barriers, although for a short while only. "I shall never let you go to him, even though you say you would have more to give me if you were held by this other relationship. I would take the children back to The U.K. I wouldn't be so concerned about what you did while I was away. Then you would taste the reality." She can see no way through the complications. She is becoming disillusioned. Without him to balance the decision she is feeling cornered. I am coming shopping soon. I really need to see you. What do you think? Bad idea? We are reaching crunch time—X

Adrian: He'll know you will want to come. Better be clear somehow— anyhow. Would love to see you, but know it would appear we were ganging up on him. Try to ask again—or just come if your intuition says yes. I'm here until 5.30. Then milking with Freya and the children again.

P.s Do you want to bring the children milking? Bona fide reason—though a bit edgy. I like to hear strong arguments like that. Much better. Something to work with, or against—and maybe The Laird's bottom line. Either you give me up or he takes the children away with him. Strong stand—and good sense. You get your cake, but in a way that means you can't eat it. You could never leave your children, and you have no grounds to fight for custody. So there it is. You are stuck. Your relationship will never return to being peaceful, yet you cannot leave because the children are held as long as The Laird decides to hold them. It would seem your most sensible choice is to submit—or is it?

What would submission look like? Accepting your fate. Your choices are dependant upon your husband's—his permission; his willingness to let you fly. So, lean back in trust. No pushing now. Wait and see what unfolds. Seek lightness and fun. Worry not. You have done your honest best. All is well, My Friend. All is open and clear. Relax. No decision is needed. At least from my seat this appears to be clear—from the man of little achievement. X

Mouse: *On my way now; just a flying visit. Is that okay? At bottom of hill.*

We meet. I am given a warm, loving hug. Adrian is wearing an aqua blue T-Shirt and the Burberry scarf I gave him last year which lends him a youthful but serious air. He kisses me lightly; platonically. Looking at me, he wonders if he is seeing properly. "I've been thinking about the dairy farm in the valley close to school—with a wooden house—and you as my wife. Or is it you?" He looks at me again; unsure. Yes, he loves my messages to be sensual. He loves the gift I gave him for his birthday, especially the white camisole top. But he is careful with his text messages. He will not write sensually. Yes, this is our new beginning. We have fought all the battles. We have claimed this place. It feels odd and somewhat flat, as predicted. We will have to start again.

"I like to get underneath your constant bubbles," Adrian tells me. "I need to go deeper. Is it unfair to demand that intensity so regularly?" "But that's what I crave and what I need," I answer truthfully. "I need your spiritual superiority and intensity. Read our story. It's all there." We speak about The Laird for a while but we don't linger. Adrian is anxious that Freya may have seen me parking outside. He pulls on his milking overalls and I head away to the supermarket. Rinky is staying with friends overnight.

P.m. Mouse: *The land is solid beneath their feet. The hidden corners of The Forest are no more. Lord Swallow and his Lady are reunited at long last—but—do they recognize each other in this earthed reality? It has been 5 months since they were close. They have faced huge ordeals. They are different. Their love has been fuelled by lyric and prose. They have become Lovers in a story; their story. How are they to adjust to this new dance? What steps should they take to dance off the pages? Or are they more at home in their literary fantasy? Lord Swallow is distant and unsettled. She remembers this familiar place. If he reads the story he will find it mentioned often; usually a reflection of adjustment to their physical togetherness. She wonders if he recalls their times of stillness—at the beginning of their meetings—to process their feelings. In a way they are starting again from the very beginning; in a new land too. "You smell of cheese," the Little Princess remarks as she greets her mother. "You have been a long time?" The Laird questions her. She is strong and open. "I shall go where I please. I may see my friend; better not to ask. That's how it is." I expect she will be quizzed later on—maybe a catalyst to his decision. We shall see. She has been thinking about the surface bubbles that annoy her Fine Sir, obstructing the way to their deep ocean meeting place. Perhaps this is her landing before she can sink to the depths.*

80

She asks him to be patient with her characteristic, rather as she is with his need to process and unwind from his long day. Their Rhythmic Dance steps have become their Spiritual Practise. It takes time to perfect. It will certainly take time to reclaim, if that is what they want. After arduous, solo journeying they find themselves strangely spent. She wishes she could accept his kind offer of a meal—a massage—a night together. Then they would unravel each other layer by layer in slow, intense sensuality and tenderness. Whispers and lips, caress and honour; regaining their private domain with ease and delight.

P.m. Adrian: The bath is so hot, even with the addition of a sixth more cold water, that he is soon more out than in—hot rushes overlap the parts that are still in—as an endurance exercise—patience until the fire is embered. Perhaps more cold, though less heroism might be sensible. He has made a cheese but the new basket he used to drain the whey has tainted it with some sort of preservative residue. The stink of it is still in the house where he tried to burn it off.

Sunday 29th April 2007

A.m. Mouse: She removes her clothes and lies close to the man she has bedded for twenty-five years. She tries to be intimate. He responds—but without any joy; without a true connection. This is how it has been for her the past 7 years. Now he knows the truth—is aware of her feelings. When he wakes she will offer her hand in genuine love and friendship. She will suggest a working partnership. They can maintain all that is positive between them, perhaps from afar. But not this intimacy. And as for Lord Swallow, {he of the scorched rear and cheesy disaster}, well—the way appears to be clear! Do they walk the path?

They stroll, hand-in-hand, down to the boatyard. The gates are wide open. They only take a few minutes to get there; his new lodgings are close by and his Landlady is away for a month; no questions dog their steps. Angels opening doors again? They approach their beloved Boat with confidence. She is sound. Lord Swallow lowers the gangplank. She doesn't show any sign of rust. He gallantly extends his hand to his Lady. She accepts with a homecoming smile and climbs aboard. They have arrived.

The quiet Marina is odd. They remark upon the open, ambivalent manner of The Marine Officials. They are slightly stunned. After an arduous five months they can relax. Inspecting their vessel close up they are a little dismayed by the neglect. In places the polish is worn thin—the brassware dulled. Some areas they hardly recognize as belonging to their beautiful Boat. But of course, they mustn't forget the harsh conditions of the past months. She is a little changed—a little older.

They hold each other long and close. "So—my Lady has walked out of The Castle Gates—bold and strong, eh?" He kisses the top of her head. "Yes—she surely has." A time of maintenance and repair is called for and then they will discover if she is seaworthy for long distance voyages or local, day trips only.

They will be patient. Perhaps the Harbour Master might relocate the entire boatyard. Who knows? They have done all they can. Now it lies with The Angels.

Running their hands along her familiar lines Lord Swallow and his Lady Thumbelina smile in anticipation—X

My day is quiet. I don't hear from Adrian; not at all. Strange. What thoughts go through his mind? Am I confusing him? Should I just walk away and leave him in peace?

Mid morning, Mouse: *The Laird departs for town. They have had their final, honest discussion. Are you there, My Friend? Busy? Disenchanted? Giving us space? Do you want me to take you to the Home Show? If so, what time? X*

Early P.m. Adrian: *Hello—my morning so busy and rich. Good, clear intentions fulfilled. Now a visit from Edwin—now a visit from Carla. New ideas form after conversation with Carla; a church; a Sunday gathering, with advice from the priests. I'd love to come with you to the Home Show, but I might need to take a trailer. Come with me? What time is our shift?*

Mouse: *Hi, My Friend—thought I'd lost you there for a moment. Our shift starts at 2 p.m. I have the Ute. Shall I come to you? What time?*

Adrian: *1.20 or so. Soon. What is happening with the kidlings?*

Mouse: *With you in 5—Children with friends—X*

I arrive at Adrian's lodgings promptly but he isn't around.

Mouse: *Where art thou, Lord Swallow?*

Adrian: *Up yonder paddock, My Love—X*

I collect Adrian from the farm and we drive to the Home Show together. He is warm and friendly, but he maintains his distance. Every year The Action Centre near the dock hosts a large Home Show for regional businesses. Kitchens, bathrooms, curtains and stoves are all displayed, amongst a host of other things. For several years our Kindergarten department has provided the crèche facility, giving us free advertising. It is a lot of work and I'm not sure it is worth the trouble. Adrian and I complete our stint, entertaining children, providing crayons and paper and keeping the seasonal display and leaflet pile tidy. Other teachers are present and we each manage a 'walk-about'.

The show is quite fun. I am surprised to find a collection of vintage motorcars close to our corner. An English couple from school is giving cookery demonstrations. They run a successful Delicatessen Shop and catering business in the centre of town. Adrian and I are left with the final shift and the task of dismantling everything. We talk as we drive back across town. "I needed a quiet, still day yesterday," Adrian began. "I spun out last night, giving my opinions too easily. I needed to reign myself in; come back to 'service', yes—that is it. I had an interesting talk with Edwin. He could see the picture we have always held; us two as catalysts for your marriage; a spiritual partnership, much as we have sensed. That felt good. Delphine is involved with Edwin! Fancy that! I am pleased for her. It lets me off the hook, anyway."

Pondering his words I wonder if Adrian would like to be let off 'our hook.' Is our situation just too complicated? He continues to be friendly—touching my leg in the car and taking my hand. He kisses me lightly when I deliver him home, but he doesn't invite me in. He leaves me feeling uncertain. I cannot let my family down and he is not totally committed. He doesn't put himself out for me. "Are you okay?" He asks as I turn away. "Okay about your decision and your grumpy husband?" "I am tired," I answer truthfully. "I'm okay. Whatever happens, happens. I'm okay."

The evening brings a troubling despondency. Adrian doesn't contact me. I sense he is pushing me away really; making me choose my marriage. The Laird and I have a long talk. He has told my parents. S—H—T. We continue our conversations; round and round we go. I see no alternative but to surrender. The negativity is too great for any other stand. I shall tell Adrian tomorrow—let him off 'the hook.' I shall say it isn't an end to 'us', but rather, an end to the possibilities, unless he really, truly wants me by his side. I don't think he does enough. I shall enter into a private world with him; probably in my imagination only. I shall think about my decision tonight. I won't text him unless he sends me a message. Like him, I shall have a 'resting' day. I shall tell myself our relationship cannot work. We have no future.

Monday 30th April 2007

A.m. Adrian: He went to bed late—beaten by the cheeses. Two big ones lie oozing on the draining board; a creamy Ricotta and two Panir sit in the fridge. He wakes early—active—almost in movement. School is big in his mind. His face feels a bit grim—has done for a few days now; driven—he knows what he needs; it has been calling for some time. Meditation—daily touching of peace—the inner smile—the peace of Christ. No striving or straining. Very well.

Her—and her—he has pushed her away with his grimness. Shh—little head—no thinking until a smile lights within.

Mouse: She is flat, dull—realistic. The final decision tonight. No going back. The English job opportunity will not hold. Her parents know. The messages from her Lover are unclear. She needs a rock if she is to step away from the shore for good. The rain falls. The dog poops quickly in the long grass—

Adrian: He feels for her—but he is responsible for her low state, he has to admit. How can he help?

Mouse: *Can I see you today? But not if you are feeling obliged.*

Adrian: *No obligation, My Love. After 11.30?*

Mouse: *I'll see you at your house after 11.30. Thank-you. I am free-wheeling down the hill. You might have to get used to it. X*

Her two men; they are both waiting. One in slouched despair, his broken ankle halting his stampede. He desperately needs to move forward but is anchored against his will. He can make no plans. The other sets to with grim determination, achieving much; his stream of creativity reaping rich reward under his direction. One is unhappy waiting; he pushes for a decision so he can return to his usual way of life. The other is content to wait, lying still, not sure if he wants the commitment. He prefers the suspense and mystery, as does his Lady. Will they find life dull when the battle is over? How will they fare in the quiet, peaceful times? But then she knows that the relentless call to go deeper, to probe the mind-talk, would keep them alert, interested, striving and keen. She imagines some would find the constant battle tedious, but she adores their joint yearning to go beyond.

She walks in the rain at Tui Park, wondering if the tide is going out or coming in; she still hasn't mastered the art of knowing. Perhaps she likes the liquid mystery. She is feeling sick, flat and tired. She must make her choice today; this evening. She and the dog turn left and walk along the row of tidy houses. The relentless ripples of the sea upon the shore keep her mind steady and focused. The water laps over her boots insisting she pay attention. What does the ocean tell her? The weather is wet; good for anxious walking. The Tui birds warble in the trees, despite the rain—and a new bird she hasn't heard before is singing; a long note finishing with a high, single 'pip'. She studies the different gardens from the shore; many properties own beached kayaks and catamarans. Their tidy lawns and inviting decks look out over this beautiful bay. How pretty the town is, with all this water and the green, green backdrop all around. One garden has a high, childproof glass fence in front of the bay, another sports a serious greenhouse. One garden is awash with autumn leaves that spill onto the sand from a large Ash Tree. The golden display is stunning against so much green. The tree looks like a caramel crunch blast, purposefully placed in a high street window.

This is their time; these lovers; the 'going-in' time to match the autumn. They fell in love last autumn on Lord Swallow's birthday when the leaves began to fall. Their Love fell from Heaven into their Earthly laps, taking their lead from the golden glory. Leafy Glade and winter burrow took them snuggling into each other under the blankets; deep into each other. Can they really give it up? They have to decide today. But she is unsure—and he is unsure. They need to be intimate to find certainty. They need to burst the bubble; to find that place again; to know its truth. Does it still exist? The Laird is soft and open, trying to love her through the chaos. He can see a way forward, with or without her. They spoke last night for a long time; open and honest. They spoke of the U.K possibilities; of building his business together. For a moment he was excited and she sensed his stature growing. This is what she gives him. He feeds off her positivity.

An orange glow amongst the mangrove catches her eye; the spikey grass becomes a hazy, warm blur in the autumn light. She will decide today. They will decide. She writes down some of the options; namely, should she ask for a separation; for time to think? But that would mean splitting the family. She could not bear the upset.

Lord Swallow and his Lady arrive at his house together. She thanks The Angels for giving them free time now, at this precise moment, just when it is most needed. The continuing events are extraordinary. They light a candle. She picked a white Camellia beside the shops earlier; someone had clipped the shrub and flowers were strewn about the pavement. She places the flower beside the candle. They pull chairs to the kitchen range and hold hands. They eat in silence. No speaking to begin with as they have agreed. "Yes, I have been coveting you again," Lord Swallow admits. "Your white camisole gift was a huge thing for me; a trigger. But—I have put it aside. Big J. asked questions about us being together at The Home Show. Kitty and Martini saw us arrive in your car. That unseated me; will they drag me over the coals again? So, I have been keeping my distance and my integrity."

They talk through all the possibilities; the only conclusion being a return to The Laird but not at the cost of their platonic friendship, their text communication and occasional visit; telling The Laird they will have the odd school meeting and e-mail communication for The Book.

"You are my Little Artemis Wife," Lord Swallow exclaims with a smile, in the same breath telling her he is trying to put her behind him, or at least aside. He mentions The Laird, wondering what it must feel like, knowing his wife is so sad without her lover. His own energy has been held and directed into creative outpourings instead of pining for her, rather as she has been doing with her writing. "You give me so much," he states. "But I have to be careful that it isn't *that* I am in love with rather than *you*; the real *you*. You give me applause, standing, self-esteem and peace."

They talk about their Spirits, how he knows his has dominion over hers and how powerful that is. How do you see my Spirit?" She asks. He thinks for a while; "I love to see you inspired and independent," he admits; "especially when I am watching you from afar. Yes—respect and companionship; this is what I feel." "I've got it!" She exclaims in excitement. "You can handle my Spirit; rather as an experienced horse trainer tames a wild stallion. You tame me; nobody else has the authority to challenge me, but you do. I listen to you."

"I need to ask you something," she adds. "If I were to get on board an aeroplane tomorrow and fly away, perhaps forever, what would you feel?" He is silent, telling her he would have to think long and hard; "I will have to dig out my heart for that one. I'm not very good at going there," he surprises her.

"Let me think about it. Big J. is worried for the children, and for the school. You know something? I think I'm getting ready for a decision. I could almost put it all on the line for us; lose my job, and the children at school. Am I being asked to do that? Maybe. But, the children being hurt by our choice is the bottom line. We must take our guide from them." He holds her gaze with smiling Angel eyes, washing her with a Heavenly wave of pure Holiness. He fair takes her breath away as once again she steps through The Garden Gate in his presence. The electric moment is divine; a Religious Experience? He notices the Holy ripples shuddering through her.

But, he is worried about others seeing her here in the house with him. School families regularly collect his unpasteurized milk. Stephanie is keen to help with the cheese-making; she could arrive at any time. His Ricotta Cheese is lovely; he feeds his Lady a spoonful. Another plate of Irish stew and he is away to school and she takes her leave, knowing and loving him.

So—another wet dog walk for me. The tide is right out and Tui Park a comforting place to be. I walk briskly in the rain, retreating to the van to write. The Tui birds call in the branches above my vehicle and I munch a naughty bar of chocolate. There has to be some consolation. "Can I come and see you later?" I asked Adrian as I left the house; "just to get clear about everything." "Lovely," he replied.

Early P.m. Mouse: The truth will be heard. It will not rest until its homecoming is given right-placed honour. The Celestial Sea rejoices in the recognition of her Captain and Lady's tentative step upon her deck. She has been waiting—an ordeal she has been instrumental in directing. Each lifetime Artemis and Apollo weave a tangled web; more complicated than the last. Their task? To find a path to joyous union using skills of deep integrity. Yes, integrity and unconditional love. They are well-versed in these skills, but this set of quandaries is a myriad of complication, involving different hemispheres as well as religious taboo, moral code and professional conduct. The Boat creaks as they tread her boards. Lord Swallow and his Lady dare to lift the hatch and peer inside their beloved vessel. She is more of a risk-taker than her lover. Lady Thumbelina would have The Captain lay her across their bunk in a jiffy. Luckily he has the matter well in hand. She relies on his control. She will try to behave. They face a grave and dangerous swell. Even her unstoppable bubbles are quiet today—X

Later, Mouse: Darling Friend, can I come down now? Or are you too tired? I have permission. X

Adrian: Wow. I have slept and am just arriving for milking. Come on down.

Mouse: Should I come to the paddock?

Adrian: *Might as well—seeking Christ in our meeting—remembering the knife-edge—the children—helping us stay focused—in service.*

I arrive at the farm in the pouring rain; goodness, it was wild driving away from The Mountain this evening! I left the family for a second time as wild night weather struck the vulnerable cabins. Supper served and all abed, I have not neglected my duties. I left The Laird reading bedtime stories to the children; his wife a complete mystery—a wild card that shocks him more each day. Poor Darling; how can I be treating him like this? My Lord Swallow is rather distracted up in the top paddock. I probably should leave him to it and meet later, but I am here now. We chat quietly as we stroll back to Vonny's house. "I should make the cheese. I need peace and quiet." He is a little distant; snappy even. My trousers are soaked, so he lends me a pair of his. Adrian is in a tizz by the time we light the fire and settle at last. He is frustrated that he cannot get clear for me. "I should know you by now," I say, not minding the familiar pattern. This is our sacred landing, although I feel more comfortable with it than he does. I must be quieter next time. Adrian needs silence, not my bubbles. I love him. I don't sit too close. He lies on the floor and I massage his feet. I notice he often lies down when I am with him, consciously or subconsciously inviting me to join him.

"Can you get some more wood?" He asks, directing me to the garage. "Oh—I don't know what to do," he shouts. "Argh!" I feel bad, creating such turmoil in my men's lives. "You aren't accountable to anyone," Adrian exclaims. "The Laird and I both have our careers to consider. You have no career, friends or family in this hemisphere. You are as free as a bird, sort of. Crikey!"

We end up cuddling a little; we kiss tentatively. "Should we really go there?" He asks. "Well, surely we are allowed one goodbye kiss," I say. "I like the way you stroke my manhood," he whispers in my ear, but I don't indulge him; perhaps just lightly brush the back of my hand against the firmness below his waist. We tease and play together. Yes, we are completely one; we cannot deny it. We adore each other. He takes my hand in his, interlocking our fingers. "Could you imagine me as your husband?" He asks quietly. "Could you imagine me as your wife?" I answer. Oh yes, and yes, and yes—we both answer 'yes.'

We speak about our funny ways; his edgy tendency and my bubbly effervescence. We balance one another. We look long and gently into each other. I try to come to a resolution. "No, don't," he says vehemently. "We don't have to go there yet; it is just an idea. Help me here; tell me you can fix it, My Love." I talk about my inspiration and ideas, often sparked by our meetings. "A slow burn—intention mulled over and then delivered. He challenges me to face up and out. I watch him with acute insight and perception. We are madly in love; crazy about each other. We hold hands and I am again engulfed by waves of Holy Joy. I never knew it was possible to be this happy. "Are you feeling The Rainbows?" He asks, wanting to know why I am smiling so much. "No," I admit. "I am through The Garden Gate, feeling a glorious electric shock that starts in my head and travels right through me;

not unlike the sensation of exploding sherbet on the tongue. I have to shake my head and close my eyes; it is so present. I hope to take you there someday soon. I have been hanging on through a tiny window of intuition without any message or hint from you. You have had messages and lovers' balm throughout. Do you like my tactics?" "Oh, yes," Adrian replies; "very clever. When The Laird lets you go—for whatever reason—I'll come running."

It is hard to say goodbye. I adore this man. Our deep connection amazes us both, but we have decided to remain as friends; to work under Saint Michael's Sword and plough our rich harvest back into the soil. It will be intolerably hard for now, but the dividends will pay later. Our thwarted lovers' sacrifice is destined to become a potent fertiliser. "What are you feeling?" He asks gently. "I am feeling tearful," I reply. "I just need to be still." We kiss again and I leave him by the fire. He waves to me from the window as I leave Vonny's yard. "Shall I walk you to the gate?" He asked before I left. But I knew he didn't want to go anywhere, so I said; "no, My Lovely. You begin your royal ways; be a King, not a Gentleman tonight!"

"Adrian and I cannot take the selfish love route. We choose to offer it up instead." My husband lies on the sofa, nursing his broken ankle, his head in his hands as I deliver our difficult decision. "You were away a long time," he states sadly. "It takes a long time to say goodbye to someone you love. You still have a wife. I am sorry to put you through such difficulties. Thank you for being here."

Apparently all the family members had telephoned while I was out. Why has everything been brought to such a head, only for us to say; *'sorry, we give up; there is nothing to it, really?'*

And did I miss a tentative proposal from Adrian? Why am I still so happy? I suppose if truth be told I know Adrian and I are not over—cannot be over. I retrieve my wedding ring from the wax and push it back onto my finger. I show my husband the replaced love token. We need to sleep. Nothing has changed; nothing at all.

{Recording this diary writing four and a half years later I find a sentence in brackets; it doesn't say who uttered the telling words; The Laird or Adrian: I honestly cannot remember: **"I can't decide whether you are good for me or not."**}

Late P.m. Adrian: *They kissed—their pact made; their decision reached. Relief and grief—tender—trusting—vulnerable. He thinks of a song by 'The Counting Crows'; one line; 'start turning the grain into the ground; roll a new leaf over,'—it's a favourite of his. He longs to share it with her—his Friend—his Companion. Perhaps it might become possible later; she has big things still to do. He sends her a blessing—grateful and warm. God speed, My Free-Wheeling Woman. I love you.*

Mouse: *—X—*

Chapter 3 Admit

Tuesday 1st May 2007

A.m. Mouse: The Laird is awake early between 5-6 a.m. disturbing her early morning vigil. He cannot sleep; a sure sign of trouble. He is uneasy. She has reinstated her wedding ring; a ceremony did not feel right. She does not really want this—she knows there is no choice at present. She senses her husband's surprise at her lack of tears, although her sobbing outburst while she walked the dog in the pitch black might have satisfied him. He knows the huge ordeal she faces. Apparently the phone didn't stop ringing all evening, the poor Laird hobbling to catch each concerned U.K relative; brother, sister, mother; all wishing they were closer. Why so much fuss? The more disciplined the lovers' stand, the more everyone worries. Hmm. She cannot tell her husband he gives her everything she needs; she has a deep fondness for him, yes, but in the light of her Soul Mate Companion? Well—

Their profound meeting last night—the truth in linked hands; acknowledgement as potential husband and wife and humble, right-placed sacrifice inviting waves of inner joy and peace. Did he notice her restraint beside the warming fire? Even after his invitation to move her hand slowly to caress him as she so longed to do? She wanted to shine in his masculinity— so much. Perhaps she can be honourable after all. She still has to decide how to lie with him every night—naked and vulnerable in his arms—in her imagination—her hand upon his Greenstone—every inch of their bodies in molten union; no space between their perfect form. She should probably not go there anymore. She sighs deeply. She is very much in love with him; so in love that nothing can break the truth of their single existence.

So—he shall plough their harvest back into the land for the benefit of the school community and she shall write—and write; her time spent in caring for her family as she has always done while carrying their creative lyric alone. They will smile at each other over the school fence, knowing for always that they belong together in celestial union.

She bids Lord Swallow a good morning—X

Adrian: When will you be mine? The puritanical way of self-denial is easy, in a way. He is used to punishing himself. He does not want this today, though an agreement of sensible, held action has been made. He never wants to forget the rich possibility that exists between them—the chemistry and destiny, and the brand new lands that thrill the explorers in them both; uncharted waters with few inhabitants and riches aplenty. Yes, he will keep this spark alight—

Adrian's ability to grasp the potential and internalize it is our only hope of retaining a real connection. I am relieved that he has written the words that make it so. We cannot undo The Craftsman's plan. I somehow manage to keep the home fires burning, maintaining our knife-edge keel at the same time, grateful that I can multi-task.

Midday, Adrian: *Hello, My Love. How doth My Fair Lady fare? Found myself easy with colleagues today—real laughter with Martini and Big J—clear. Just meeting Edwin. Here he is—X*

Mouse: *My Darling, hi. Just finishing a visit to Wellspring Hospice for the College project. The Bog-Brush and I have had a spectacular dash in the sun and waves at Pillans Beach. Felt you with me as I ran into the crashing water, dog and all! Loving you—X*
P.s Say hi to Edwin. I waved to him this morning—not sure if he knew who I was? My thought today—am I being honest? Seeing as I have absolutely no intention of waving goodbye to you. The Laird senses my reluctance to let go. "I am still feeling uneasy," he admitted this morning. "We need to talk about how we are to repair our marriage." I suggested he will only feel safe once back in The U.K. Hmm—will we have to choose—again? Sorry to load you. I'm so glad school felt good—X

The beach was so exciting this morning. I felt the thrill of freedom as I ran into the waves with the dog. The sun was hot and the waves full and wild, like me! Another sensational Rainbow arched across the sky as I left The Mountain. It is a hot, hot, autumn day. Wellspring Hospice was calm and quiet when I visited; a peaceful place to die. I was moved by the special atmosphere. Death brings us face-to-face with life—and what is important. I recognize the intense vibes. Do Adrian and I face a living death? St. Vincent de Paul's charity shop outside wall needs a mural painting; I help direct the artistic meeting, trying to feel enthused. I won't be climbing any ladders. Two college parents will help the students. The famous murals through nearby Katikati might inspire the budding artists, keen to complete their service projects.

I sit in the van after the meeting and write—there is always so much to log. I drive to the hair salon beside the Waikite Bay roundabout; I must book haircuts for the boys. Adrian drives out of the small esplanade as I drive in! He must have been visiting the holistic animal centre. We kiss indulgently through the windows; hands to lips as we pass; The Angels allowing us a glimpse of each other today.

Early P.m. Mouse: *Thank you Angels, how lovely to see you today, Fine Sir—and we didn't even break any rules! Love you—X*

90

The Laird is sad and gloomy when he walks in through the cabin door. His ankle is not repairing as it should. He mentions the returning depression. Why doesn't he feel relief that she is home for him? They talk openly.

P.m. Mouse: *Simon is phoning The Laird at ten o' clock this evening. Poor Laird. I feel for him. Is it my entire fault? His injury is slow to heal—an ironic metaphor. The wretched depression raises its ugly head again. He has been told 'no driving.' His will to work is paling—perhaps because the battle is over, or is it? Say a prayer for him as you milk your lovely ladies. Your Artemis wife in velvet—or should I say gum boots—will be watching you from the poplars; not disturbing you this time—just loving you—X*

Adrian: *Take him a big shot of whisky and a kiss of reassurance. I'm off to milk very late—my poor, bursting girls. See you in the poplars—*

The Laird and I talk again; round and round we go. We speak honestly as the children put themselves to bed. He clutches his big blue notebook; "I need to know how you feel about us returning home," he announces. I consider his statement carefully; a return to Sussex would be a backward step for me; he would have to go there alone. "A new place might be okay, but I am reluctant to leave the country—and Adrian," I boldly admit. "I need to wave to him over the fence every now and then; to know he is there. If he didn't feel the same way I could go, but he does feel the same way." "Well—he has a beautiful woman loving him," The Laird retorts. "He hasn't told you to go away, has he!?" I argue that Adrian has done his very best. I mention the religious experiences I felt with him yesterday. "Yes, I was looking into his eyes and he was holding my hands," I admit; "but we were sitting in different chairs." The Laird speaks of my brother Wilf's phone call to my older brother Jonathon; "Wilf hasn't seen you looking so free and happy since you were twenty-one when you worked on board that Turkish boat. You really are free here, aren't you?" Like Adrian, The Laird comments on my unencumbered state. "There's no way you would have done this at home. It must be a mixture of New Zealand and the artistic school." I mention my sun soaked dash on the beach today; "that wouldn't be so possible at home as autumn arrives."

The telephone rings, so I head upstairs to bed, leaving my husband to tackle my concerned mother. "This is all very tiring, indeed," I hear him say. "Running from New Zealand would be a mark of failure—yes, I might be able to hold my head up again at College, soon." I don't linger on the stairs. The Laird is buoyed up by the attention and concern from family and friends.

Wednesday 2nd May 2007
A.m. Mouse: *Her husband sleeps peacefully. They spoke openly last night. Her family were there for him on the phone. Strange that she does not seek, or feel the need, of their counsel. She is not confused. She feels strong. She tells The Laird she would find it hard to move back home—that she needs*

to know she might pass Lord Swallow in the car—or at school—or in town; that they can smile at each other over the fence. She has told him about the extraordinary channel to direct communion with The Holy Spirit that she achieves through their bond. So—now she will live her own truth; lay her cards upon the table for Lord Swallow and his Lady to view. The truth is—that she needs him in this deep sanctity. She will keep their private dialogue alive. She may acquire a different phone for its privacy and protection. And—she would like to take occasional trips out on The Celestial Sea to keep their spark glowing; not as fully engaged lovers, but as guardians of the treasure, much as they were the other night beside the fire. This would be a light-filled place for her, even though there is an element of secrecy. Her sacred growth needs him in this way—has always needed him. She can hold her head up high in dignity and honour. She does not expect her Fine Sir to feel the same way, but she needs him to know where she stands—X

Adrian: *Good Morning, Friend. I am concerned about The Laird. Knowing I am loved gives wings to my life—it is clear to me—and it is probably what has fuelled my recent creations in the world in some unobtrusive way. The Laird has rested on what he presumed was your complete love and now he knows it was not all of you loving him—that it was the love of—a mother, maybe, not a lovers' love. Not fully held, deep respecting love and admiration. So, now he feels alone, even though actually that love has not changed. Now he knows, aware there is a big part of you he does not know or touch. Old rejection comes flooding back—anger—depression—gloomy thoughts—failure —because he is now conscious of what has been below the surface. A Class 3 experience? It can't be patched. It has to be grown. The old rot needs cutting out to encourage fresh growth. The tender parts must be protected—work and attention. So, you and I could help by getting clear with a witness—a meeting with The Head Marine Official. Our agreement ratified in the presence of a clear light conscience. The decision to arrest the crop before harvest and plough it back in—this needs to be witnessed or it may never be done. Then the grieving can really begin—or not.*

Come, Good Friend, let us arrange a meeting to complete our agreements formally. Let's have them witnessed to show the strength of our commitment. The Laird's immobility is such an opportunity to explore old wounds if he were willing. Your actions have opened a door to them; more like the door has been blown apart exposing these old emotions. Who is the young man before the injury? Is he prepared to drop all that he thinks he is? Can he stand vulnerable to find out?

Mouse: *Good morning, Darling. Hmm—food for thought. Think we might be getting there? How does your morning's intention sit with mine? A combination of both? Is it positive to deny ourselves completely? Perhaps—or perhaps not. Loving you—X*

The morning is blissfully quiet. I am up early. For some reason my watch has stopped. I send Adrian my morning message later than usual; The Angels must have wanted him to write his at the same time. Our messages crossed. This is important; a witnessing, yes. I have visualized it. What does it mean? The dog doesn't want to go far down the drive today; I don't know why not. I check the clock—goodness, it's an hour later than I thought. Time to get going. The Laird is soft and relaxed this morning. He has slept well. I kiss him sensually and profoundly. He is listening to Sting on the C.D player. I can tell that he is feeling open. The Holy Spirit is present. Dear Lord in Heaven, please help our quandary.

Mouse: *Goodness—a divine light is filling The Castle this morning. She takes her husband a cup of tea—and kisses him deeply. She senses him letting go; even some joy creeping in. The 'beloved land' appears through the mist. She sends her love; sacred blessing and unconditional love—always—X*

The autumn mist lies in ghostly pockets along our road to school this morning. I haven't seen the volcanic Mount so disguised, only the top is showing, like a mysterious, floating island. The children are mesmerized by the eerie wonder. Rinky's comments last night are still with me; "Who would you be married to if you weren't with Daddy?" She asked quietly. "I would be married to Adrian," I tell her. "He and I love each other very much. We are very close friends, but it is a bit of a secret." "From who? From Daddy?" She asked. "No, darling. Daddy knows, but not other people." I hold her back in the school car park. "About Adrian and me—it isn't a secret that we are close friends." "Is his farm a secret too?" She asks again; bless her. Please, Dear Angels, please ease this passage. Please keep Rinky from any faux pas, thank you.

The dog and I take our usual turn in the park. The mist hangs like a lightweight blanket over the ripple of darting fish. We stride right out into the bay again; the water reaches the top of my thighs. The Bog-Brush points even in the water. The White Faced Herons reign over the bay this morning. Their yellow stockinged legs are obvious, despite the poor visibility. We watch a seagull catch a flounder. The hazy sun tries to dapple our passage, but it is obscured by the mysterious shroud. A native bird calls in the dense brush opposite the estuary. The exotic song bounces across the still bay diving headlong into the mist like all the sounds today. And my feet are brushed by a group of little fish. We stay in the water a long time. Our fate lies in the lap of God—and The Angels.

The Laird is reclining on the sofa when I arrive home. He isn't as relaxed as I hoped he might be. I make him a good lunch and sit next to him. "In letting the Sussex job go I am trusting—trusting that all will be well," he informs me. "I don't want to return to how things were, though," I say. "We have to find new ideas; a new way." The Laird is working a half day today. I drive him down the hill at one-thirty. "Do you feel safe in my hands as I free-wheel down the hill?" I ask him. "No, not really," he answers truthfully. "I think you should just let go," I reply. "I don't have much choice, do I?" He retorts. "Keep an eye on the N.Z and U.K job vacancies," I suggest. "We are being held. Please don't worry."

I deliver The Go-Getter's mislaid games kit to school and then drive to the Waikite Bay shops to collect some homoeopathic remedy for The Laird's injury; 'Knit Bone,' {comfrey}. "Don't give it to your husband until you are certain the ankle is set properly," the knowledgeable Kiwi pharmacist with the henna hair and round figure advises. "Comfrey is a powerful healer. I've heard of cases where bones have had to be re-broken because comfrey has worked its magic before a setting was correct."
I have a strong desire to see Adrian.

Early P.m. Mouse: *Are you home? Just waving over the fence as I drive past. Trying to be a good wife; giving The Laird lots of care and attention. Hope you are okay? X*

Adrian: *On my way home now——*

Mouse: *A visit from your Lady? Or just a wave from Tui Park? X*

Adrian: *I'm having a snack, then heading out.*

Mouse: *—Love you—do you want to come by the park? Or had we better keep our distance?*

Adrian: *Don't know actually. How would The Laird be with it? Be nice to see you, but quick. Might look bad if seen—I'm okay with it though.*

Mouse: *Okay—quick—just to touch base as we stabilize The Boat. Park or home?*

Adrian: *Come here.*

Adrian is not overly friendly this afternoon. He is busy making lunch; fried cheese and salad. I lend a hand without getting in his way. I can tell he doesn't want to be interrupted. We sit down eventually and he unwinds, as I knew he would. "I *do* want to hear every detail," he tells me between mouthfuls. "I want to know *everything* that has happened; that *keeps* happening." I talk through our marriage wrangles; I tell him that I have told The Laird I cannot move away right now. I mention Rinky's question—and my 'secret' answer. "Funny, I had a nice chat with both The Go-Getter and Rinky this morning," he divulges. "The Go-Getter tells me he has been filming his Lego models; in fact Cedric has sent me his recent mountain-board film;it's excellent! And Rinky loved the song and dance I taught the class; you know the one; 'when

I first came to this land—and I got myself a wife;' we looked sideways at each other when that came up; 'and I called my wife: Joy of my Life,'—"

"This witnessing of our pledge," I begin; "I'm not sure we aren't being dishonest; do we *really* intend letting go completely?" "My intention is not to make love to you," Adrian displays his moral high card; "um—I think, but, given half a chance I would shag the pants off you! Now—come and look at this; I have been creating an astrology and astronomy chart. I can see the patterns in the night sky. I can't wait to show you."

I kiss my platonic lover a few times but he is slow to return the compliment. It is so good to see him. "Mmm, My English Rose", he sighs, abstaining from my intimate invitation. Freya arrives to collect a bottle of milk just as I am leaving. I pretend that I am collecting some too.

P.m. Mouse: *Can I collect some milk tomorrow? Just to be bona fide?* **'I was diving in for milk and cheese'.** *It felt okay to be seen today—time for us to face the community—gently—in check. Also a couple of school matters I need to discuss. Shall I telephone first? X*

Adrian: *There is no need to fear. Surely Freya knows and blesses us— don't you think? Will your family be okay drinking milk from my enterprise?*

Mouse: *Surely they will be alright with that, Sir. I shall cook with the milk if not. They have to get used to the reality of our friendship—now is the time. I would like The Laird to make a connection with the Buddhist Monastery close to school. I think it would calm his fears and help build some inner strength. I need to talk to you with my Festival Hat on. Apparently the teachers need a presentation tomorrow for the up and coming Festival; {St. Michael and the Dragon.} We need to articulate the deeper meaning behind the impetus; something to be printed in the school newsletter for the parents. X*

Thursday 3rd May 2007

I didn't sleep at all last night—not one wink! I have been working on all three Books since 3.30 a.m. I send Mizzie the work so far. The e-mail can't cope with the large amount of script. I will try again tomorrow. Drat and bother. The Laird is restless, aware that I am absent. He wakes early again, disturbing me at the desk. He is kind and helps me send the pages again. I don't text Adrian this morning. For some reason it feels right to leave him alone. I am super-organized by **7**.30 a.m, even managing to stop the pig from raiding the rubbish bins. I deliver The Laird to College and complete the school runs on time.

Late a.m. Mouse: *Hello, Sir. When is a good time to collect some milk?*

Adrian: *Could I ask a favour? I need little plastic containers for children to collect mud for a model tent base. Garden Centre for some seedling* *punnets? Their giveaways? Then you could come round here. I'm going into school late today. Lazy boy still in bed—*

Mouse: *Okay, as long as you don't forget to woe me occasionally with your sweet lyric, My Fine Sir. Just pulling into the Garden Centre now—what shape, colour, size, holes in the base? Flower pots? How many? X*

Adrian: *You gorgeous creature whom I long to wrap up in a deep embrace—holes are okay. 19 pupils. Big enough for a little model tent? X*

Mouse: *Amorous messages will get you anything, Lord Swallow—as long as they are genuine, of course. I shall know if they are not! Pots it is. See you in 10—loving you—X*
P.s Are 16 by 8cms okay?

Adrian: *Yes, perfect.*

I arrive at Vonny's house in glorious sunshine. Adrian has installed some curtains separating the kitchen from the sitting room. He wraps me up in a gorgeous hug behind their shield. He is clean and yummy, wearing the new orange shirt that I like. How I adore him. We kiss lightly before he dishes up a bowl of homemade, warm muesli; "soaked in whey overnight," he informs me; delicious. We sit together in the sun, enjoying each other so much. We have lots to talk about. "Do you want the old corrugated iron up at your place?" He asks, intimating that he could do with it on the farm. We aren't really using 'Alcatraz', so sure, he is welcome to it. "Big J. is really impressed by my flowing, creative juices," he divulges with pride. *"As long as it is just the creative juices flowing",* she had said, raising an eyebrow, telling him that an attractive, single male teacher at school was a liability with so many mothers on the scene. "School is such a loving place to be right now," he exclaims with a flourish. "Big J. and I spoke about Edwin and Delphine; I admitted I was pleased to be freed from that one! My conversation with Edwin the other day was stilted—I couldn't really explain what we are to each other, you and I; it's just too complicated so I didn't bother going there with him. I've been invited to sit on the school property group," he continues. "Sammy has some great ideas; she is really motivated about the community village and senior school initiative. I know you are involved too—let's press ahead; some interested parties want to get on board. Can you get us some photos of the eco village you know in Sussex? Thanks."

Adrian is on a roll today. I hear all about his 'More to Life' course, and the parenting workshop he is running with another parent. He is certainly in full creative flow. No wonder Big J. is so pleased with him. I am slightly stung by her 'mother' comment. Does he see me in the same light? Is that why he is reluctant to commit? "I'm off to Hastings soon to learn about woodwork teaching and cheese-making," he adds. "I'll probably catch up with Jules there." "Having your own home suits you," I tell him, noticing his life increasingly spread about Vonny's place; laundry all over the sitting-room, creamery filling the scullery, woodwork projects under the house and the hot tub in the garden. He certainly takes over. I hope Vonny doesn't mind. "We'd better hurry up and make a success of The Books, I tell him. "You might afford a house of your own if they take off."

I roll up my sleeves and lend a hand at tidying; I have always enjoyed organizing and sorting. "It's good to have a woman's touch," Adrian admits, indicating the plumped cushions and clear floors. We are like an old married couple working side-by-side. How strange to have bypassed our regular intimacy, tackling the domestic jobs as if we have been together all our lives.

"Oh—about The Book," Adrian adds. "I don't like the idea of The Boat speaking; it could sound cheap and trite. You know what I mean? I have had an idea I'd like to run with. I am almost ready to pick it up again. Forgive the delay after my initial start." "I know the timing is important for you," I reassure him. "I look forward to you being involved." I am so excited that Adrian is taking the concept seriously—really giving our Book the time it deserves. "I've been up all night, working on the chapters," I tell him. Adrian pulls me towards him and gives me another warm hug. We kiss more passionately today. "Remember your husband," he whispers in my ear. We could so easily get carried away, but we hold back. "My soft-bodied woman; My Lady in velvet and lace," he sighs, smiling at me so beautifully. I disengage reluctantly—"My Smiling Minstrel," I reply; "in buckles and breeches—mmm—goodbye, thanks for the milk."

I take my leave, our punnet and milk transaction complete alongside the steadying of our fine vessel. She is standing on the slip-way, checked and ready. Will we remove the chocks? Will we sail again? Something strong and vibrant is keeping our love alive. I feel more certain than Adrian. Ah, yes— but I have a few years on him, remember.

The remainder of my day is busy. I swim in the indoor pool with half the town's primary school children. It certainly isn't peaceful today. I collect the family on time, including The Laird. The boys have haircuts and then we drive up the hill to feed the animals and organize supper, or tea as the Kiwis call the main meal at the close of the day. Goodness, I am tired. The Laird is pensive; still very hurt. I suppose everything is such a big shock. I just can't feel it because I am the one who has received the golden package.

P.m. Mouse: *Dear Friend, I'll look out the photos of the eco village later on this evening. Should I wait for you to send me the mythology of The Boat before contacting Mizzie? My sister just needs a beginning paragraph or two— to set the tone. Let me know if you feel inspired and I will delay sending more attachments. T'would be good to give a proper taster; do you agree?*

I have been watching you from the poplars. I am tired—expect that you are too. I have had a busy afternoon. Thank you for our lovely, late breakfast meeting. I am chopping cheese for tea, trying to avoid the crazy, humping dog who is chasing the children all over the house. My patience is wearing thin tonight. Time for my evening kip. I'll work later. I send a loving smile your way. Big love to my Smiling Minstrel, from your Singing Gypsy Companion with a Russian twist—X

Adrian: *Yes, he has wondered how she is. So nice to share the day's events together; the meetings and interactions—all the busy achievements— full indeed. The cows ran out of water today; thirsty. He watches them drink, deep and long. Sorry, my loves. He has just booked into the nursing course at Stephanie's —the only male; so useful to know this stuff, particularly as a teacher. Yum. Tomorrow he is teaching all day—festival practise—pack up— then picking up car.*

The weekly accountability meeting—where I remembered all that I said I would do—went very well, winged though it was—sigh—full and relaxed—run with a hand of casual professionalism. So nice to have time to catch each other—and those kisses—boy, holding this agreement is going to test him sorely, but hold it he will he adds quickly, in case she gets any ideas. He sends his love to their family—his family—liking the sound of how it is—

Chapter 4 Agreement

Friday 4th May 2007

I slept long and early last night. I had meant to complete work for College after my short, evening snooze, but I never woke again. I am awake now at three-fifteen in the morning. Reaching for my phone I find the message Adrian sent last night. His words thrill me—as always. It is wonderful to feel him so close. His phone doesn't wake him; "the reception is poor in my room, you needn't worry about disturbing me. I have to go outside to receive your messages." "Perhaps you need a new phone?" I suggested last week. His is worn and erratic. I shall send my reply now:

Very early A.m. Mouse: She finds his message from last night at 3.15 a.m—her evening doze taking her way beyond her regular, two hour slot. Yes—how good it is to share their days; how blessed to start the morning together, a most unconventional, married couple, allowed on this level, but not on another. The stricter they are with each other the more together they become—it feels right-placed. The kisses—mmm—she can sense the knife-edge—can feel integrity in Holy brush of lips and cheeks. But—will they know when The Boat slips down the ramp? She could travel a long way down on steel blade, the cutting edge a harsh guide as they seek purity. But this may be too much for the male drive; too tempting. She will stay away today; luckily they are both busy. She desires him—cannot keep out of his arms at night—hopes that he can keep her fuelled—wonders if he wants her to keep him fired? Tentatively, of course. Perhaps over the next few days an opportunity may arise for them to find an acceptable rhythm; a natural, private gauge that provides for their needs but keeps to the agreement—their own rules. At the end of the day, that is what matters. This is our life, My Darling Adrian—and we decide.

She would lie with him and stroke his noble brow this morn; she would take him in her arms and soothe the heavy cares away—with lips and breath and dance. She would find his very core, as he would find hers, and therein The Garden Gate with all its potent abundance would open and they would move together in the land of Rainbows and smiling promise—X

Adrian: Little Mouse, Little Mouse, in my house, a cheese was made for the flea and the louse. Set out to write the first draft of The Boat Mythology but was waylaid by a rogue e-mail from the good Big J, calling my creativity to school work. Just arrived at said place. See you at Festival practise. I am being Sienna today.

Adrian strolls up to my car when I arrive at school this morning. It is so good to see him and we chat for a while. I tell him about Molly who is busy ploughing up the garden. "Will I need to put a ring through her nose? I understood Kune Kune pigs were grass eaters, not turf rollers! She is stacking the grass into neat piles everywhere." "Molly can move to school in two weeks' time; to live in the new pig pen Class 3 is making—what do you reckon?" Lord Swallow comes to the rescue, again. "Oh, yes please," I am relieved. "That would be good. I don't think I can cope with her on The Mountain for much longer." Freya draws up beside us. I haven't seen her since our slightly awkward meeting at Vonny's house. We chat about the pig, and the unpasteurized milk; how different it tastes, and I mention the potential community village around the school. We are open and friendly—and it feels good.

I dash home to walk the dog in the field beside the house. "Look at this amazing toadstool," I say out loud. Wow, it is hiding in the pines on the neighbouring land adjacent to the Pa Site; red-topped and spotty; a perfect specimen. I manage to work on the College project when I get in. I can't say I am enjoying it much. I nearly wiped the entire lot off the screen by accident just now.

"You are just in time—follow me." I meet The Laird at College after lunch, as we agreed. He has organized a meeting with the students about their Service Project and I need to be there. Each candidate must complete twenty hours of charitable works before they will be awarded a College Certificate. It is a good scheme and right up The Laird's street. I should be more interested but it isn't creative enough for me. Anyway, I do my bit and talk through various options for the students. I have visited a number of Old People's homes etc.—all are happy to have students helping out. As I leave College I bump into Ronnie Vascher, {one of the mothers from The Go-Getter's class}. She teacher relieves at College some days. Her husband Michael is also a teacher, working with the troubled boys in the big Boys' College in town. It is good to see her; I like both Ronnie and Michael. They were the couple that gave Adrian the little green car which he crashed in Auckland last January.

Despite The Laird's excellent presentation he is feeling low and grotty. I remain up-beat. My relationship with Adrian is so complete; I feel no lack in any way. I take my sad husband out to the supermarket for some food. I deliver him back to his office and then sit in the park, writing up my diary before school pick-up time.

* * * * * * *

Oh, great—Adrian has sent the potential beginning of our Book:

E-mail from Adrian:

Hi my friend. Had a crack at getting ideas down. What do you think of this? May not be right—might need less character. Not bad though. Lots of teasing out to do in any case. Off to milk then to see some pigs, {looks like I can have them for the farm; friends for Molly, eh?} Then a meeting for M2L Course. Talk to you soon. Adrian X

"Wave slicer, watery dancer, long and deep—shapely, full-bellied sails to sense the air—use the air to its full potential—harnessing the driving power of each puff and gust, and inside—warmth and style—homely comforts—a generous galley—a cushioned cabin—wood and velvet—canvas and brass—

The Craftsman checks his models. He feels what comes from her—the line—the purpose—the lofty heights—the finish. And from him the balance—the weight, the depth, the warmth and strength of the timber.

I like Adrian's take. Mizzie has also sent an e-mail. She and the family are so pleased I have chosen to maintain our marriage. She asks if The Laird has given his permission for The Book to be publically aired:

Dearest Sis – well done for making such a difficult decision. We're all so relieved, and hope and pray you two can now work things out again as a team. The magical thing you have had with Adrian will always be there for you – some people never get that, married or otherwise, which is the saddest thing of all. On a cheery note, I'm sure you know about Simon getting down to the last 12 for the Joseph and His Technicolour Dreamcoat TV show here on the Beeb. He was sadly voted off on Saturday – but if you haven't yet found it, look at bbc.co.uk/joseph and watch his performances, as they are videoed on there for all to watch!!! Yes I'm still prepared to be your editor – but with a proviso. I feel guilty that I put on my editor's hat before my personal one and failed to fully appreciate the gravity of what has happened and how it so nearly ended your marriage, (and may yet do so?). It is the writer's failing – that everything in the world happens as if in a book, with no real effect on people – and something I need to work on. So, the proviso: If The Laird is OK with me editing this, then I will become involved. If he would rather it stayed private, then I want to respect his feelings and not edit it. Does that sound OK? If he's OK with it, then I look forward to reading it and maybe clarifying what the hell has been going on. It's still so mysterious – so conceptual and emotional but no hard factual skeleton as yet! Much love to you all. How I wish you were here so I could give you the biggest hug. Mizzie XXXXX

Early P.m. Mouse: Hi there, thinking of you. Have you collected your car

yet? Was it at the garage? Had a warm welcome and friendly chat with Frances' man, Braden, in the school car park this afternoon. What a nice, gentle man he is. I am swinging on the ropes in the Twealm Realm, giving the dog a dash before the usual domestic chores kick in. How was your teaching day? Longing for you—know I shouldn't be. Take care—X

P.s A sudden thought. My father is into genealogy and I wondered if I should ask him to investigate the strange coincidence of your mother's maiden name being linked with the Sussex village my own mother called home as a child. If you can give me details of Jenny's family; when they left The U.K; dates etc, he might thoroughly enjoy the exercise. Just a thought. What are you up to tonight? Apart from the milking and star-gazing of course. I shall be with you, looking up at all the wonders in The World's magic ceiling—X

Adrian: Nice idea it is too—the genealogy that is. I'm seeing Jenny tomorrow. I'm on my way to see the pigs now, then on to 'More to Life' course this evening. Thinking of you too. Did you get my e-mail? Have a look. Let's have a long, slow, early morning tomorrow before hockey—virtual, I mean. I'm here—text you later.

* * * * * * *

Later, Mouse: She cleans the kitchen—the children both abed, the bigger males stuck into computer and rugby in the top cabin. She spied a wonderful fairy toadstool this afternoon; the brightest red and white magic under the pine trees. She must tell the boys; they love to photograph such treasures.

She is free tomorrow morning—early and then again after dropping The Go-Getter at hockey. Normally she would slip away and find Lord Swallow in a duvet dream. He would invite her to join him, waiting as she unlaced her leather boots in a slow, deliberate ritual, the longing to be joined with him so strong. He would watch her remove her jeans—and then her top. At last the contours of their form—as one—warm and still in the morning hush—complete.

But, tomorrow she must drive on past—pretending she no longer needs his adoration or his blessed balm. She will try. She will drive past—

Adrian doesn't respond to my provocative message. He is out this evening, occupied elsewhere. I miss him.

Saturday 5ᵗʰ May 2007

*A.m. Mouse: Am—mmm—kissing you. Just walking the dog. Have to leave by **7**.20 a.m, so our Go-Getter informed me last night. He almost slept in his hockey kit—gun shield at the ready! Everyone else is fast asleep. How was your evening course? Loving you big time—X*

Adrian: The sun diffused through the plastic roof still carries warmth, which makes it bearable to have his bare feet out on this lovely morning. Breakfast steams from a bowl held on his chest and the porch swing chair creeks its protest at the forced action. He is interrupted by a hockey phone call mid-prose. {His class game is later than The Go-Getter's.} Soft, sweet apricot explosions continue. He is cautious this morning—cautious not to let things get too hot—the line of agreement feels blurry. He wants to know where The Laird is. Where is Christ in this? Where do we stand? He asks for clarity— calls on The Angels—the higher self—the weaver of destiny to reveal the meaning, the task and the lessons. He launches his lovely, lyrical lady a loving letter and leaves to collect a heater. Loving you too. X

Later, Mouse: Dear Friend, I am at Tui Park with The Bog-Brush. Are you off to hockey? Apricot explosions sound good—mmm—am hungry this morning—hot and hungry—blurred edges—X

Adrian: Quick, come visit now.
P.s Actually, I have to go. Clock wrong. Sorry, My Sweet, unless you're here for a super quick squeeze.

Mouse: On my way right now, My Love—X

Adrian leads me quickly behind the temporary curtains when I arrive. He hugs me close and long, but again, he is unsure of our integrity; my tempting messages unseating him—"I like them though." "I know you do," I reply with a chuckle. "So—you are feeling hot and hungry, eh?" "Oh yes, Fine Sir," I reply. "I certainly am. You had better leave fast." "I reckon our boundaries need replacing," he announces. "We should consider the witnessing too." I am disappointed—all I want is to be held by the man I love. "I think there is an element of infatuation with you," he comments. I don't ask him to elaborate. I suppose he means I am infatuated with him, rather than the other way around. Am I infatuated? Not with Adrian personally, but with the Holy Magic we access together, for sure. Who wouldn't be?

I take The Bog-Brush back to the park. She is particularly unfriendly with other dogs when she is on heat. She barks furiously at every canine creature, especially when she is in the car. We stride into the still water to avoid a fierce-looking, black dog. The park is cold today. The sun is out but the water stings my skin. Three young people are fishing. I keep out of their way, distrusting my grouchy hound. The children are with friends for the day; Rinky is staying with a German family who has built a comfortable family home in Waikite Bay. Joanna's father is an electrician and her mother works in the kindergarten.

P.m. Adrian: She is slightly set-back by the scolding hint in his voice— but she is a bold explorer; the passage opener. Her job is to try the ways—a Mouse in a maze—he is coming after her, but bringing a nest. He doesn't want to take it up a dead-end, or be surprised by some unexpected danger. She shrugs and looks for the next passage—hmm—that one didn't work, where to now? He has told her to go to her husband, ensure his well-being before they can enjoy each other. Is she reaping the harvest? Can she not bear to turn it in? 'Just a little bit—surely we are allowed a taster?' He thinks not. He realizes that turning it in means giving any personal gain from their union to others— selfless sacrifice—perhaps for a bigger reward, but perhaps not. Can she feel that edge? The pang and but of humility? Lord it is yours. We serve you, expecting nothing—trusting in our providence.

Later, Adrian: He reasons on—perhaps she, having grown up with sacrifice—and lived the good life for so long—perhaps her view on it; her take on it, is quite different to his. For him the burn of it helps him find clarity, certainty and purpose. Uprightness too, where everything he achieves is given over with a sob of gratitude. Nothing is kept to bulk up his own body of self-worth. Is this puritanical? Not sure. But the feeling is deep and penetrating and moves his heart—

Mouse: she can imagine that pang—that pain in humility—oh yes—but she does not feel its nourishment; it does not lure her as it does him. She wonders why not? Is she too selfish? Or has she been forced to go there through 16 years of motherhood? When it is not chosen the guilded edge of denial departs with its bounty—perhaps. She inhabits a 'no-man's-land'—no husband, no lover. A seeker, yes—a Mouse seeking passage, definitely. She can see it all so clearly, but if she tries to put it into words it sounds like a pipe-dream—a crazy, unobtainable dream. She is undeterred, however. An organic emergence is the only way things will unfold. They are not in control of the plan anyway. So, she cannot turn her back on their truth; it would have passed by now if it were merely infatuation. She knows—as she has always known. She sends him apologies for blurring the edges. She won't do so again, not until things are clearer. He is right, as always. The Laird needs her now. His is a long and arduous journey. She will take him out on a trip somewhere today. Love you, My Friend—X

I take myself to the indoor swimming pool. Need to clear my head. I'm not sure about Adrian's righteous stand. The pool is pleasantly quiet. I am cold after my dip, even though I ended my swim in the hot pool. I pass an upturned car and trailer in a ditch; a navy blue car similar to Vonny's. The Police are there. For a horrible moment I wonder if it could be Adrian. Surely his heater collection didn't require a trailer?

Mouse: My Love—just tell me you are okay? I need to know now. Tell you why later—M—X

I text The Laird, asking him to join me on an outing. He responds, sounding keen.

Adrian: Yes, I'm fine. Just been supporting the little team in their first game. Caught up with Tammy's father. He's been through the ringer with separation. He isn't working; looking for something new. Sherwood Forest? Not sure. Invited him milking. I saw Justin—says he needs to send me an e-mail. What's going on? Why do you ask how I am?

Midday, Mouse: Past an upturned trailer and car in a ditch after my swimming—dark blue—police—gave me a fright. Realize I need to stop being selfish. The health and well-being of those I love is the most important thing; no more confusing them. The lull time is important—go with it—no longing. The Book is the key—my strong sense. And Justin? Not sure. Land stuff? Us? Keep clear and safe, oh beautiful man of mine—X

I re-run our morning conversation in Vonny's kitchen; "what do you think of my Boat mythology for the story?" Adrian had asked. "I like it very much," I told him. "I particularly like the way you earth the detail, balancing my lofty idealism. It is lovely. Did you read Mizzie's e-mail?"

* * * * * * *

Early P.m. Adrian: The colour has fled from the day—grey clouds mount, casting their shadow over the land. The harbour doesn't sparkle as it did this morning. He can feel the heaviness in his face—maybe just lack of food—he'd better eat before moving the cows. Interesting come down from the thrill of possibility that was there earlier—a quiet drawing in—feeling into what's there for us all. A weekend away—loving you—X

I take The Laird out this afternoon. His depression deepens. I cannot shift his mood; understandable I suppose. He cannot get over the choices I have made. He cannot be in this town without thinking of me with Adrian. "Perhaps you had better go home then," I suggest. We have reached a stalemate. We walk around a park and rugby ground we haven't seen before. It is situated on a small peninsula close to Waikite Bay. The Laird lies down under some trees, watching the sport. "Go and write your Book," he says unkindly. "How am I supposed to feel positive? You are always asking me to make decisions. Now I have to decide whether to allow your writing to be edited. I feel bashed and broken by you, woman." The conversation reverts to Adrian. I speak of his strengths at school; his plans for the farm. "Yes, he is everywhere," my poor husband groans. And so we go home; the special outing yet another nail in our marriage coffin.

P.m. Mouse: Hi Darling—where are you? Off to Auckland for the weekend? Who is milking the cows? I am back home now. I took The Laird out—not very successful. Reached an impasse. He continues to be very frustrated; exacerbated by his lack of mobility—his worst nightmares all at once. His negativity is tricky to be around. I hope the skies are less grey.

Thinking of you—not doing too well on the 'no longing' front. Will keep trying— hmm—love—X

Adrian: *Hello, My Friend. Hope your Spirits are calm and steady through the lull—The Boat halted in her progress down the ramp. The wind has dropped; no point in launching now. We are both waiting to see from what quarter it will blow again. The wind was present when you and The Laird were in real and honest discussion. Things feel stagnant and swampy again. Can you press into the negativity? Find your friend again? What to do with the smitten heart? Bridge the separation between you. Keep together, especially in the dodgy weather.*

The Swallow Man is breathing again. The thrill of travel stirring in him once more; a simple walk with the dogs around an industrial complex in Papatoetoe soon awakens his eye for trees and branches—herbs for his thermos. The plastic tub he bought through the Internet from a fireman is gigantic, just squeezing into the car. The dogs are squashed together, better than being put inside the tub—humour again—yay. Is she freed as well? He hopes so.

Sunday 6th May 2007

A.m. Adrian: *Where is his Lady this morning? His Friend. He lies in his mother's house—pigs—calves—tub—Big J—Laird—Justin—Sasha—all fly around his mind. He is reactive. He knows why. Friday's life shock with Big J. at festival practise—unprocessed mind-talk; fear and resentment clouding everything—even the biggest light in his life—Her—His Friend—His Lady. He sets to; to clear the mind and find the truth. See you soon—clearly.*

Mouse: *The Laird is in better spirits this morning. He is friendly, warm and accepting. His wife has been fully clothed all night—not quite the boots— but certainly the jumper and jeans. An early night—a stressful day yesterday—a drop in temperature—her intention to spend some of the evening writing did not materialize. She didn't manage to send her Love a goodnight message. The call to sleep was the greater force. She wakes early and snoozes. She is overwhelmed by his embrace—by the set of Rainbows that shudder through her constantly. She must subdue them—still them—lock them away along with The Boat's sails. Dangerous, yet wonderful to take them out of the dark cupboard. They refuse to fold back into the constricted bundle of before—too much air and movement to re-stow them neatly, if at all. Hmm—*

She is walking; the Tui and Bell Birds so close above her head at the end of the drive. The Bog-Brush loves to be still; she is a Pointer, after all. The air is crisp—her fingers cold as she writes to him; her Lovely Friend; her Soul Companion; her Apollo. The water in the stream is so loud this morning. The dog stops at the same mound of medicinal grass—must contain an important vitamin for the canine reproductive system. Good morning, My Darling. Thank you for your lovely massages, {oops, Freudian slip, I mean messages!} I am

106

so glad you are feeling better on one level—hope you are processed on another. Let me know—love—X

P.s Say Good Morning and Happy Mothers' day to Jenny from me. Tell her I really enjoyed seeing her the other day. We are off to church at 10 a.m. Wonder what today might bring? Loving you clearly—no confusion in unconditional love. A slight ripple from the sails but I can control that. Have a blessed and Holy day, My Beautiful Friend—X

I deliver The Laird a cup of tea, giving him a warm cuddle as well. I coax him into making love with me. We are tender and close; the first for a long time.

Adrian: *Breakthrough! Mind talk about Big J. mostly cleared; life force again. Humble servant. Thank for your 'massages' too. Sails, eh? Fine looking they are too—sets the helmsman quivering at the sight; heart racing response. Jenny and I are taking the dogs for a walk. Is it Mothers' Day? That's good timing, eh? Loving you lots and lots. See you soon, Yummy Friend.*

P.s. Could you phone Sammy about a Monday meeting for the school development/land group? A ring around maybe? Pim and anyone else? Auction of the next door land is this Wednesday and we should have an intention ready—proposal for the developer whoever that might be. Sammy and Pim might go to the auction. Could you follow it up? I suggest a meeting on Monday morning at 8.30 a.m. Might be better after drop-off later on, but I might not be available then. Maybe Sammy could phone Big J. and let her know what is being planned. Louise too. I wouldn't mind keeping my name a little out of it just for now—if you know what I mean—XXXOOO

Mouse: *My Fine Helmsman, how I love you to handle my sails. We are well and happy, The Castle Mistress has given The Laird tender loving ministry—and he is soothed—more restored. Her message to him always; 'there is lots of me to go around. Please do not be afraid. No negativity.'*

I shall get down to the phone calls, Lord Swallow. We should get The Laird talking to Martini about his senior school ideas. The call for a new horizon is strong this morning. Loving you. X

The morning's church service feels alive and full of celebration; probably a reflection of my state of mind. My optimism is racing to take off, to remove the chocks and let The Boat splash into the water; and not just for Adrian and me; for The Laird too. What a fantastic team we could be. The Holy Spirit fizzles through me at the moment of consecration. The Laird is buoyant around the church-going families, but then his spirits dip noticeably. Is he unwell? Why do his moods fluctuate so dramatically? I'm sure they are getting more pronounced. Perhaps he is reminded of his unhappy childhood when we are alone as a family—whatever the reason it is tangible and not just because I have stepped away with Adrian. I also sense Cedric needs to be back in England; his negativity is increasing and I think he would be better off at his old school in Hampshire. He even looks like an arty public school boy with his tight jeans, trainers and floppy hair. The Laird and I have both remarked upon it.

Early P.m. Mouse: *They filled the church pew today—a positive, happy group; even Cedric, in church for Mothers' Day. The Laird sat at one end, Lord Swallow at the other. Little Arthur sat amongst them, close to his father. Today's sermon? 'To embrace the Holy message of unconditional love—to give more than to receive.' The folk band was playing this morning; not exactly reverent but it lent a tone of celebration. These two fine men are guardians of the unorthodox family group. As the service progressed she wondered at the effect her billowing sails might have on those around her. She harnesses the gale force levels of love when they are fully stretched; her positive energy reaches extraordinary levels; something she needs to share for the greater benefit. This is why the stowing of her sails, the dampening of her Spirit, denies their selfless value. The dark cupboard nourishes her not. She knows what her fully rigged Boat can achieve; a gift in itself. The Boat is as free as a light-filled bird; her horizons limitless. As the church service ended she looked up to find Lord Swallow on the deck of The Celestial Sea. He had the sails up in a jiffy—his passionate skill thrills her. He knows how to handle the intricacies of her wild Spirit. No one else can manage them. With his expert eye and strength he worked the sheets, hunkering down to fasten the final cleat. The wind was blowing his hair away from his face—she gasped at his handsome figure—his skill. He glanced up at them as he completed his task, a beam of pure delight and boundless joy across his face. Yes, they are ready to re-launch their Boat. Perhaps they might all climb aboard!*

We watch a family film this afternoon. The Laird is friendly again, although he continues to struggle with the lack of concrete plan. I take the children and the dog for a short walk through The Bush above the drive. We spy a whole host of treasure mushrooms.

Early P.m. Adrian: *Walking the dogs around the mangroves—wide clear sky above—God's glory. Spent the afternoon studying Biblical discoveries; phewee! What a tale I have to tell. Watching a video tonight, then home early tomorrow morning. Nice time it's been—stimulating—might be tired, but worth it. And you, My Love? You sound well. New horizons? I'll send you a goodnight text. X*

Mouse: *Hi, My Friend. Thanks for the lovely 'massage'! Not all of it came through. Biblical discoveries sound interesting. Anything for our quandary? My thought today? All this taxing waiting and debating time has really been for others to get used to our situation. We were acclimatized months ago. Also thought—perhaps we are allowed a small sailing trip when the wind is set favourably. When everything is harmonious. Just a thought—possibly not right—we could sleep on it—M—X*

Late P.m. Adrian: *Wait til you see the movie; 'as it is in Heaven'—oh boy! My mother just sent me the weirdest text, saying that she has a little tambourine for my son when he is born to my new wife! Life's a whirlwind and I'm loving it. Take care, My Dancer. Stay grounded—sails spilled and at rest. Relax, really relax. No need for any action; just honesty and depth. See that Movie with The Laird. How is he? Then come make music with me. See you tomorrow. X*

Later, Mouse {unsent}: *'Come to me,' she whispers. 'Come to me in all your wisdom and grace. Come wash me with your smiles and revelation. Come merge with me inside our celestial knowing—come.'*

Monday 7th May 2007

A.m. Mouse: *'Stay relaxed—really rest,' he has told her, his intuition so at one with her's. She is sleepy—not pushing herself. She went to bed for her evening snooze and didn't get up again, the stress of the last few months catching up with her at last. Mothers' Day is next week in fact; sorry! Don't known why we thought it was yesterday. Nice for you to have that sense while you spent time with Jenny. You sound inspired after watching your film last night. I will try to hire it—sounds a 'must' for all novice and advanced Angels. The Laird goes up and down—warm and loving—exasperated and lost. 'Dear, oh dear—what am I going to do with you, Mrs!' 'Just give me my head,' I reply. 'You'll take it anyway,' he adds; 'I shall cut it off instead!'*

But, I am set. The Boat is resting and the sails stowed; sort of. It feels right to tread gently and slowly. So, My Lord Swallow shall return today. He will be tired. He will need silence and cups of lemon and ginger tea. His Artemis wife will kiss away his cares if he desires her love, reuniting with shared anecdote, wrapped up together where they feel most comfortable— while holding their integrity. Come home to me safely, My Fine Sir. Come home to me and lay your head upon my heart.

Good morning, My Darling. A few of us are meeting for a short get-together re land at 9a.m. Keep safe—M—X

Adrian: *Still dark—driving-lights looming up, out of the mist. Driving by faith. 100km of journey under his belt. One third—heading home—back to milking updates—collegial accountability—rabbits and cats—children, projects —and of course—his Lady; The Seeker—the one who loves him—who stretches him and her family beyond the limits of convention—she who lets loose the songs of the heart as wind to stir the sails—she who asks more from him.*

He drives right into the eye of the dawn, the strains of the love story he watched last night still playing in his mind—the beautiful, full-hearted lover who saw Angels—the courage—the emergence of truth; the shake-down and wake-up that rattled through the town. He is tired—ooh, a sleep would be nice. He went to church yesterday, even though the service wasn't on. A grey morning is revealed. She must hold them all today—especially her husband. Still, the need for permission sits heavily on him, perhaps indicative of an unprocessed life-shock or fatigue from over-stretching himself. He is a little weakened and heavy today. Comfort would be lovely—but it could bring discomfort, in a way. These weaker days are useful because he gets to see his default setting, which today is revealed as cautiousness—and also longing and need—no—best to stay away today. Wait for the great restorer to have his way with me.

How well I know the soft touch of your sails—how tender the care you would administer. BUT, the truth is your husband has far greater need than I. Minister to him. Your sails recoil? He doesn't understand them? Try again— sail up boldly—trust him again with the same tenderness you would show me—holding nothing back. First your family, then us.

Oh, Lovely Lady, how I would love thee—were you—

Mouse: *I shall, Fine Sir—I shall stay away. May rest see you restored. May your day bring you peace—X*

Mid-Morning, Mistress to The Laird: *I'm being 'The good Wife'; the sun gently coaxes warmth into the wooden beams of the kitchen ceiling. A light sponge cake is cooking—'we are tired of your usual recipes,' The Castle Inmates complain. Some flapjacks too. The Bog-Brush slumbers, and the pig; rotund and content after her morning's digging. The Mistress cannot shake off her tiredness. The children are delivered to school and the dog has been walked. She sends him her love. She is here, will always be here. X*

I will try to do as my Swallow Man instructs. Oh, how I wish I were free for him to love me. His final sentence clutches at my heart. I am tired. I sleep on the sofa and I continue logging texts. My pile of notebooks is growing by the week. I walked the dog in the sheep farmer's field next to our house. He may have seen me. He isn't very friendly; unusual for a Kiwi, although most landowners guard their property fiercely and detest dog walkers. I imagine he might come over and have words with me.

"So, you are bored with me—bored of our life, and bored with us?" Yesterday's conversation with The Laird returns to me as I write. "You are not boring, My Love. It is just our energies don't spark together, that's all. That is what I am bored with. Of course I love you."

What strange times we face. I should tackle the growing pile of paperwork on my desk. I am usually an organized, 'on-to-it' kind of person; my controlling nature taking charge. Not any more; I have let go with Adrian at the helm. I couldn't be less interested in sorting through the pile. The papers have been glaring at me for weeks, but I have more important things to do. My light sponge cake is as flat as a pancake. Bother, I forgot to add any raising agent. The sun shines on. I send a belated birthday message to my nephew. I keep forgetting the family birthdays; hemisphere divide drives a huge wedge between us. I shall ask the children to draw a picture and we shall photograph it and send it through cyber space. I remain apprehensive. Something is in the air. I shall maintain my distance. The close-up work is taxing. I shall stand back and watch events unfurl. The Boat is more than ready to slip quietly into the ocean.

The phone rings at lunchtime. It is dear Cordelia. I haven't spoken to her properly for a long time. Does her call herald a change? Today is the **7th**-

She doesn't sound very happy; financial and relationship issues I understand. Adrian and I have both commented on her absence. "I miss you," I admit. "Perhaps we can get together next term, when things are easier." We don't linger on personal problems for long, chatting instead about the handful of families who are looking to join us from Rotorua; from the little school Cordelia helped run. The Rotorua initiative doesn't go beyond Class 1. She is excited about seeing her old friends. I chat about the school development and how I would like The Laird to speak with Martini about taking on a group of school leavers; running a programme for the 14-16-year olds. How he would love that. I have spoken with both Stephanie and Lois about the idea. "Best the proposal to The Laird comes from Martini," I suggest. I didn't add, *'not from any woman'*.

"The children and I have been relief milking for Adrian," Cordelia tells me. "And we've been feeding the bunny this weekend." Vonny is still away, that's why Adrian took her dog to Auckland. Cordelia is pleased that I left her a message yesterday. I must be a better friend. We say goodbye, promising to spend time together soon. I spend the rest of the afternoon writing more pages of 'Dry-Dock' and this 'Setting sail'. I hope to send Mizzie more script. Will The Laird allow the editing? Yes—we are all waiting; the interminable 'wait.' I half expect Lord Swallow to change his mind and suggest a meeting. I would possibly say no today—possibly. But then, I can never refuse him anything.

P.m. Adrian: *Little Mouse, Little Mouse—can I call you at your house?*

Mouse: *My Dear Friend Adrian—am just on my way to school. Text me- when you have slept? I am free 3.30/4.15—X*

The Go-Getter is spending the afternoon with his friend Keenan; Lisa and Andy's son. Rinky and I are delivering Lucia to the riding stables. Lucia is horse mad. Adrian hasn't replied to my message. I expect he has guitar lessons. A flurry of autumn leaves rushes ahead of us beside the road as we drive. There is a fresh breeze today. The wind is picking up. A magnificent oak tree on our mountain road in the lower residential area grabs my attention today. Spinning oak leaves shower us as we pass; they dance gleefully in the wind. They are so happy—and free. They fall in slow motion. I snap the flurry moment, storing the golden scene in my mind for another time; like now. A girl with a boxer dog chats through an open car window. The dog dozes in the long grass that has escaped the mower; Kiwis mow all year round. They are very particular about tidy edges in the town; a complete contrast with much of their pioneering make-do's.

I have some clothes for Bernard and Felicia's young son, so we dive in on our way home. They have been away for a month. We greet each other warmly and I hand back Felicia's Eckhart Tolle book. "Thank you; I found it most interesting."

P.m. Adrian: Two reminders—he doesn't seem unduly affected by Friday's discomfort. A story is playing around his mind—from his Biblical research. He has been in Egypt for most of the day—strange—taking a while to return home. The rhythm of cows and stars is good for him. And somewhere his Friend is working, her mind busy with the chores of parenthood, or perhaps gazing out for new horizons, fondling her sails. He sits like a sadhu on his hilltop—quiet, heavy and tired. She works like a titmouse cleaning her nest. What will the daybreak bring? An interesting break it has been—tiring but filling—curious—what next? X

Mouse: My Friend—hello there. I was just reaching for my phone to send you a loving text—to ask how you fare—when your message came through. You sound as if you have landed. I have been still—quiet—slightly flat all day; overtaken by tiredness. My father has sent me a long, hand-written letter of disapproval and plea. He underlines the huge upset I am causing, suggesting how I should behave—gulp. My parents have always had a strong voice, but they can't do anything while I am on the other side of the world. There is no way I could have aired my sails in this way back home. Ho hum—need to be with you—seems like ages. Loving you, despite all odds.
I stir the onions and bacon; the boys are in the top cabin. "So, what next?" You ask. "The Book, Lord Swallow. The answers are all in The Book." Let's use this lull to push ahead. Can you send me The Boat Mythology again? Also, have you read the letter I sent about our writing? All the pointers are there. A small introduction might be good. What do you think? Am with you—M—X

Tuesday 8th May 2007

A.m. Mouse: Another night fully dressed—exhausted—I even slept in my apron! Deep sleep took me to your arms. You were kissing me so sensually—mmm—I miss our kisses—where we linger in our secret. An early rise and the daily rounds begin. A warm, spanking wind ruffles the long flax leaves. The sun is still abed; the moon highlights different things. The stately pines in this high place are crowned by twinkling stars. My feet crunch on the gravel, taking us along the often-used path in this, our Kiwi home. But for how much longer? The Laird needs a new project. He slips into depression unless an exciting new agenda shines ahead. He knows I don't want to leave—knows it is because of you. He scans the pages of U.K teaching vacancies several times a day. Hmm—I saunter on—wondering. Loving you—X
P.s I have sent you another idea for a synopsis—by e-mail.

112

E-mail to Adrian:

My darling Adrian—another idea for a synopsis—a passage from our latest Book, 'Setting sail.' I think it reads well; a combination of yours and mine; our prose married for all time. I thought I might send it to Mizzie, as well as our two original synopses. That way she has enough to work on. The Laird still hasn't given his permission. I shall find the right moment to ask again. It needs to be when he is feeling up rather than down. I shall send the rest of the story to Fair England if and when he agrees. Gentle kisses and gossamer wings; your partner in quill and kiss—XOXO

A.m. Adrian: He can stand again after a wobbly day—a day where the knocks brought up fear, and thoughts of self-preservation. He has a faint dream memory of a passionate night with his Lady. He also slept fully-clothed. He feels ready to add his weight to the wheel—to be a friend to Big J; completion is the call, and organization. It is time to rise—an early trip to school pre-Sienna to tidy up the model houses that have driven her wild—and to offer her love. Touched by the task; the call of St. Michael—drop your personal needs, petty grudges, hurts; the stuff of the lower ego. Raise your concerns to the greater battle—the uplifting of humanity—joyful sacrifice in the service of our Mighty Lord—stir me. Rouse me with your call. Awaken me with life. Heal this vessel to carry my task through to the end of my days. Open this heart to Love—over and over—bridging the gulf of separation again and again—courage—

P.s Come see me this morning at drop off—at home til 9.30.

Mouse: I shall be there, My Friend. Let's take our swords together in blessing and love for all—and for each other. See you early. 8.40 ish—M—X

Adrian ambles ahead of me as I motor down the school drive after morning drop-off. He must have completed his morning tasks for Sienna. His dog is on a long rope. He looks fresh and gorgeous. He stops to talk to Gertrude; "goodness—she gave me a life-shock," he tells me when we meet at Vonny's house. "She thought I had treated Jessie unfairly by sending her out of the class. Others had been difficult too, but they weren't punished. I handled Gertrude well; acknowledged her concerns. I spoke to her daughter then and there; I really listened. She seemed pleased. I didn't claim to be totally in the right. I said I would watch that next time. Perhaps Jessie could help me out. I wasn't really fazed. I feel strong enough to handle these knocks. Man, I'm hungry and tired again. Let's make some porridge."

So, we sit together in the siting room, each holding a steaming bowl of oats and dried apricots; a yummy mixture. "Good—we can be chaste," Adrian announces. "No snuggling." We are natural and easy together. I speak about my father's letter; how that made me feel; "his words haven't really unseated me," I admit. "I am in charge of my life and something other holds whatever is going down. I shan't turn around." Adrian is full of an article he has read about the possible Noah's Ark remains having been discovered. The burial place of the Arc of the Covenant is also mentioned. "Look—here is the newspaper article. Amazing, eh? They have photos and everything; look at the size of that hull! Of course, there is an article that decries it as a big fraud, but read this—they have even found a passage through the Red Sea where Moses is supposed to have led his people! I reckon I believe it; exciting or what?"

We move on to other subjects, namely The Laird's need to begin a new project. I mention the seed I have sown with Stephanie and Lois—about The Laird working with Martini on a senior school project. It is a long-shot, I know. Adrian is unsure. "Could I really have The Laird in school? Working together?" Perhaps I shouldn't have suggested it. The Laird finds it difficult when Adrian is on The Mountain, and likewise. Two rival bulls together? Are they being called to overcome that? They might pull it off. The plot thickens.

There is still so much to discuss and never enough time; "you really must get that movie out," my Lover insists; "it is so *us*." We acknowledge the difficulties my husband must face, knowing the deepest and most intimate part of his wife belongs to another. "The Laird knows that you are really mine," Adrian admits. "We desire each other; we long for each other," he admits, gazing at me for a long time. "We cannot deny that we do." His eyes are soft and my heart melts. How strange that each passing day increasingly highlights the truth. Lord Swallow holds me close before I leave. We allow ourselves a gentle kiss that lasts a while. "My, oh my—when we kiss like that I can feel my integrity slipping," he sighs. "I can travel a long way down that knife-edge and maintain my integrity," I explain. "But I know it is different for a man." We smile at each other. There is no need to say anything.

The sun is hot enough to walk in a vest top along the shore at Tui Park today. Autumn strolls slowly into New Zealand, unlike his British brother who makes his presence immediately felt. The dog is still on heat so we head off, away from the main area where a family is picnicking. We walk into the sunlight that drenches the houses and gardens on the Waikite Bay side of the Park. I particularly like a wooden house with dark green paintwork and copious deck. Adrian's words are ringing in my ears; *I try not to get excited about a future with you; our being together,"* —his face brightened when he admitted his true feelings.

There are so many sun twinkles on the water today; one spot looks as if the stars have come down for a daylight bath. The dog and I watch, enthralled, alone with our thoughts and our hopes. "I can see you later on," I told Lord Swallow; "probably without permission—for a quick visit."

I have an appointment with the College Principal this afternoon; he is keen to know how The Service Project is progressing. Bradon is a jolly man and we have a good meeting. He had heart surgery recently and tells me how he must walk for half an hour every day. "Regular exercise keeps the small capillaries open; best do that rather than undertake bouts of stiff exercise."

Early P.m. Mouse: *every time they come together their bond strengthens. Against all odds—the highest obstacles—their love and desire lay a solid foundation. To deny its felicity is dishonest, but to plunge straight in is a selfish act. The Angels must take the lead, gracefully and discreetly, so they can follow the right path unfolding within their lives. Each day a movement. Each morn a blessed kiss—X*

I have some spare time this afternoon, so I shop and log our text messages before collecting The Laird from College. He has an appointment with the surgery at five p.m. Cedric is in a frightful mood, but the younger two are very happy. I collect Lucia with my two from school; she is staying for the afternoon.

P.m. Mouse: *Shopping—tick. Stowed away—tick. Dog walked 3 times—tick. College meeting—tick. All school and college delivery and collections—tick. Laird's new plaster applied—tick. Cup of tea and soothing care administered—tick. House tidied—tick. All text logging—tick. Inspired meeting with Sammy, {must tell Lord Swallow}—tick. Glorious breakfast with said gentleman—tick. Sensual kissing—tick. Integrity maintained—tick. Supper cooked and served—tick. One friend delivered home—tick. Laird delivered back to college with his sleeping bag for a Community Service Workshop; students staying the night in the sports hall—tick. Phew!!*
Quick visit tonight? Tick? Or not? Thank goodness I had all those big sleeps! Loving you. Am with you under the stars—M—X

Adrian: *Tick—visit is possible. A school meeting has been cancelled. Time? Milking for another twenty minutes or so. He is learning to navigate astrally. The constellations become more familiar to him every clear night. What is his fellow Helmsman learning? How to use the sails—the right moment to raise them—how to stow them—how to capture every breath—this sounds like a voyage is impending. But where to? And with whom?*

Mouse: *My Darling Friend—should be with you between 8/8.30. Just at Papa Poi roundabout—X*

I drive straight to the farm once The Laird is delivered to College. As he left the van, clutching sleeping bag and crutches he turned to me and said; "when I was talking to Barnie the other day he said *'now is the end of the beginning rather than the beginning of the end."* I look at him sadly, unsure how to reply. "I shall do what I am meant to do," I say. I must sound harsh. I don't want to be unkind, but I won't tell lies. I suppose I am really saying; '*I do not choose to be here. I am only with you because there is no other alternative at present.*' I feel sad for my poor Laird; he has been patient and generous in many ways. At what point should I choose truth as opposed to a selfless act? Or should I reverse that question? Am I meant to lie for others' sake?

How wonderful that Adrian has Vonny's house to himself this month; I know The Angels have planned it so. I pray we might find a clear way forward before long. I pray that Cedric might be offered a place at our old school in The U.K. for his final two years at school, {he is being particularly difficult this month,} and of course, I pray The Laird might find a new project to lift his spirits and take his mind off 'us'. I continue to hold my line—that I can carry my domestic duties while he is away adventuring—if I am allowed to see Adrian. "But I want you to come with me on my adventures," he tells me. "Your adventures are not exactly my kind of adventures," I say, although I suppose I can go there; I have been 'going there' for years already, without any heart and soul connection.

My Lord Swallow is warmly dressed in two jumpers and a woolly hat; the Dairyman and Woodworker. Light spills out of the basement space under Vonny's house. Adrian uses the space as his woodwork shed and extended dairy store. I am duly greeted and shown the new steel milk container that fits in the fridge. "I met this cool guy in a farm supplies shop. He was so enthusiastic; amazing! He found me a tap for the container. I love meeting these people; sharing our interest and knowledge—pipes and rivets, milking equipment and dairy engineering. I also met an old boy in Mitre 10, {DIY store}. He was buying rimu door knobs. I told him I had dozens of them back home if he was interested, taking my phone number he said; *I just love it!*"

My Lover is beaming; woodchips in his hair and a sparkle in his eyes. "It's so nice, knowing each other is there in the background," I offer. "Yes," he agrees. A group of thin branches lies across the workbench, clamped in the woodwork vice. Shaving off the bark with a clever little device he ordered through the Internet Lord Swallow is engrossed. "How cool is that?" I help sand the finished pegs, driving them home into the rusty heads of the school's small spades; perfect for young hands. We sharpen the blades and talk about painting the handles. "We start work on the piggery tomorrow," he tells me. "Several parents are coming in to help."

My Lover eventually pulls me to him, holding me close. "This is sad for The Laird," we agree. "Let's send him our love and best wishes. "But I won't be untruthful," I repeat. "It's lovely to come home to you, laying my head against your chest." "That's nice," he hugs me tight, kissing the top of my head. "We aren't opening the lids of our Copper Boxes," Adrian voices, "but we are certainly tapping into our deep reserve of respect and true friendship." I feel so at one with Adrian—restful and quiet—and right. It is the end of the day. How lovely it is to start and end the day in each others' arms. We kiss gently and slowly, without sexual invitation. We kiss again beside the car; "thou shalt not covet thy neighbour's wife," he says to me. I cover his Greenstone with my hand, just finding it beneath his woolly layers. "We are not going to that place," I assure him. "We are still in integrity, odd as it may seem." "Do you think Little Arthur has anything to do with this?" Adrian wonders. "Hmm—he/she has been on my mind a lot," I answer. "Rinky keeps talking about me having another baby. If we had a baby girl she would have to be called Arthur." Adrian shows me the text message his mother sent him about his wife having a baby son. "I'll send it on to you. How strange is that? I'm sure I was with you; loving you last night," he admits. "I certainly knew you were kissing me in my dreams." "Perhaps we will invoke an immaculate conception," I suggest. "Well, my mother has anointed me, so I'm all set!" Adrian's response makes me smile.

I leave my platonic lover and drive home. The cabins are quiet; the children are in bed under Cedric's supervision. He is watching television. The Laird is at College for the night so I have the house to myself. I enjoy my solitary bed tonight.

P.m. Mouse: *Goodnight, My Lovely Adrian. Thank you for a perfect evening of woodwork, integrity and gentle ownership. Hope the hot tub is wondrous. One day I shall join you there and lie against your chest in a steamy wallow—watching the stars together. See you tonight in our virtual reality—maybe. What is Little Arthur planning?*

Mmm—sleep well—I love you—'softly, gently, quietly'—X

Part Three Rat Lines

They have polished her brassware and completed the repaint—The Celestial Sea shines with an excited sparkle. But her Captain worries she may attract too much attention. "Best get her in the water and find a discreet berth somewhere;" the crew agrees. One of the Marine Officials has already reprimanded Lord Swallow through the office window—a wagged finger and a questioning glance. He is rattled by the warning. He has his eye on the quiet waters where fewer rocks lie in wait to catch even experienced sailors unawares.

The Boat slides silently down the slipway, holding her breath; or perhaps that should read 'stilling her steel.' She hardly dares believe she is nearing the water at last—after the long and tedious months of 'waiting'. She makes no sound as her repainted hull kisses the lapping brine. Her excitement is checked, although her keel shudders with pleasure. She is nearly re-launched. The truth will be heard. It will not rest until a homecoming berth appears. The Celestial Sea rejoices in the recognition of her Captain and First Mate's tentative step upon her deck. She has been waiting for so long. Each lifetime her crew weaves a tangled web; more complicated than the last. Their task? To chart a karmic passage using skills of considered integrity. Yes, integrity and unconditional love. They are well-versed in these skills, but this set of quandaries is a myriad of complication involving different hemisphere as well as religious taboo, moral code and professional conduct.

The Boat creaks as they tread her boards. Lord Swallow and his Lady dare to lift the hatch and peer inside their beloved vessel. She is more of a risk-taker than her lover. Lady Thumbelina would have The Captain lay her across their bunk in a jiffy. Luckily he has the matter well-in-hand. She relies on his control. She will try to behave. They face a grave and dangerous swell. Even her unstoppable bubbles are quiet for once.

Chapter 1 Recognition

Wednesday 9th May 2007

We have a gentle morning. I make everyone a good breakfast. Cedric eats well; let's hope it improves his mood. I don't feel a strong need to communicate with Adrian, but I do eventually. I am feeling so close to him that messaging takes a back seat.

A.m. Mouse: My Fine Sir—a light dusting of wood shavings—a double layer of woolen jumpers; The Master at home with plane and lathe. She loves to see him so. She feels at home; at peace in his ownership; in his claim upon her heart and soul—

Adrian: Beautiful message. Have a joyous day of progress. I'm a little nervous—big day on the farm—X

Mouse: Good luck with everything. Not sure what it entails; I think you mentioned pig-sty building? But I'm with you, whatever. No need to reply—X

Both my menfolk are especially occupied this morning. I shall send The Laird a morning greeting too:

Mistress to The Laird: Darling—hope the event was everything you hoped it would be. Try to keep the ankle up if possible. Dog has had a splendid beach dash—my jeans are soaked! Garry Govern, {a parent at school working on a house in the bay}, shouted cheekily from the shore: "keep that dog under control!" I didn't know who it was at first, but then I recognized him. Am just about to swim—need to shift some of that chocolate! Then I'll go back home to make more phone calls for the service project. I need to bake for the children too. Roast chicken tonight after your school board meeting. Are you still going to that? Just let me know your movements. Loving you, despite all odds—X

The water in the bay was noticeably colder today. It stung my feet and legs until I got used to it. The dog and I enjoyed our usual amble together before the domestic chores of life called me away.

* * * * * * *

P.m. Mouse: *Hi there. How is the pig-sty? How was your day? I have had a productive time—domestic and achieving. Thinking of you—X*

Adrian: *Sunset silhouette—dusky peach—grey-swirled pink—wispy threads— the night fills in. The cows nuzzle heads—empty udders—milking complete. The blue water trough fills slowly and requires a hand to hold the tap fitting. The bubbles remind him of——*
He surveys the day's work; a dozen posts stand proudly upright; children's names written equally proudly upon them; a workable skill that saw each of its builders depart the site with a rousing cheer. The beginnings of the sty are well underway; they can imagine the finished article. They feel the pride and surge of confidence as the first successful part reaches completion. The project manager is bold; his judgement holding strong. Yes, it feels good. Being on the land offers him a certain freedom. He is on the sea—The Captain of his willing crew. How nice it would be to have his First Mate beside him. But not on this voyage; this one he captains alone. His thoughts turn to her family ship; the poor vessel tossed cruelly about. Not built for these conditions it is being hammered—ill-temper rife amongst the crew—The Captain absent or ill. What will become of this wallowing ship?

Mouse: *The screen lights up. She has missed his sweet lyric today; his beautiful message swells her heart. Her man has been so busy—a meaningful and creative task—a palace for the lucky pigs; Molly included! She sighs— tired—usual routine day for her. Roast chicken in the oven. The Laird is still at their school; another board meeting; he will get a lift home with The Chief Marine Official; 'a good chance to talk,' he told her. The pressing urgency today? To organize Cedric's future; his constant negativity and foul moods reaching concerning levels. He is refusing to join activities with his friends and he is unbearable at home. His behaviour pattern needs to be broken—probably leaving home for part of the year. We shall see. He and The Laird rub each other up the wrong way—too many negative vibes together in a small space compound the problem. "He should return to The U.K," says The Laird. "I should have taken that job; the school would have been perfect for him—and for me—and okay for the other two."*
Hmm—she thinks on. In many ways splitting the family tension for part of the year would be a relief, although a strange idea. Something needs to change; these two males with their heavy, brooding pessimism invoke a silent nightmare. She needs a positive mantra at hand. Please send a prayer to The Angels of Domestic Quandary. Wish you were here. Loving you. X
P.s She would so enjoy being his First Mate—in every way; building, designing, writing, in his arms all night; her limbs curled about his. Perhaps he might sometimes allow her to lead; she is used to leading. She knows they would achieve a happy balance. For the first time in her life she is happy to let go of the reins; she does not need to hold everything. She feels safe in his capable hands. A sudden thought comes to her: Perhaps The Laird should take Cedric back to England and really concentrate on him for several months. He

always blossoms under one-to-one; set him up in every way. Hmm—this could be positive; or not? They aren't good together.

The Laird arrives home late. He had a big meeting at school and Simon drove him back up the mountain. They chatted about our on-going quandary; an acknowledgement that *'no, my wife doesn't make me deeply happy either.' 'Are we prepared to work on that?'* Simon asked. My constant line that we keep what works but loosen the bands is confusing. My perception of our bond has not changed, even in the face of Adrian's presence in my life. But for my husband it is a huge change—of course it is. "What is more important; the institution of marriage or the pursuit of truth, even if it comes from outside?" We retire to watch the film Adrian told me about. "I heard it mentioned on the radio," I tell a little white lie. *'As it is in Heaven'*—a heartfelt tale of celestial love.

Thursday 10th May 2007

A.m. Mouse: *"knock that bloody chicken off the shed roof—go now woman—use one of my crutches; hurry!"*

It is dark—she needs to rouse herself anyway. The dog is expectant, keen for her usual routine to begin. Should she tether her for the rooster dispatch? She will bark if she leaves her inside, causing even more disturbance and fury. Armed with crutch and tethered hound she balances on one of the stone water troughs—success—she dislodges the feathered cacophony. But—she forgets the dog chases anything that flies—too late—with alarming speed she is yanked to the ground, landing with a great thwack on her side. She is covered in water and mud; a serious bruise to her left breast. She is shaken but okay, thankful that no hard object was in the way. She would have been knocked out. She walks the dog—she is in pain—finding The Laird's crutch still in her hand. Minutes before she had been dreaming of her Lover's tender embrace. She dreamt they were in a new environment. She was in his room. He was annoyed by The Laird's arrogant tone at a recent business meeting. He stood behind her; their hands and arms adoring and touching. His fingers moved to her left breast. {Did he know of her impending accident?}Their love deepens every time they come together.

She will be black and blue—better find the rescue remedy and the arnica. She sends him her love. Good morning, My Darling. Wish I was with you now— M—X

Adrian: *Oh dear, he reads her text with a wince. This Lady—this family needs some tender loving care. Is this just a painful entry into a new life, or is it the grinding crash of sinking ships? Is this his doing, he wonders? Is he responsible for their pains in some way? Has he acted wrongly? Does he need to hold them more—take them as his family and step into their dynamics, from a physical distance, but more consciously on a psychic level? Is this the request?*

Mouse: *No—it is not your doing, My Friend. Are you at home?*

Adrian: *Hi—up on the land, working on pig-sty. Two pupils just rushed over to see the progress. Feeling good. Come on up?*

I saunter across the new playing field in the warm sunshine. I climb over the stile. Adrian looks vibrant and so handsome; his boyish haircut is more noticeable today. His 'work in progress' is exciting too; tools lying about everywhere, a trestle table propped up by the fence and a series of completed posts upright and solid. "I can't believe how focused the children are," he tells me. "Look how deep Joni dug his hole!" I peer in—goodness; it must be three feet deep. "How did you get them to stick to the task?" I ask, as surprised as their teacher. Another man is helping Adrian today; a friendly parent I haven't met before; Sean Kimble. Two children are busy with hammers, continuing their thrilling project. The novelty certainly hasn't worn off.

"The Laird and I watched the film last night," I tell Adrian. "What did you think of the leading woman?" He asks; "she really told him, didn't she!" We smile together. "Well, better get on with the day. We probably shouldn't be seen together, eh? Bye."

* * * * * * *

My day is slow. I am tired after this morning's accident; shaken up I expect. Adrian didn't ask how I was. I had better keep on taking the arnica. I walk the dog in the low tide; the mud is especially gloopy. I notice the renovation progress of a dear little Bach amongst the reeds on the shore further around the bay. {A Kiwi 'Bach' is short for 'Bachelor pad'; huts originally used by single men when they worked away from their families, often built along the coast and now used as holiday homes.} I can hear someone working inside the small building; the radio is playing. Smoke curls from the chimney and a car is parked beside the sand. Oh, I can so imagine owning a small property like that with Adrian. How we would enjoy the opportunity. A strong wave of emotion brings an image of Little Arthur playing on the beach. His father would tell him the names of all the birds, the plants and the shells. He would teach his son to whittle the pieces of driftwood that he has stuffed in his little pockets.

I spend the afternoon with the College Students again. Tom gives me a friendly smile; the English boy whose parents moved to Hong Kong, leaving him behind to complete his schooling. He looks happier. I meet with students individually, hearing about their different projects and checking their recorded service sessions. Some have been fund-raising for the Hospice, rattling tins outside a supermarket. I was at College for several hours. We are all busy this week, especially Adrian. We haven't seen each other much. Cedric is even tetchier when we get home. Why is he so angry all the time? His old school in Hampshire has sent an e-mail, offering a place for his final two years at school.

124

Will we accept? We managed a trip to the library before we came home. Rinky's friend, Lucia, is staying with us tonight.

P.m. Mouse: Hello. How goes my Fine Sir? Milking? Out this evening? Thinking of you. M—X

Adrian: The milk is still inside its drum upon the grass. A noisy plane approaches the airport. He lies on the wet grass, massaging an acutely sore belly; the result of an intense meeting and tiredness. The day was good though—more progress on the farm project. New areas reclaimed from the blackberry with Sean's help—a new friend? The man you met briefly this morning; a nice guy; good to work with. It is a busy week. I still haven't caught up—and—

Kiwis don't use the term 'brambles' which surprises me. So many words/phrases hail from traditional Britain that I had presumed 'brambles' would be a given. Nope—'blackberry' is the commonly used name for the prickly plant.

Our domestic conversations go round and round. The Laird and I discuss long into the evening. We list our thoughts and deductions. The Laird doesn't feel I have really moved on in any way since our decision of two weeks ago. That if anything, Adrian and I are more of a couple than ever! How strange is that? We both place the children at the top of any prioritizing. The Laird eventually admits that he needs to find some inner peace himself, as well as a host of other things. "How I wish I had your lack of worry; your faith and trust," he says. "I suppose I draw on your positivity." "I cannot move forward in our marriage if you are not prepared to really face yourself on a personal level," I tell him. "This is what we are missing in our relationship." "I know I am not secure," he admits. These personal wrangles are mixed up with our parental decisions about Cedric—what would be best for him? The Sussex Monastery has offered The Laird another job; as a sports master. "Tempting," says my husband. "But it would mean a backwards step into old habits." "Perhaps I *do* need to be away from you to see the bigger picture," I suggest. "But that would mean splitting up, and I don't want that," he replies. Hmm—

P.m. Mouse: They have been talking—and how—my goodness—round and round; too much to explain in a text. They discussed Cedric's future too. She is still reluctant to agree to her husband's demands—except the 'no jumping into bed with your lover,' agreement. He claims their married bond is important; solid. They reached some profound truths about the spiritual work The Laird needs to address for their marriage to succeed. He has committed to undertaking that work—say between now and December. We shall see—X

Cedric sits in silence with his hat on and hoody pulled up as we tell him about our marriage troubles—The Laird thinks we should, although I am less sure. We don't mention Adrian. We speak about his return to England to complete his schooling. He is interested. Now we just have to make it happen. Dear Lord in heaven—please help us with this difficult decision. Life would certainly be easier if we didn't have constant financial worries. The Laird has a relatively good salary, but our mortgage is crippling. Kiwi salaries are unable to support a hefty mortgage. New Zealand is one of the most expensive countries in the world to purchase property—if you are receiving a Kiwi salary. Europeans who purchase their properties outright have a much easier time of it.

P.m. Adrian: How is she—his Friend? What magic has unfolded in her day? He has forwarded a text from someone interested in the community land project; Trinny from Rotorua. Want to make contact? Loving you—X

Mouse: And so, My Darling Adrian, I have been working at College for part of the day. I ate far too many chocolate biscuits. Missing your touch—your magic inside me. I have steadied the family ship. The Harbour Master is a little soothed; a little clearer in his goals. Now is not the time for any ship-rocking. Empowerment to the ruler at the moment—and The Book. Yes, a step forward. For you and I—work and care, love and holding. Sleep well, Fine Sir—

The Laird and I continue chatting into the night. The quandary never ends. "I think you are hoping I will say 'yes' to us three; is that it?" He asks. "No," I reply. "I don't know where it will go, all I can say is that my intuition indicates this is right." "I would have been okay about it if you hadn't slept with him," he says. "Oh no, you wouldn't," I reply quickly. "It is only because of my choices that we are here; really opening up to face the issues." "Hmm," he sighs. "It is all very odd. But I would NEVER, NEVER give you permission to sleep with him." "Fair enough," I respond. "The structure of marriage is what makes me tick," he continues; "holding it all—and allowing things to happen inside it." "Yes, I can see that, but it isn't working for us," I maintain my claim that something needs to change. "I know that I have broken the rules; rules I generally agree with, but in this case I have allowed myself the taboo. For me it is the happiness and joy that provide the structure, not the other way around; like the film we watched; unconditional, God-filled positivity. And what about your constant negativity within *the structure*?"

The Laird's parents lived in constant strife, but they stuck it out to the bitter end. Does he want to follow their example? I stay solid in my opinion. I will not budge. The Laird's escalating, negative vibe cannot continue. It damages us all. Eventually we climb the stairs, warm and friendly.

Friday 11th May 2007

A.m. Mouse: She is stiff this morning—her thoughts with him—her Fine Sir; her companion on every level. The evening's work was powerful. She was strong in her stand; that things need to change. They shared positivity, despite The Laird's refusal to share his wife; {understandable}, and her refusal to let her lover go completely; {perceived as unreasonable in the eyes of those unaccustomed to Angel tactics.}

So—a new day—a decision to try and get Cedric back to England for his final two years of school—a commitment from The Laird to try and let things go and not to worry—to find a new opening for his personal and spiritual growth. And from her? She would give no other commitment than to continue steering their ship—her hand steady at the helm, and not to leap into Lord Swallow's bed. She will not deny their close friendship. She had better begin her day.

I love you, My Darling. I am with you. Good Morning—X

I remember something I said to The Laird last night; "so, am I meant to give up Heaven? And my partner in this too? When he feels the same as me?" "You haven't really moved away have you?" He replied. "Your decision two weeks ago wasn't a decision at all." "There isn't any choice—not really," I said. "There is always choice," he told me. "You just cannot face the consequences." And in many ways that is true.

A.m. Adrian: *A warm greeting from the cocoon—his bed so snug and comforting. He too is steady—he shouts a cry of celebration into cyber-space. She has done it! She has spoken the truth—what she wants and what she will not put up with. She has asked for growth—called for change; hurray! Arriving at a shared vision—deeper alignment with her husband—helping him to move from wounded child to adult learner—breaking the back of habitual chauvinism. He is proud of his plucky woman; very proud. Somehow he knows this is right. Things are lining up; an important movement. The heavy old ship is being moved from its breached position—where it had been blocking the flow, forcing traffic to swirl and jostle awkwardly around the ends so dangerously. Now it has become traffic itself; a vessel in movement—going somewhere—never to really sail like The Celestial Sea—but at least ocean-bound; bobbing.*

And his dream—last night he met and greeted The Laird. There was warmth. The details were hazy, but he was there—ahhh! Outbreath—relief—the pushing and tugging has achieved something. I wonder if the movie helped? So—the day calls. The many animals in his life call for his attention. The cows are low on feed and get feisty if not pampered. The hens have been cooped up all day and need greens and corn. The rabbit and guinea pig need shifting. Was it a dream about numerous commitments? Too good to believe that a reconciliation might actually come about! Just sent you a text from Trinny—the parent interested in the land project. I'll forward what I sent to her.

Oh, yes—do you have a contact for Keegan from the home-schooling group? I'd like him to play hockey with my class team as we are short of a player. Loving you lots X

Message from Trinny: I car pool with three others from Rotorua. I have dreamed of a community village for many years now, but felt it wouldn't be here in Rotorua. The Waikite Bay area gels with me, and may fit in with your plans.

Adrian's reply to Trinny: Hi Trinny. Thanks for your message. Great to hear. The more people interested, the more drive the project receives. A meeting is being planned and some radical ideas are brewing. I'll put you on our list and keep you informed. Adrian

We have a rushed morning getting The Laird to College in time for a student trip. And then I deliver the younger two to school. I wander up to the farm to find Adrian. I can see his car with its door open, but no man?

Mouse: Come to find my Gentleman Farmer, his waiting steed with stirrups set; he must be here somewhere; an impressive amount of pig-pen cleared. I call—no answer. Are you stuck in a thicket? Or in a meeting perhaps? I send you my celestial blessing. Will inform Mountain Molly of the progress made to the Porcine Palace. Love you—X

Tui Park feels different today. The tide is right out and the exposed coastal landscape one I haven't seen before. The dog and I walk right across the new definition towards the opposite shore. Flat pools of shallow water await our discovery. The calm water mirrors my inner quiet. I like the new form; interesting that it was there all the time, just waiting to be exposed. Sunshine wrapped in envelopes of thin cloud spills from a peaceful sky, dappling the different landscape. Heron skim the surface of the standing water. I turn to view the residential shoreline of Waikite Bay; finding the line of the now empty estuary sitting stark before the backdrop of the ever-present green hills. Close by lies our school with its new farm and impressive industry. Love abounds. My Lord Swallow presides over his realm; my man—the man I adore.

Midday, Mouse: My Friend, I have e-mailed you Keegan's number. What a great idea to get him playing hockey with your class! I just had a good chat with Pim about our Community Village enterprise scheme. Meeting planned for next week. Trinny's message is exciting too. Something has moved. The Boat is shifting. Hold on tight. Set the sails!! Big kiss. X

"You must be hanging out to catch a glimpse of Adrian every time you arrive at school." Last night's stressed conversation returns to me as I drive. *"No, it isn't like that,"* I answered my husband. I didn't add that our relationship is way beyond that stage; like a mature married couple we don't *'hang out to catch a glimpse of each other.'* We are happy to see each other— and content when we don't. We have almost by-passed the need for touch. Odd, really. I spend the day copying our copious texts; the passages abate not. I walk the dog, shop and make some college phone calls.

* * * * * * *

Vonny's dog is loose in the lower car park beside the road when I arrive at school this afternoon. I take him to Adrian, finding him engrossed in the woodwork shed. Jock has escaped the kitchen stronghold; naughty dog. My Fine Sir is busy making a wooden spinning top; a clever item. He is very pleased with it. The woodwork shed is neat and tidy. "Two children received electric shocks from the farm fence this morning," he tells me. "Oops—parents were informed and we asked the hospital for their advice. The children had sore arms and chests." Adrian appears happy and content, although he must be shaken by the accidents. He doesn't suggest we meet for a quiet catch-up. His week is busy.

I collect Rinky the Minx while The Go-Getter departs with Stephen's family for the night. Stephen is Ronnie and Michael Vascher's son; the couple involved in education. Rinky and I visit one of the primary schools assigned to the College Community Project and then we come home. The black moods of the senior males continue. They have just walked in through the door. How I loathe the heavy negativity. Who needs it? Their potential dispatch to The U.K suddenly looks very appealing. I don't think I can take much more.

Early P.m. Adrian: A complete week—a full, rich, and complete week. A big week where he felt like a real teacher. And now he is breathing out—about to relax in the warm, healing company of mothers and nurses at Stephanie's nursing course; an antidote to the week's busyness. And what of her, his Lady? What will assist her in healing this week's end? He wonders if they could meet—just for a catch-up?

Mouse: My Friend—how lovely to get your message. I am feeling alone on a wild, rough ocean. The two depressives have just arrived on deck with their heavy despair. I could do with your lightness and your balm. A catch-up is a must if this sailor is to avoid drowning at sea.

So—a good week for my able teacher, and now the nursing course. Are you at Stephanie's all tomorrow? Text me with your movements and I shall fit in around them. The Laird wants me to take Cedric for an outing tomorrow. Had a thought that he could help with the pig-pen—seeing as we have a vested interest—X

Adrian: Oh, My Lovely Friend—would love to be spending time with you. So many things to talk about and share. Passionate living needs springboards. It's about relationships. Desire for community is growing stronger—ways to help each other—non-taxing ways; systems of mutual support inspired by the school's philosophy again.

Lovely, older nursing teacher called Katherine from Hastings is running the course at Stephanie's—Light of Spirit in her—humour, hope, purpose. I had to ask her how she views the needs around her; she must be constantly surrounded by need in her nursing job. "Yes," she agreed; "but aren't people resilient? Living in this technological mine-field and somehow managing; coping with it. And there is Angelic help, but of course there is deep suffering and poverty. And yes—there is a Community Spirit; present at births and deaths and tragedies. The Spiritual World can work most effectively when we come together. X

Mouse: *Hi Friend, thank you for your message. Good to hear about the course. Wish I was there by your side. Things are easier on The Mountain. I just found the senior males snuggled under a duvet watching 'Black Adder' together. Relief! Supper delivered to them both. The Go-Getter is with Stephen tonight. Texts all logged. Some writing done. Loving you—X*

* * * * * * *

I reckon my 'Mouse' mantle is rather apt—I dash and scurry about all over the place, making sure everyone and everything is nourished and content. It is only with Lord Swallow that I really stop—stop and 'be.' Perhaps this is why he is so important to me; I am not entirely rodent!

Late P.m. Mouse: *I am up after an early evening sleep. The boys haven't appeared. Expect they might stay in their cosy nest all night. The Bog-Brush is still upstairs—a weekend treat to be allowed on The Mistress's bed. Rinky and I have been watching 'Swiss Family Robinson'. The hound demanded a quick step outside just now where we gazed up at the perfect star formations together. Thinking of you and how I could learn their shape—mmm. Are you home? Asleep I expect. Keep wishing I could jump on my trusty steed and slip quietly into your arms. I have been there already—won't tell you how you enfolded me—how we have been turning each other inside-out. Oh, no, better not tell you. Sleep really well. Lots of our own special love comes from The Mountain to My Fine Sir—X*

Saturday 12th May 2007

A.m. Mouse: *Part of his message about the nursing course arrived at 4.50 this morning. She has logged it where it should be. Was he texting her then? Or was it a cyber-space delay? She longs to hear more, wondering if he slumbers this drizzly morn. Imagining she was lying in his arms earlier she wondered at their perfect contrast and alignment: dark and fair, tall and not so tall—angular and rounded—hard and soft—lofty and earthed—spontaneous and planned—Sun and Moon—Northern and Southern—male and female—a true match. She feels herself opening deep inside; senses his body seeking hers—their lips meeting in a silent conversation. Her desire for him quickens as the dawn breaks. She opens even more, waiting for his sacred seed to be placed in her womanhood. She wonders, is this The Small One? His constant* *knocking audible through the dark. 'Go for it,' he urges; 'the consequences will work themselves out—please give me a chance. I have chosen you; don't you understand?'*

She pulls the pillow over her head, trying to drown out the call. Hmm—how could it be? How could it possibly be? Subduing the Rainbow showers she rises from their drowsy, imaginary lovemaking and heads out for her regular dawn amble and rooster despatch. They must get rid of them this weekend; the roosters, that is. They do nothing for the already inflated mood of the senior male inmates.

Good morning, My Lovely Man. How are you? I can be yours sometime early this morning if you are about? X

Adrian: *Nice—yes—he woke early and found his unsent message. He has been studying Rudolf Steiner's speech on The Dead, and The Spiritual Realms—how we can read to The Dead; how starved they are when they come to our sleeping souls at night for nourishment; and what the clairvoyant perception is like; important. He has given a 'trial-run' lecture to some dead relatives; Grandparents and Little Arthur and step-mum's recently departed friend.*

So—if she was to bear his child she would have to be within his care. He would not let her grow a child in a home of tension—so—a wife—with permission from her husband and community?! This is a tall order for any being. Can The Small One; the mighty Spirit who wishes to come, really organize this? Affect that much change? Wow! Or does it take us to have faith that what his Lady is receiving is accurate—spiritually sound—Christ blessed. He would deeply enjoy her close, sensual company, but does not lust for it. 'The consequences would sort themselves out', eh? Maybe, but right now agreements have been made—time has been taken—movement impending—soon maybe. Events seem to be moving fast. Who knows what is approaching. His day is mostly free. Only hockey at 9a.m. then shopping until 12ish. Home jobs, tidy up, lawns, dairy, then farm and school projects. No plans tonight—

Mouse: *Funny that she should have those strong intuitive feelings at the same time as his nursing course. The timing? Hmm—she has had them for a while, but today she needed to voice them. Strange. Thank you for your thoughts. Yes—how do we tell if the voice comes from a blessed source? Christ blessed. Does a Holy intention drive it? Better think on that. I will pull the pillow further over my head. Shall I come and visit you now? Restrained of course—to swim.*

Adrian: *Of course; leaving at 8.15. He was also thinking of child-bearing—last night too—at useful nursing course—aware of his childless status—quite fine with that but ripe for it. A question; does Little Arthur know what he/she is doing? Is it possible for The Dead to make mistakes? To influence the receptive willing to serve selfish needs still? How harsh this sounds, but he*

131

has to ask it—to test it—not meaning to offend—and how strongly he longs for her too—but without having to have her—

Mouse: *Just on my way. We won't have much time; probably just as well. Forgot my chastity belt—oops. With you in 15—X*

The kitchen door is open and the dogs bounce up to greet me when I arrive. Lord Swallow turns to greet me, indicating that he is on the phone, his slim frame shown off to perfection in mid-blue, denim jeans and T-shirt. A short-sleeved green shirt completes his attire. With Vonny away he has entirely claimed her house as his own; it certainly feels that way. I love him, encroaching habits and all. He gives me a wonderful hug and we allow ourselves the pleasure of some tender kisses; each one bringing us closer together. Can we really keep them under control? Mouths slightly apart—lips brushing untold promise; not sexual, but oh—so tender—so caring—laden with promise; with the promise of belonging. Yes, belonging. We chat for ten minutes; "what is The Small One about, then?" "Perhaps he wishes for media highlight," I suggest; "through The Book if it takes off. Get everyone guessing and waiting for his arrival; something like that!" We laugh; "yes, that sounds about right!" "But how do we know the impetus is Christ-centred?" Adrian again voices his important question. *"One is predicted to come who is the negative force,"* Adrian continues. "Well, I don't think so in this case, but we must ask these questions. The Dead are not always right. They look to us as a seat of learning. They look to those they have known before, not others. They like to be read to; spoken to. They absorb feelings—amazing really; look, here's a copy of the reading we shared at the nursing course; it's fascinating."

"I found you three winter shirts at the Opp. Shop yesterday;" I give Adrian his gift before I leave; "three for eleven dollars; this purple-checked one for Mondays and two pale blue ones. I suggest you turn out the caramel one you were wearing the other day; it doesn't suit you." Adrian takes the shirts gratefully; again he is happy for me to be directly involved in his attire. We also discuss the possibility of Cedric helping to build the pig-sty and pen later on today. He may not rise to the challenge, but you never know. Of course we run out of time; hockey starts in twenty minutes. Glancing at the clock on the kitchen wall Lord Swallow pulls me to him and kisses me so gently. The Garden Gate opens and we gaze into that sacred place, instantly tasting the magic.

The sun is shining and the world is a happy, busy place. Saturday mornings in New Zealand are vibrant. So many people play sport and in a large town like this everyone is out in the sunshine. I catch the end of The Go-Getter's hockey game; Michael Vascher drove the boys there this morning. My keen young fellow scores twice! I have a nice chat with Fo on the sidelines; a friendly mother with a daughter playing in the same team. I tell her about The Laird's ankle; "Oh—what a great opportunity for learning." "Great indeed!" I agree wholeheartedly. Like many in our alternative school, Fo is a natural therapist; a masseuse and healer. She is great fun. She and The Laird get on well. Stephen comes home with us after the game. We stop in The Warehouse on the way, purchasing a bar of dark chocolate and a couple more of the diary notebooks that I seem to fill up so fast.

Mid-morning, Mouse: *Love you—hope the hockey was good. Just passed the Giant Cow model on 15th Ave; it has a calf today! Off-spring definitely on the cards this morning! Had to smile. Dog and I are on the neighbour's land. Bernard is visiting The Laird with tales of his recent Scottish Whisky Tour. He followed us up the drive while I had the boys on the roof; "oh, you have caught me being an irresponsible parent!" The children love that thrill.*

"So—have you been milking the cows?" I was asked on my return. "No, but I did visit The Cowman; platonically,{sort of}. I didn't break any agreements."

Anyway, Good Sir, I will let you know Cedric's response to the pig-pen build. I told The Laird about the suggestion.

Adrian: *Hmm—you ask Cedric. Say that Adrian asked. Not for too long or anything. Hockey was pretty full-on. I stayed for the second game. Talked to lots of parents. Need a kip. Off to buy some medicines. Let me know about Cedric. I will text him if you think it would help.*

Mouse: *It would probably be better coming from you. He is more positive with others at the moment; especially if you mention Molly's new home. I'll send you his mobile number. Bernard is leaving shortly and Cedric is up. Bernard could drop him in Waikite Bay.*

Loving you—in your arms—beautiful kisses to start the weekend, your Lady in Velvet, or scruffy jumpers, I should say—M—X

Adrian: *And The Laird—how is he with the suggestion?*

Mouse: *seems to be fine. He didn't really comment. Like me, anything to get Cedric out and positive would be great—*

Well, that idea didn't go down well. Cedric is *not* keen to work on the pig-pen, despite Adrian's kind invitation. The negative vibes continue. I shall give up on the senior males before long. My honest declaration to The Laird about visiting Adrian was initially received light-heartedly but led to problems later on. He will not accept my need to see my friend. "Was it planned?" He asked. "No," I told a small white lie. "I just dived in for five minutes." Shute—he is in an awful grump again, muttering that we have to leave New Zealand as soon as possible. He mentioned a friend whose wife wouldn't leave the job where her lover worked; their marriage didn't last long. He cannot accept my vision for our future. My judgment where he is concerned is all wrong. I am resigned to my fate. "We'll have to go home then," I agreed. "I am trying to organize it!" He exclaimed.

Autumn is definitely here. I spy a few bare branches and piles of leaves under the occasional deciduous tree. We are all missing home; apparently England is enjoying a fabulous spring. But the return of the NZ hockey season is good; the sociability is fun with the same school parents as last year: Lisa, Fo, Michael, Andrew and Louise. I do enjoy their company. Kiwis are wonderfully open, honest and especially friendly.

Mid-afternoon, Adrian: *Hi Friend—sent Cedric a text, but no reply yet. Think he might be keen? Maybe tomorrow. Hey, do you want to bring them all milking?*

Mouse: *Darling Friend. Thanks for messages. I am overtaken by exhaustion—I'm trying to get some kip. Thanks for texting Cedric; we shall see— he is reluctant but I might persuade him otherwise. The Laird is reactive after my morning's honesty. Should I just tell him straight? Not sure—I'm sticking to the line that I need to see my Friend every now and then, and that we aren't breaking any agreements. But—you and I both know what we know—hmm. He wants me to just 'drop it'. Better not suggest the milking, lovely as it would be. Another time perhaps. I told The Laird I thought it would do Cedric a power of good to work at the farm. Might be possible tomorrow. How goes your day?*
Thinking of you—lots of love—M—X

Adrian: *Angry thoughts—does he not get it? He does not meet your needs! His 'I'm grumpy so I can do what I want behaviour' sends you further away. To give me up you need him to fill the space I leave. He needs to be actively working on true partnership before he can demand you drop it! Fume—fume—*

Mouse: *'I feel sad that you might not be my wife in the future. I'm not sure you want to be married any more. It is time to be honest with yourself.' She held The Laird close, his eyes were sad but accepting. She cannot be dishonest any longer. He is willing to try, but only if she gives up the man she loves. Understandable. Is she being unfair? Selfish? Events are going at such a pace; everyday another avenue appears. 'But the truth'—they have not properly voiced it.*

Adrian: *The truth—what is it? He feels a quiver of fear pass through him— she can't mean tell The Laird they are dreaming of having a child, can she? That is too much pipe-dream material—too unsettling for the cows— unleashing the tidal wave that would blow him off the land—wash away the pig-sty—bring into the open all the hatred held in check by those who know. Or is this his paranoia? How would Big J. respond to that one? The father pauses—she holds a bomb—a weapon. He entertains the idea of it, but cannot see how it would manifest without great pain. Maybe this is what is required, but no—not with his settling and community building shaping up so strongly around him. He waits to see what happens next.*

134

Later, Mouse: *He is right—it is perfect as it is, for now. Their world is not of this one. She must steady the ship—she could not abandon her crew anyway. Yes—steady the ship—concentrate on The Book—the land—the learning for them all. This suits them. It is better The Laird does not know about their inner world. He cannot handle it. He is set back each time she is totally honest. Lord Swallow, your Lady is heading to the Garden Centre with Stephen; meeting Ronnie there. Would you like a goodnight kiss, or are you a-milking? Leaving in 20—X*

Adrian: *Swing by. Am at home until **7**. Aren't you just going to 'drop it' though?*

Mouse: *Better not come now—got to serve supper once back. Happy milking—X*

The family sits around the table; the senior males remain stormy and hopeless. I light a candle, holding the moment and the rocking ship. I serve a good meal; gammon with parsley sauce, mashed potatoes and mixed vegetables. Everyone enjoys their food. Ho hum.

Late p.m. Adrian: *Just finished milking. Rather late but the cows were pretty contented; already waiting in their little stalls. Milk up a bit today; Daisy's at least. I gave her some vinegar yesterday. Her eye was a bit gunky but looks better tonight; never knew what trace mineral she might have needed. Tonight I walked up with my buckets—realize I need this—walking—slower pace—less driving—leads to more peace and connection. I might make a harness for the dogs to pull a cart. Are you still using pre-pay cheap text offer? Text 2000 is one you can get; 2000 texts per month for ten dollars—good for the amount of texting we do; only to 01 numbers though.*

New thought tonight—maybe I'm acquiring all these skills so I can set up a farming village for the disabled, here in Waikite Bay; like the one you know in England. Looking after Lois' Ben and other youngsters at school with learning difficulties. We have even got the land set aside—imagine, eh—workshops, milking; using your descriptions and experience. Then I got to thinking if 'here' was where I would do such a thing—and that set me thinking about the energy of other places around the country. And then I thought how cool it would be to go touring together, checking them out—don't you reckon? Looking at stars—visiting farms—camping—sailing; hmm. Dream on, Piper. No way could that happen right now, is there, Fine Weaver of plans?

My camomile tea is drunk—and my back is cold—time to walk home; heavy with ¾ pail of fresh milk and a head busy with plans for the dog cart. Text me a sweet goodnight—X

Mouse: *Dear Lord Swallow—I have much to say—as usual. Might need to be later. Can you wait? Loving you—M—X*

* * * * * *

Later, Mouse: *"We are sorry," Lord Swallow and his Lady tell The Small One. "You tried so hard today—enticing us to leave the pages of The Book; the eve of Mothers' Day." They ask him/her to be content with a parallel life for now. He/she is loved—included—held—acknowledged—even dressed and tucked up—taken on trips and introduced to the wider family. Is this enough? Lord Swallow has learnt that life beyond The Book runs alongside its spine. This way, he can care for his child while attending to his vocational calling without the exhaustion and constant call to administer on a domestic level. For believe you me, parenting is a mighty draining, full-time job! His Lady would be with him now—lying in his bed—attending to his needs. They would stroke each other so tenderly, their held eyes keeping open The Garden Gate, maintaining their Boat on a knife-edged keel—his masculinity taking her in their celestial union—the rhythm dancing in full motion; their joy and fulfilment off the scale.*

The Laird was forceful, rough with her earlier in his attempt at ownership. He was not at peace afterwards. She did not like it—understanding his take, but not interested in the physical if it isn't rooted in the spiritual.

The Ute is parked at the end of the drive, two roosters awaiting deportation in the back. She could so easily slip away—X

Chapter 2 Rough

Sunday 13th May 2007

Very early A.m. Mouse: Art thou awake, Lord Swallow? Your Lady has been dispatched—voluntarily—to find the third cockerel that is driving The Laird mad. Blast—no torch—her mobile phone will have to do. She stumbles under the house—wooden panels and unkempt machinery left in untidy heaps, making her passage impossible. Why is everything left to her? Probably because she has always done everything in the past. Hmm—no luck in locating the unwelcome bard. Sliding on unseen pig pooh she makes it back inside— thankful she didn't break a leg. The pig is making a shocking noise—shouting for an early breakfast. The dog demands her walk—the star-lit canopy is calming; a patch of hillside lit up by the brilliant moonlight.

She thinks of him—so peaceful when he walks to the farm. Lovely. She is with him. Aha, there goes the missing bard; he is under the house after all. Back under she goes. Success! Lying flat on her front she tucks the surprised victim under her arm and inches her way out. No torch—impossible obstacles; feet disappearing between ankle-breaking, {better not use that expression}, crevices in the wood pile. At last, they are out! Down the drive in the moonlight—how far away did Cedric drive the Ute? Ah, there it is. The third bird joins the two younger ones. He is probably their father; has been on the land since they first arrived. Male deportation appears to be on the cards this month!

However, young Wonky of the twisted beak seems to have found his strangled voice at last, his male status declared loudly from the 'shid' beside the house. The metal structure acts as amplification! My goodness, this is turning into a comedy of errors! She grabs her chicken friend, he can join her in the bathroom as she soaks the morning trials away. That should shut him up. Oh dear—it doesn't! He shrieks his head off, right under the master bedroom! Shute! She gets the giggles—dashes outside with the surprised bird and pops him into the small hen house. Perhaps that will keep him quiet. It is cold—luckily she is half dressed—just! Oh—that is good—the bath beckons. The dog has settled, watching the irregular morning fiasco from the sofa under the mirror. She looks like a mystified spectator struggling to understand a quirky West End satire.

At last she can turn to her Friend—down in the calm of The Forest. He would have had it sorted in a jiffy. She loves his idea of a Community Village; how she would give her eye teeth to be his travelling partner; investigating, planning, net-working, and then in his arms every night. She would run her hands all over him—he would press her beneath him and tell her to stop talking. And she would. He is the only man she listens to. How's that?! She fingers the fine hairs on his arms, remembering how they catch the bubbles in the sulphur-rich waters of the thermal hot pools. She loves him. Good morning, Fine Sir. Would you like me to drop in after the rooster drop? If I am able? —M—X

Adrian doesn't respond to my long message. I am surprised not to hear from him. My day begins. A good breakfast starts the day off well. I even light a fire this morning. The household has woken early. Let's hope we have a better twenty-four hours without any disclosures upsetting the apple cart, or should I say capsizing the vessel?

Later, Mouse: Are you silent today, My Friend? The bacon is cooking— the dog rests beside the roaring fire and the eternal rugby will keep The Laird occupied in the top cabin until 9 a.m. Take care—M—X

Adrian: Like a shot—perfectly placed—I can trust myself. Staying deep and true my body will act in harmony. No fawning—holding—worrying. Perfect. Good morning, My Friend. I hope your well-earned bath was pleasant. Could do with one myself; maybe a fire bath later, to celebrate the assessments I will do this morning. Sore eyes and stiff joints today—up until 1.30a.m. in the workshop whittling helicopter toys out of willow branches—so good, but a bit driven. Lots of chocolate biscuits; a whole packet actually. Yesterday could have been the cause, so I am a little subdued today. I'll make a rich beef stroganoff this morning and invite Little J. and her man round for tea. I spoke with Sammy at hockey—Community Village meeting on Friday afternoon? 3 people very keen. We could attract more if we advertised. I told Justin about it too. I sometimes get a life- shock from him—probably the reason for the chocolate biscuits. I bought a contraption called a themette; a home-built water heater for camping with a jacket around a chimney—very cool. I got an oilskin at the same garage sale, and a whole lot of tools; a hose and a contact for some big, 1000 litre plastic tanks that used to hold vegetable oil; great for water tanks. I also had a good idea that I want Cedric to help me with—any noise from him? Drop in—platonically—X

Mouse: Off to chicken drop and church. Chat later. Chocolate bicys, eh? Sounds just like me. We are sooo alike, My Friend. Big breakfast—bad for the hips. More to grab hold of—ho hum. Text after the service—X

* * * * * * *

Midday, Mouse: Dear Friend, are you home? Cedric is up and he might be keen if you let him know what you need help with. Can you send him a text on my phone? Then I can show him and encourage him out. How are you

138

getting along with the work? We are back from church—a sombre mood all round as the negative vibes continue. 3 roosters dropped at the bee hives halfway down the hill. Castle Mistress is in a positive mood, encouraging her menfolk to throw off their blues and get working—cleaning house and garden etc.—X

Adrian: I'm doing two main things—building a pulley system to carry buckets up a hill to the house site—then designing and building a milking shed. Ask Cedric—but not if it's going to cause a problem. I'm too tired for more excitement.

Mouse: Sounds truly Swallow inspired, but I'm afraid he hasn't taken the bait. Perhaps another time. Am tired too, but doing well with the improved vibes. Lunch is made and 3 loads of washing flap calmly in this gorgeous weather. The views are astounding today. Sorry you are tired—you could have done with your Lady luring you to bed instead of chocolate driven helicopter making last night! I'm sure they are brill though. Wish we could curl up in a Leafy Glade somewhere—watching the clouds together.

The boys set to, dismantling the unsuccessful dog run. The Bog-Brush always escapes. Now we can phone the caravan company to remove their property. We haven't used the caravan for ages. It is too expensive to keep as a play house and if we are thinking of selling our Mountain section, then the eye-sore needs to go. Bother, the children have broken one of the bed legs. I should be able to fix it. Cedric continues to be very off with me. "Why are you so cross all the time?" I ask. "What have I done?" "It's all your fault—this mess we are in—all your fault—spending money—not working—running hopeless businesses that don't work." I ask Cedric about my writing; has he been reading my work? "It's a romance—part imaginary," I tell him. "Oh yeah, I really believe that!" He replies. So, I tell him about Adrian, how we are the best of friends and that we have placed strict boundaries around ourselves. "And that isn't easy when two people get on so well. Yes, it is a challenge for Daddy. We are working hard to get you back to England," I assure him. "But I need your help, not your hindrance; please understand that." I think Cedric took my words to heart. I hope so.

It is good to see The Laird and The Go-Getter together down the drive, filling in the pot holes. Our little lad is being a complete Angel at the moment, acting as vital ballast to our damaged ship in these turbulent waters. Rinky has been a little off-colour; pale and tetchy with regular questions about a possible return home. She doesn't want to leave New Zealand. Her friends are here.

Late P.m. Mouse: —X—Sleep well, My Friend. Hope your day has been blessed and achieving—X

Adrian: A quiet goodnight, My Friend—much to tell—but when The Angels allow it. Sleep Holy. Love to your family. X

Monday 14ᵗʰ May 2007

A.m. Mouse: *Their early dawn stroll bears no fruit this morn—a dull, cloud-covered sky says it all. She is wearing two jumpers. Is she too hot? The temperature is lifting. The church service yesterday—a gloomy affair. They were spent—heads bowed in submittance; not knowing. The Laird was at one end of the pew, she was at the other. The children tried to get a pen to work, distracting themselves by doodling on the hymn sheet. They didn't succeed.*

And he? She imagined he stood in the church lobby—partially present, his head also bowed, a pile of interesting garage-sale trophies at his feet. Their Sunday was one of resignation—of dismantling dog-fences and filling pot holes. They sort through their physical lives, preparing for a return home. She goes with it, seeing no alternative today. She humbly accepts whatever. She must put the family first. Hmm—

There is an unusual highlight in the cloudy sky this morning. The obscured sun creates a pattern; what is it exactly? A back-to-front question mark? Hmm—again.

Adrian: *He wakes with a start—action. He musters his thoughts and sets to, training them to stay in the pens and paddocks of children and farm. His mind bucks against the constraint, wanting to be free and roaming. One by one he checks each child in his class; their need—their riddle—a vow to make this a morning practice. Duty and service—sacrifice. He thinks of Rudolf Steiner burning out his life in service. A new thought comes to him, but it is tinged with fear. He feels a life-shock lies there, coiled around his Mana, {Maori word meaning Spirit/being/life task}. He has had a low weekend— feeling burnt out yesterday; achieving little. But these times are often fruitful. His new idea which needs checking in the light is that together they can be great support partners to streamline and enrich their lives for greater service to their communities; she to her family and school community and he to his colleagues, children and school. He would not covert her as he has done, but would plough it back in before the harvest, and think always on how to use that longing for the greater good. Sounds a bit fear-based. Better go process it. School meeting soon and planning still to do. Cold fingers around his heart, he goes to seek the warmth and strength of love.*

I try to send Adrian a single kiss by text; just as acknowledgment, but for some reason my signal cuts out and I fail. The house feels more organized today. I am trying to be strict with my diet. If truth be told I am feeling a bit glum. I sent Mizzie the ending of 'Dry-Dock' last night. The Laird has given us permission to work on The Books together; "*am I putting a bullet to my head?*" I rely on my husband's blind faith; he has always followed my lead. Will he be able to this time? Pray God I will encourage The Light to shine and magic emotional as well as financial assistance; we really need some money to smooth the passage. I suggested to Mizzie that she reads the story as a flashback; as Adrian and I have imagined. "The second and third Books are more serious," I told her. "The first Book is relatively light-hearted.

It is a dull, damp day. I run the dog on the beach, but not for long. My leather boots are wet. I forgot my gum boots. I am grateful for my double jumpers now; the autumn is definitely here. I closed the van door after our walk just as two, rough-looking dogs arrived on the scene. Oh my—that was a lucky escape. The Bog-Brush continues to be tetchy.

Midday, Adrian: *Oh, My Love—saw you drive by—couldn't catch your eye—no loving message on my screen. Are you okay, My Sweet?*

Mouse: *My Darling—I am sad today—on the beach—a soggy walk—forgot my gum boots. Thinking of you. The Angels wouldn't let me send you a loving message earlier. I will try and resend. Missing you—X*

Missing Text, Mouse: *—Love you—M—X*

I spend the rest of the morning logging all our messages—my goodness, there are almost fifty since Friday morning! Perhaps I should investigate that cheaper line. I shall ask for Adrian's help. I am soothed by my Lover's tender words; how I love him. He usually restricts himself, allowing me to dish out the goodies but not often following suit. I know he is holding himself back, in check, although he doesn't refuse the loving balm I send his way. I know he cannot go there. We are both frustrated.

I write, and write, and write, dashing back and forth to the bathroom as I am back on the cleansing Supergreens. Time for a trip to the recycling station. Adrian doesn't call me to join him today. The strangest thing happens at the Transfer Station, {recycling depot}; a piece of rubbish in the paper bin catches my eye. I pull it out. A picture of Christ looks back at me with an invitation to join a Sunday Worship meeting. The address on the back of the paper is somewhere in the centre of town. I carry it to the car, wondering about its relevance. Am I meant to investigate further?

Early P.m. Mouse: *Hello, My Friend—are you home or are you working all day? A strange thing happened just now at the Transfer Station; a piece of scrap paper caught my attention. I put it in the car. I found it was an invitation when I looked closer. I need to show it to you. Thank you for your tenderness; your kind message of concern earlier.*
I realize I am in need of some loving balm, although I know it gets too close to the line for you. Thank you anyway. M—X

My message-writing is interrupted by a call from Gordon, the local farmer who hasn't ever been very friendly. He suggests we join a neighbourhood helicopter weed-spray to avoid trouble with the local council; we are required to keep the gorse under control. "It would cost you three thousand dollars," he adds. Hmm, I suppose we should do it, although I am deadly opposed to chemical intervention. We don't have that kind of spare cash anyway, even though our property value will decrease if we don't address the issue. I take the opportunity and ask if we can walk the dog on his land, {we have been doing so for a while now}; "no," he answers. "The sheep will be at risk from worms and measles." "You aren't very dog-friendly here," I tell him; "attitudes are different in Britain." "Well, we are serious farmers here, in New Zealand. We have to protect our livelihood," he concludes. I don't like him much. Most Kiwis are delightful but Gordon isn't one of them.

I pass Adrian chatting to a parent in the courtyard at school pick-up time. He looks great, wearing one of the new shirts I recently found him. I drop both Rinky and Lucia at the riding stables at three-thirty. Driving past the huge oak tree I notice a beam of sunlight highlighting the face of a little girl walking home from school. Like many Kiwi children she is unshod and carefree. Some Maori children remain barefooted throughout the winter. A scattering of autumn leaves, beautiful sunshine, laughing children and freedom—how different life is to home. I like it.

Early P.m. Mouse: Dead cool shirt—yummy man—keep your eyes averted, woman! No longing, remember? You keep forgetting. Am free for half an hour this afternoon—X

I don't hear from Adrian; he must be busy. I continue with the usual taxi service rounds; collecting family members from hockey, college and the riding stables. The Go-Getter helps me prepare the steak for supper. Cedric asks me to *"please stop singing when I am in the house!"* He can be a little so-and-so. I slam my way about the kitchen, venting my frustration. Perhaps he might notice my upset. I won't speak to him for a while—see how he likes the moody, silent treatment!

P.m. Adrian: Finally he sits down—a taxing day behind him. Still things to do with a More to Life meeting at 7 and cows to milk. Teaching guitar went reasonably well, somewhat restoring him, but his mind has been tricking him big time today—life-shock hit—still more processing to undertake. Will do it now; curl up in bed and catch up. And her—why was her day a sad one? Why this sense of disconnection between them? Could it be an attack? Angry tidal surge—hit him squarely, knocking him right over. Goodness me—and not being able to send messages either. What is happening?

Mouse: Supper is cooking—the fire lit. The Laird reclines in state on the sofa in the top cabin. The lethargy is becoming a worrying habit; a natural mode if his 'go' button isn't flicked. The Go-Getter is particularly sunny and positive at the moment—a natural sunbeam; thank The Lord. He has been making tzatziki—the Greek dish with cucumber and yogurt. Steak is done—spuds boiling. It took hours to log three days' worth of text messages.

P.s—yes, what is going on today? Your messages were all over the place. Last night's one arrived at breakfast and this morning's one arrived in the wrong order, leaving your Lady unsure of your whereabouts or feelings. I have been thinking—could The Small One be having a wee tantrum? Because we aren't delivering what he/she wants? Just a thought.

Loving you, my busy, busy man. Take care—X

* * * * * * *

Later, Mouse: *Need to be close and still—need to look through The Gate together; need our gentle kisses. I think the disconnection arises when we can't touch base.*

Goodnight, Lord Swallow, I hope the late hour finds you refreshed without life-shocks. Was that my doing? All is calm on The Mountain, as long as I don't mention anything linked with my Forest and Ocean existence all remains tranquil. Reliance on established structures and blind ignorance seems to suit everyone better. My Darling, I would hold and love you if I could. Sleep well. I am beside you in the realm of our Celestial Sea—M—X

Adrian: *Tomorrow afternoon is free. There is so much to catch up on. What is this invitation she found? What is the meaning of his dream? What course do they set, given the wind and tide? He drives home, stopping to move the body of a possum he hit on the way to his meeting.*

Mouse: *His dream? The one he can only speak of when The Angels allow? The mystery gains pace. She dreamt of him last night. She entered a room to find him reclining in an arm-chair. He handed her a $50 note. What does that mean?*

Take care—tomorrow afternoon would be lovely. What time? A serious catch-up is needed, these past two days have been so full. These friends like the detail; the intrigue. It suits them well. Love you—X

Tuesday 15th May 2007
A.m. Mouse: *The morning routine kicks in. Less rooster clatter, tidy, clean house makes all the difference; clearer mind too. She was with him between 3 & 4 a.m; a beautiful hour in their private realm. Mizzie has responded to my e-mail; she says 'Dry-Dock' finale is too confusing without 'The Celestial Sea' preceding it. I have forwarded you her message. The kettle calls—and the eternal lunch-boxes. Love is around you, My Friend, M—X*

P.s Just realized I have a college meeting at 1.30 p.m. It might not last more than half an hour. Am free early this morn and again after your Main Lesson—X

Adrian: *I'm heading home for a late breakfast at 8—swing by. We may have milk collectors calling however. Still a bit jumpy am I—*

Mouse: *I'll call in for some milk—above board—jumpy-*

My Cowman looks peaky, wearing a woolly hat framing a pale face. He gives me a hug, but not for long today. He asks how I am. He is feeling shot to pieces. "I'm in a no-man's-land," I reply. "I'm okay with it though." I tell him about Cedric's behavior and that unseats him further. "I think we are all psychically linked. Let's have a pause; just to get straight. I have so much on, and so do you. Let's stop awhile." "Until Friday?" I suggest. "Yes, but we can text if we need to," he adds. "Edwin phoned to see how I was; how everything was going. He told me it wouldn't be good if you returned to The U.K. You would probably never come back."

Hmm—we are both feeling flat. We speak about The Small One and his/her possible temper tantrum. Perhaps Little Arthur has given up on us; taken the wind from our sails. I am not too sad about the still waters. It feels right, somehow. We are secure in our love. "I had a strange dream," Adrian adds; "the one I mentioned in my message. I was climbing a tree. There was an eagle's nest right at the top with four chicks inside. The mother wasn't with them. I took one of the chicks but it gained in size as I descended; it turned into a huge, fluffy creature before disappearing! How peculiar is that? The Eagle is often mentioned in the bible, but usually for its swift and secure speed, not for any carrion activity."

"Here's the invitation I found in the recycling bin;" I hand Adrian the picture of Christ with the town address on the back. "Do you think we should accept?" "Can I keep it?" He asks, a serious expression wrinkling his brow. "Of course," I answer. "This is all very intense, My Friend," I offer. "You know, Rinky is rattled at the moment. She doesn't want to move back to England. The Go-Getter is the only positive member of the family."

I leave my partially platonic Lover quickly, knowing he needs peace and quiet right now; his vital 'processing time' is calling for attention. The constant restraint and denial is exhausting us both. Transferring the energy into something life-giving is both wonderful and distressing, spending more and more of our energy. It's almost as if the last magnet link has been overcome and we have fallen backwards, spent and shattered but at peace. We miss the challenge though. The wind has certainly left the shore. We are becalmed again; but for how long? I walk the dog when I get home. The sun is out but I have lit a fire in the wood-burning stove. The cat lies on my desk and the dog at my feet. I like their happy company. I complete the diary writing and try to turn over a new leaf.

Eagles
To see an eagle in your dream symbolizes nobility, pride, fierceness, freedom, superiority, courage, and powerful intellectual ability. It also represents self-renewal and your connection with your spirituality. You will struggle fiercely and courageously to realize your highest ambitions and greatest desires. If you see a nest of young eagles, then it represents your achievements and your climb to the top of the social ladder.

Adrian stole a baby eagle in his dream; does that mean he has stolen an achievement? An achievement that grew out of control and then just disappeared?

Midday, Mouse: Festival practice? Would you like me there? Time? Just texting a quick question—X

Adrian: No practice today because of Maori lessons. Tomorrow; 2.30 p.m.

I work, I shop, I cook and I drive. I have a College meeting with the painting team at the Saint Vincent de Paul Opp. Shop. I am not being paid to actually *do* the painting, thank goodness. I don't want to get too involved. The team is excited by the potential. The children and I visit the library where I am reprimanded by the traffic warden in the car park because my Warrant of Fitness, (M.O.T), has run out. Bother. I don't seem able to keep on top of the domestic duties. Perhaps these quieter days will make it possible.

Early P.m. Mouse {Unsent}: We have reached a stalemate. I cannot move forward in my old life—I do not want it back. We cannot welcome our love that waits in abject longing. A stalemate in these days of waiting. For months I have given out, receiving little back. I am drained by endless, one-sided caress, knowing how it could be—how we are being called. My weekend surrender—my flat acceptance of no alternative hits hard, surprising even Lord Swallow in its effect.
I had a strong dream last night; the vision filled with honest clarity. I looked at The Laird and told him that if we were to maintain our marriage then it really did matter where we lived. "But," I went on to say, "it wouldn't matter where I lived with Adrian; it could be a shack and I would be perfectly happy." I was vehement in my conviction as I held my husband's gaze.

Any next step—the final move into serious life change.
They are all aware.
The halting minutes are a daily drug.
Attention! A potential future—

But which one?
A trial—a tight-rope waver.
The crew is nervous upon decks of glory and disaster;
The two go hand-in-hand.
She holds the helm;
They are all reliant upon her steady vision.
Too vast the huge swells;
Too distant any tranquil harbour.
None will make a decision.
They await their sentence with heads bowed in dull duty.

I miss Adrian's text messages but know it relieves him to be free of the anxiety, much as we share the excitement. I text him a few questions, nothing romantic. Does he want the drum kit? The metal and the old baths? Is he free to work on The Book over the weekend? Mizzie is waiting for more from us. The Laird is away on Friday night and the children might well be out too. He e-mails me a reply:

Adrian: Hi Mouse, a few answers:

1. **the drum kit could live here for a while—do you want to give it away? I know someone who could use it as a practice kit.**
2. **I might as well collect the baths and things but can you ask The Laird? After all, to stay off your land was the agreement I made way back there at Christmas time.**
3. **I could make some time to work on The Book if the Angels decree it, this weekend; this Friday night could be fine, but need some openness with The Laird about it as he will be wondering, will he not? Hope you're doing well? I'm feeling heaps clearer, a bit more energy and a few more things ticked off the list.**
Blessings upon you—and your lovely family—and pig. Swallow.

Wednesday 16th May 2007

I don't hear from Adrian this morning. Our e-mail contact is very different; I miss the intimacy. But we have agreed to keep intimacy quiet, so quiet we shall be. I have a normal day. The weather is overcast to begin with, just like me. Wonky the love-crower is in fine voice. I bundle him out of the shed and into the hen house in our regular routine. The vacuum cleaner has a new resting place; it has only taken me twenty months to find a proper home where we don't fall over its bulk. It just fits under the bathroom sink. How great is that? Life must be returning to some normality. I take the bull by the horns and telephone Andy—can he look at the repairs needed before we place the house on the market? I wonder about The Mountain; is it bad luck? We are spiralling into disaster and Cedric is especially rough. We are worried about him, deciding he should return to England as soon as possible.

Mouse {unsent}: She misses the anticipation—the daily swings of his turbulent ups and downs; the riddles waiting to be unlocked, explored and loved. They stimulate her. But a constant stream? Would she tire of the endless need to explore self? She wonders, knowing that if handled carefully they are, in fact, a vital component of The Key; the special Key to The Garden Gate. She misses the waiting, hoping he will continue to e-mail her.

Adrian runs up to the van as I pull into school this morning. "Do you have the verse for the teachers? You know; the one we mentioned yesterday—holding the essence—Michael B's book." I have remembered the book and hand it over. He bounds away to morning verse in the staff room. I stand beside Michael B. later on at our festival practise. "You *are* the author of the book, aren't you Michael?" I ask hesitantly. I brought the wonderful book of verses with me from England where it has been a firm favourite for many years. "Yes," he tells me; "I loved doing the work. I lived in Bermuda for a whole year and re-wrote the well-known, weekly verses. I could do it all over again. I'm so glad you like the result. Here," he offers; "write down your family names and I shall put a dedication in the front cover." We are privileged to have Michael B. in school at the moment. He specializes in speech and drama within the school's specific philosophy and is teaching every class this week. Adrian and I spend time in close proximity; he comes to stand beside me and together we sing another Saint Michael song featuring dragons and swords, encouraging the pupils to sing confidently. I say goodbye and take Big J. the story she is waiting for; one she will read in assembly; a story about a young Warrior Knight—a Knight of Saint Michael. Cordelia, Lois and I have been writing the assembly stories. We appear to be under control; swords and dragons are high on the agenda. Our new metal sword will make its debut at the festival this year; the sword we bought last year.

I spend the remainder of the day writing. I am trying to get the story done; it takes so long to produce. Cedric has gone to stay with a college friend for two days; let's hope his mood improves. Does he need psychiatric help? College has mentioned his depressed state. Should we have told him about our marriage problems? We must shift the negativity; sell our Mountain section as fast as possible. Perhaps that will help. I don't see any of our roosters as I pass the beehives. I hope they are okay. The sunshine is glorious. The drought is bad for the farmers though, especially those in the Hawkes Bay region. The livestock is running low on grazing.

*P.m. Mouse: Dear Friend—am heading down the hill at about **7**.30p.m. I could drop off the drum kit if that is okay? I don't expect you to see me—days off and all that. I could leave it in the workshop as you will probably be a-milking. I will presume you would rather leave it for now if I don't hear back from you-X*

Adrian: Hi Friend—so tired! Just had deep, after-food sleep. Waking up now. I'm going to Michael B's talk at **7**.30, but I would like to see you too. What brings you down this way?

Mouse: My Friend—am on my way to collect The Laird from College. He has been feeling more positive and has been cleaning his neglected desk late into the evening. This week is definitely one of sorting and shifting; a bit like us! I have to collect him at 8.30. Timings? I am serving supper at **7**ish. Probably won't be down the hill until **7**.30. Do you want the drums and a quick goodnight? Perhaps I could come to some of the talk? Let me know—be nice to see you too. It was special, singing our Archangel songs again—X

Adrian: Have to be a quick hello. Drums can come now but there is no hurry—unless there is for you. I'll store them at home until the new owner shows up. Might see you, might not, eh? Will be tight—

Mouse: Okay Friend—might miss you. I might dive in to the talk. I'm running late; unexpected phone call. What time does the talk end? I will drop off the drums if that is okay—in workshop? X

Adrian: I'm not sure what time the talk ends. Probably goes on until 9p.m. Drums in workshop fine. Good luck. Take care on the roads you free-wheeler, you—X

Mouse: —X-

Supper is served and more of The Book logged. I don't see Adrian but I store the drums in his workshop and leave a little note in his room: *'Sleep well, Lord Swallow—my kisses lie upon your pillow.'* I had a strange dream last night where the family collected an older lady from a house where she was house-sitting. She was alone there, a huge character called Christine with a shock of white hair. She climbed into the back of our van settling in the well between the front seats with her back to the steering wheel, close to a surprised Go-Getter. She had a talking chicken with her! Needless to say we were hugely amused and we laughed so much, especially Cedric who creased up in delight. That was good to see. "Ah," I thought, "this is just what we need; some frivolity and fun, yes." By the time we reached home she had become a lot younger with streaked hair and bouncy energy. She told us about her break-dancing; "it's great for my wings," she said, waving her arms up and down like a bird trying to take off! We were all very surprised. I looked up at that moment and saw The Laird and Lord Swallow standing together in the room with us. They each had an old wooden desk beside them; both were in pristine order, not a scrap of paper in sight. The men looked smart wearing linen jackets. They didn't look at each other. "Well," I said to them with my hands on my hips, {I was wearing my apron}; "I'm glad to see you are both sorted! Look at my still-bulging desk! You shall have to talk to each other soon." The two men left the room together, walking towards the kitchen. I didn't recognize our 'home'. I saw the men giving each other a big hug. At last.

P.m. Mouse: My Darling Friend, finally; the finished breakdown! Writing takes ages. Thought I had better send it before too many more days keep us distant. Would you like to brainstorm The Boat's story? Or would you rather tackle it single-handed? Some more of our alchemy anyway; good to put one's hand to when we would rather be wrapped up in each other this coming winter. I will leave it to you as to whether you write a long passage for each PART, or a shorter one for each CHAPTER. The early part of The Book will have other things added, I am sure. I will remember details as we progress. Mizzie only needs the first 3 chapters to get a flavour, but I will probably send her PART 4 &5 as well. Let me know if I need to add any details; all the small gems are important. I imagine that The Boat's impression of events will be Lord Swallow's—might need to make that obvious; i.e. a link with The Boat that goes further back than that of his Lady—after all, she bows to his authority so he must be an older Spirit. I keep wondering if we are destined to become an artistic pair of Lovers/Writers—giving to the world through our inspiration; living one day on a quiet shore in a wooden house with a wide deck, a host of friendly pets and gentle involvement in a local community to stop us becoming too introspective—with regular trips all over the world to promote our work. This picture keeps returning to me, inspired by a film I saw years ago of just such a couple on the coast of Maine, U.S A. Hmm—probably more pipe dreams. But—the world needs pipe dreams and we have some expertise in the realm of vision. I think we also have some MAKE IT HAPPEN skills; all in the hands of The Angels.

Adrian: Hello again, nodding off—decided to sleep on it. Don't wait for my writing input; may be too distracted, but something may come in sleep. Finding the phone? It has disappeared. I do get a wave of appreciation as I read The Book's index, seeing reference to the poems you wrote—such richness you bring—and all this amid a busy life. Well done/top marks for completing your assignment. X

Mouse: Darling Friend—have been missing you—thanks for being in touch. I know you need to focus; sounds very busy. Wonder if you got my text with latest ideas on chapter names etc? I don't want to bother you, but I really need to send this off to Mizzie tonight. I would rather you were happy with the idea though—tis a joint project after all. Mizzie might have other suggestions anyway. Here goes: PART 1: QUASI DRAFT Chapters 1-4 Questions, Qualify, Quantity, Quintet. PART 2: UNDERWAY; Unfamiliar, Unwrap, Utility, Unify. PART 3: EDDY;

Entertain, Elevate, Embrace, Elect. PART 4: SCUDDING; Solo, Signals, Splashing, Sunshine. PART 5: TOE THE LINE; Tremor, Tiller, Tacking, Tell Tale, Treasure {pieces of eight}.

Let me know if you approve. Wonder where your phone is, old friend! Send some prayers to St. Anthony; patron saint of lost items, {good Catholic stuff}. Hope Daisy hasn't eaten it! I'd better not send any loving messages in case it gets into the wrong hands. Big hug to my hard-working Man—can't wait to see you—when allowed. Sleep well—M—X

* * * * * * *

Later, Mouse: Hi Friend—not a nice feeling losing our pocket contact is it? Even though we have agreed to be silent. I like to know you are really close to me, and vice versa, at all times. Hmm—vulnerable is definitely the word. So, My Love, the missive is dispatched; prayers to St. Michael that something may come of our tale. Are you in school early on? I will be down at 10a.m. to work in Class I on window cleaning and to meet with Lois & Sandra about the land etc.

Big Love—sleep well. Funny, this e-mail connection is not as intimate as our beloved little pocket screen. Let me know if you want the new phone I bought the other day; hopefully yours will turn up. May The Angels hold you as you sleep; prepare you for the new term and bless your every interaction over the coming weeks—X

Adrian: Hi Friend, thanks for contact. Yes, losing phone left me feeling quite vulnerable—quite a life-shock all round today. My, that Big J. is a sharp one. I was drained after meeting. Went home to bed and stayed there til 8 pm. Wow. Crash landing, all mixed up and anxious. Passed now and back to rosier territory. Part of the re-entry into school. Big J. is however very supportive of my farm initiatives, even suggesting I get two goats. He he! Martini gave a favourable report on Next Steps meeting. I will look at chapter headings now. Email you soon. X

Later, Adrian: Hi Friend—about to head off to milk. A brief hello at school today—you can see that I am focusing hard at present. It's okay without contact though different—really need to put the effort into making school happen—such a roller-coaster for me—always relaxing too soon and putting my energy elsewhere only to get it slammed back to class and school. A successful day today and I'm all relaxed—watch out cocky teacher, you'll come unstuck—there's not much planning in that book of yours, no clear and tied-down ideas yet—still a bit sketchy. Teaching is good when it works, so hard when it doesn't. I hope that you're well. Funny occurrence isn't it—losing the phone—could reveal more to stay without it, watching the effects of deprivation to then see more clearly the effects of our usual usage. Relying more on memory and imagination of course—can take us miles off-track, or be spot on. I am always looking forward to more news from your side—The Book? The Laird? Your state? I'm getting tired and haven't attended the cows yet, so will away. Don't expect too much out of me over the next couple of days—big readjustment to school relentlessness once more. I do hope you're well and focused yourself; sure that there is much in the way of events occurring around you now. Let me know.

Been thinking of a new phone—take care X

Mouse: Hi Friend—feel unhappy without the phone contact, but perhaps it is better for you to stay focused. Can you work better; get down to things more easily?

Ho hum—wet, wet day—poor moos—thinking of my Gentleman Farmer braving the worst. Interesting meeting with the Real Estate Agents re school land; they have already been back to us to say we are zoned 'green-belt/educational'; meaning we can only sell to another educational body unless we get the zone changed. There has been a suggestion that we should move the entire school. Lois was looking into that this afternoon. We do have a potential interested party in Waikato Uni. wanting a site for 1000 students in the near future so we shall see. Lois also discovered that the piece of land we thought was for sale on the corner of Reilly Rd. is not the exact piece ear-marked, but the more interesting land behind it. I shall keep you posted as we progress. The boys have had a good day; The Laird is much stronger I would say, although he claims to be still 'stuck'. However, I notice a new strength which is good—he keeps looking at me in a resigned sort of manner and I keep wanting to say that; "yes, I am deeply in love with Adrian—what are we to do?" Not quite the right time yet though—still can't see a way around it all. BUT—the truth doesn't go away. Hmm—missing you—take care; how did you get on with the list? —M—X

Adrian: Hello friend—bedtime soon, {after late milking}, a time to review your list and say goodnight. Nice terminology. The Minx eh? Scowler is a good one. He he. Hope your belly is alright. I'm abed, strangely with great amounts of energy. Must be that terrible caramel slice I ate today. Yeech! Wish I hadn't. SO lots going on for you and your team. Standing by—feeling a little bit distant—not sure why. Things went well today, but it is a knife-edge all the time; just staying afloat. Easily swamped and reluctant to bail it out and get on top of all my stuff. Why won't I get down to it? Very reluctant—defiant part says no, no it can all wait.

I approve—do send writing to Mizzie. Hope you had a great day. 3

hour professional development workshop looking at Assessment; sounds bloody dry and boring but was pretty interesting; helped to integrate us as a College of Teachers once more. I certainly feel more connected and at ease with the term. Spent two hours drawing the class; each child and two adults. It will be worth it though—a great focus activity for them to draw—great term starter and a way to bring in the new children Miles and Hanna. It's a measuring Main Lesson where they learn to measure in feet and inches. Also put a little thought into the play of Noah. Should be good creative focus—writing a play—well, rewriting. Of course it will take a while to hear back from our editor—be interesting to know how she will receive The Book—if she has time to read it. So, I'm resting my weary body and overtaxed chocolate biscuit-filled-belly before I head out for milking; poor cows out in this cold rain—need to give them some more hay for warmth. It's never as bad as it sounds when you're snug and warm inside; wet weather gear and out you go, no problems. So, hope The Laird's day went well. You'll be on care duty all round, eh? Staying-focused-man signing off.

Must to bed soon—will pull you close as I close my eyes. Take care.

Chapter 3 Rain

Thursday 17ᵗʰ May 2007

A.m. Mouse: Subject: Cold legs—no fire—good morning. Hello there—are you awake, My Friend? No need to reply; know you are busy and focused. Had a thought yesterday; could the phone be in your car? Slipped into the door pocket? Under the seat? Fallen into a boot? I'm sure you have looked, but as the picture came into my mind I thought I would send it on. Lots of swearing, tossing and turning from The Laird all night—poor man; I wish he wasn't so tormented. Still, all potential learning. I just wish he would take the opportunity. As he says, tricky to feel positive when your life is falling down around your ears. Hmm—however, The Lady will not deny her truth. I forgot to say that Lois went off to the council yesterday and had a good chat about our various school issues. Although the school is zoned green belt & educational, they are in the process of re-zoning us to 'rural residential'—fortunate for us if the school decides to move site. The land will be worth much more when they have passed it. Apparently there is an objection, {not specifically to our piece of land, but to something in the bigger picture}, so it may take a while to come through. Lois also discovered that the Educational Board has ear-marked several sites for new schools in the area, so it is worth speaking to them as they would undertake the complicated process of resource consent.

Anyway, My Lovely One, your Lady is back to dog-walking at the park, swimming at the indoor pools, Supergreens and writing, with a dash of household errands, cooking and shopping thrown in—oh, and festival work and future school plans too. I'm still trying to get ahead on the paperwork! No news on The Book—Mizzie is either too busy to read it, or she has passed it on to someone at the publishers to peruse; let's hope it's the latter. Running out of cash again—time for another loan; yikes! Take care—X

* * * * * * *

Later, Mouse: Dear Friend—feeling you so far away, although I know you are nearby. Hope you are well? I am tired, but have had an achieving day. I am really enjoying the writing; am nearly at the end of PART 2—this time of year two years ago; it's helping me with the descriptions of the trees and plants and the climate etc. Funny how many memories come flooding back; all the little details; our first encounters; you asking me to wash the class drinking glasses for you, watching you greet the children from the kitchen window; mmm, feels quite a long time ago doesn't it? Still no sound from our editor—better e-mail her tomorrow and see if she actually received anything; our internet is on a 'go-slow' this month after Cedric downloaded a film and used up a lot of our allocated air-time. I keep ringing your phone, just in case someone hears it in a bush or a box somewhere; is that a good idea, or is it switched off? I am missing you—would love to see you on Friday for a picnic or something; speak nearer the time, okay? Hope your focused days are working well. I have had an interesting time searching the net for temporary classrooms to tide us over if/while the changes take place. If you tap in 'Dome Buildings' the first choice that comes up shows the most wonderful, moveable buildings—low cost, eco-friendly and great fun; I could easily live in one—with my writing partner of course. We would have a roaring fire in the wood-burning stove and a soft, feather bed in the middle; a stunning view of the ocean through an open clearing and the sound of the sea-gulls mixing with those of the Tuis in the trees above us. Sleep well, My Love. I am beside you—M—X

Adrian: Good Morning, Friend. Yes, I'm up and about—have been awake since four—gurgly belly and a dream about Delphine and you. Lots of muddled dreams before but one scene I can recall had me in some kind of black and white pyjamas in bed, waking up to find a plate of toast and a cup of tea in black and white too. I ate it up and then Delphine came out from somewhere wearing the same pyjamas and holding more toast and tea—a bit confusing but I welcomed her and thought this must be how it is now—and just as she was about to sit in bed you appeared also in pyjamas and bearing tea or something. Well, Delphine got mighty offended and stormed out without speaking, slamming the door! I wasn't too worried but I followed her out to see if I could figure out what was going on. She had sneaked back to listen to our conversation. Then I woke up.

Aren't dreams hilarious? I had been thinking of her because she has been trying to get a book back from me for ages and when I saw Edwin a couple of days ago I looked for it and to my embarrassment couldn't find it. I ordered another one but in the meantime found her one. Phew. She's been on my mind. And then yesterday as I walked to guitar lessons I saw her driving off—didn't catch her though. So a few touches but nothing sinsister; I don't think. My mind running through the load of guilty thoughts. I have been for a longish run last two mornings at 5 o'clock sharp. Could become regular; wait and see a bit more. Pretty tired, but that's a little stress as well. A small flash of anxiety about what I would say if Big J. asked me if I were sleeping with you. Trust is needed here, and adult kingship. Yes, I am missing you too. Forces me to connect more with spiritual beings actually. Without you to 'talk' to I turn more to God—did so this morning anyway, and would like to keep it up. Runs up to the top of Rangi Rd under the stars offer a pretty good place to connect.

So, let's try and pull our energies together again through this distance, to hold you, hold me, hold your finances, (remembering that they are like blood or water; need to keep flowing), hold The Laird, hold Vonny, hold school, hold Book, hold houses, children; all with great love, trust, faith, respect. God strength to you today, My Friend. Let's be together in Spirit. X

* * * * * * *

The morning passes normally. How the days tick by—tick, tick, tick—like a time bomb, just waiting to detonate. Should I build an air-raid shelter underground? I don't know. How I wish things were clearer.

Midday, Mouse: My Friend—what a lovely surprise to come home and find your wonderful message waiting for me. I couldn't get to it this morning for the reasons I described yesterday. Perhaps this distance communication is preparing us for a friendship from afar? If I have to return to The U.K—maybe—maybe not. I asked Cordelia yesterday if she had any inside information we would be interested to know! "Ah", she replied, "that you have to discover for yourselves." Hmm.

I'm glad that you are finding richness in the different approach—I'm not sure yet, although I'm sure it is good for me. I shouldn't be making any claim on you anyway—Naughty Mouse—be content with the distance—use it wisely—tend to your desk and family and get sorted. Yes Sir, I will listen. I will join Lord Swallow under the stars. I am thinking about his suggestion that he can speak to God more if he is not speaking to me. I suppose I have always seen our connection as opening the paths to God on a very deep level, but I know what you mean by private conversation without 'Us' as integral; strengthening and vital, especially if we are separated. My Friend—I was amused by your funny dream; do you put me in the same category as Delphine? Hmm.

So, yes; to hold all these important things together—to hold each other at all times—to know that His grace and holding is keeping us safe and maintaining the vital 'blood flow' of all that needs to shift. This is our gift—this is where we really 'plough in' our precious Love; the powerful turning point at the start of the change; your ritual seed scattering as it entered me and our beloved Earth together. Keep well, keep focused. Your Friend under the exploding stars—M—X

Adrian: P.S. You are far more to me than Delphine; there is such a good fit with understanding and communication, dreams and lift-off between us that was never there with her. This dream is unprocessed life-shocks and stress induced, I think. Go the black and white pyjamas! Here we go then. School, love, cows, pigs, woodwork, home, Vonny, dog on-heat shananigans, Molly, Sienna, Big J, Martini, Little J , running at 5am, planning, reports, fire, guitar lessons. Could be great. Sleep. X

P.m. Mouse: Thought we were meant to be focusing—middle of the day too! Tut tut-mmm. Hi Friend—how are you doing? How was your day and did you have a good teachers' meeting? You must be busy—hope Big J. hasn't asked you any difficult questions; can you not claim close friendship and leave it at that? Hmm—I know that it worries you, and that you like to be up-front at all times.

My day has been wet—soggy dog walking on several occasions, swimming; definitely wet, washing-up; more wet—and driving all day through big puddles; splashy and wet! Don't think I'll get in the bath! Well, a fairly cut-throat e-mail from Mizzie was waiting for my return to The Mountain this morning. Here are some of her suggestions:

1   She doesn't think the chatty, daily account sits comfortably with The Craftsman's mystical theme.
2   The story is more of a diary and as such may not be of interest to anyone else, even though she herself enjoyed reading it all.
3   The use of the present is notoriously tricky to pull off.
4   Too many exclamation marks and flowery descriptions; better to keep it simple.
5   If it is going to be a novel then it has to follow a set pattern to work.

What I would like to suggest is the following:

1   As you originally suggested, perhaps we leave out The Craftsman all together, although I did wonder if we could turn some of the lovely prose into a poem or two and scatter it in amongst the writing.
2   Claim The Book as a diary and discovery account rather than a novel; in other words, keep it true to the original. A further storyline could always come in to one of the other Books later on.
3   Nobody has seen the full content of the story yet; judgment has been passed on the introduction. I would like to complete the parts I am working on and ask someone to judge it as a whole. I have a feeling that it will only make sense in its entirety.
4   Go through the content and cut back on the over-use of descriptive language and exclamation marks!

5   Complete a short passage for The Craftsman for parts 3 & 4 & 5; if only for our own sense of completion; food for future work if we go in that direction and potential use as poetry throughout the whole. As the daily texts increase the more mystical element does walk side-by-side anyway—hmm—I am not deflated; still think we can make something of it.
6   Lie in my Lover's warm embrace and kiss him for a long, long time. I read an article in the supermarket queue today that gave ten different reasons why kissing is so good for us, from increased blood to our brains to security and self-esteem! There goes another exclamation mark!! Oops. Loving you—hope you can still make tomorrow? If the weather is fine shall we go land-hunting in the hills for the Star Dome enterprise? If it's wet? Are we allowed to curl up somewhere, or is that too risky?

Sleep well; peaceful and complete—M—X

Adrian: Hello friend, Here I am feeling in a bit of a mess—stressed—overwhelmed—not coping that well at all—don't know what is wrong, but perhaps a decent early night may help. I think that this indicates that there is something I am not accepting and that it's going to get worse until I do notice and welcome the change that is needed. Arrrghhh! I hate this—so uncomfortable—and then so blessed easy when you finally stop and look. So what is it? What new depth or understanding do I need to face? I'm missing you too. Would like to see you if only briefly on Friday after 11 a.m. I have a meeting in the afternoon and must be away by 12:50. Perhaps a picnic lunch at the Everglades? 11:30?

Meantime I will get an early night and try to unravel which of the many life-shocks of the day was the one that sent me over. Eek. Such a battle to accept being a teacher. Out out out is all I want, much as I love the children—there's something there that makes it so hard—so sensitive—so vulnerable—could be sleep and good planning.

I'll have an earlyish night. This morning's early start and extended sleep left me no time to connect. So, now I have just returned from Stephanie's house having dropped off some milk to Mat the yoghurt maker and picked up an electric fence unit to keep wee pigs in captivity. Also went to see the pig farmer as my lost phone had his phone number; the only source. He was welcoming and informative telling me that come 6 months pigs can definitely mate—bad news for wee Molly; also learned the method of dispatch and scalding the carcass to remove hair and skin—yech. Apparently they are very noisy as well—gulp—hope old grumpy-bum-new-home-builder up the top is going to be okay with it—not too noisy little ones please—other neighbours may have things to say as well, but we shall cross that bridge when we come to it. My tame farmer Mel has been looking for pigs so can always take them there—actually might be good to put them there soon to eat up all the calving milk currently being tipped away. I go up there on Sunday. Could really do with a new phone now; sick of being without, so if spare one is available I would be very grateful, although you may want to save that one for your family; new budget ones are not overly expensive.

Had a moment today where dog met up with the next door Jack Russell after being away from him for a couple of days—had to call her reluctantly away and whisk her into the car; don't really want weird little mongrels, but sudden realization or wondering if this is not exactly how it is for us—being kept apart when all we want is to be together. Should I let her go—trust her instinct—or not—hold them apart rather cruelly for the possible good of all. Anyway, had a good process this morning after small meltdown—same old nonsense. Felt much clearer and could manage School again. College of Teachers Meeting today blew it away, but should be able to bounce back. Can you meet briefly tomorrow—thought about swimming?

Oops—just nodded off. Awoke to a screen full of p's and s'. Better go. Just looking forward to catching up with you again. I'll be home at 11.30 tomorrow so leave me a message or call me in the morning. Also, I could dash home around drop off time if you wanted to come by quickly before School. Okay. Supergreens too? XTop of Form

Friday 18th May 2007
Mouse: Good morning, Fine Sir—thank-you for the lovely, chatty message. Disappointing about Molly; she doesn't make much noise at all. What about keeping the others away from the farm and getting a female friend for Molly? Then you could bring in the males for mating, {when they are old enough}, and have a wonderful, piggy nursery at school without any of the noise or distressing part. Just a thought anyway; may not fit in with your plans. You could have all the chickens in that space too—if there were a beam in the piggy house they could roost above the pig or pigs; it's what they do at the moment. The only thing that would need to happen is the baby chicks should hatch out elsewhere, and the laying boxes need to be high up—otherwise our grunty friends will eat both chicks and eggs!

Feeling you far away, yet close beside me at the same time—strange; frustrating and lovely, both. I have Supergreens in the car for you, and the new phone, although you would need a new sim card. I keep thinking your old one must turn up soon. Perhaps I'll try and help you remember your movements when I see you today. Can't wait to catch-up. I can drop in at 8.30—and see you again at 11.30. You can always leave a voice message on my mobile. I have it on silent. Let me know if you can, otherwise I shall just turn up at Vonny's at 8.30 and wait for you. You could always leave me a message there. I

will bring my swimming things down—hot pools? Or land-hunting? Anyway, My Friend—go gently—wake smoothly—M—X

I see Adrian briefly at eight-thirty. He has farm duties he had forgotten about. I give him the phone and agree to meet again at 11.30. We are celebrating the Festival of St. Michael and the Dragon this afternoon. We shall both be busy with that. He is very grateful for the new phone.

Midday, Adrian: Lying beside a freshly dug grave his face is grim. The aborted calf lies in the wheelbarrow, its still form twisted, awaiting burial. The mother so upset and anxious earlier on when the girls from his class discovered it, now grazing in the lower field giving him time to bury her calf discreetly next to the milking stall—possibly where the foundation for the new school build may go. What is this symbolism? Grave digging on the morning of their St. Michael Festival. A curse? He has been struggling to shake off a sense of gripping—little spaces of clarity—then shocks that bring back the tightness. The secret of course—that he discovered yesterday—is to practice loving himself. A mirror is useful for this. The winds blow strongly. Autumn is here, and soon the colder weather and rains will begin. He will try to build the milking shed this weekend. He has been asked to stop the building projects in school for a week; the children are looking tired and not so well. Oh—feels like rain. Better keep going.

Mouse: My Love—I was just reaching for my phone when your message came through. I am so sorry about the calf. What a terrible shock for you. I don't like to think of you alone on the hill, sad and unsure; nature's way—a cruel fate, but a reality in every farmer's life. This high wind; battering—digging deep—exposing. Saint Michael, where are you? Burnished autumn colours exchanged for mild uncertainty. But, tomorrow will dawn as it deems fit. We cannot hold and shape everything. She takes his hand—he lays his head upon her breast—reaching out they are there for each other. I am missing you, but I am here. Sleep well, My Love. Don't stay out in the cold overly long. Please let me know when you are safely home and warm—X

* * * * * * *

Later, Adrian: Home and warm I am—so much leftover milk that I have to sterilize more bottles and make extra Panir Cheese. I'll be busy for an hour-and-a-half, I'd say.

Mouse: I'm pleased you are home. Get some rest before The Festival. The Laird's comment last night: "your body; your kindness, is here—but not your Spirit. What am I going to do with you?" "Honour my needs," I replied. The Book is coming along well. I have reached November 2006. See you later, Friend.
P.s had the thought that an old life could be done with; a burial on this

important day? Was that your ex-partner I saw at school yesterday? The Archangel sweep in a direct hit—a new beginning; a powerful sword laying claim. Are these warriors set? What are they meant to be? I had an interesting dream last night—and a strangely empty Friday night and Saturday lie ahead. What does it all mean? X

Adrian: *Thank you for your thoughts—can't penetrate the lesson here. Confusing events—dreams and people, set-backs and failures; a shakedown or an angry backlash? I can't see my way through it. No visible outcome. Just hang on and trust that the train will emerge from the tunnel. The storm will pass and we'll see where we've been blown. Hang on! Any better view from your vantage point? Foggy as hell down here.*

Mouse: *The Sacrificial calf—The High Priest with bowed head; the pain that had to be—it might have been a heavier burden—giving thanks. She thinks of him—of the afternoon ahead. She sends a blessing; a benediction. The stars welcomed her early morning amble; they waved a friendly twinkle. Even the pig accompanied me on my dawn walk, stopping for a pee at the same time as the dog! I hope this afternoon finds you restored. See you soon at the great event—our day. X*

Adrian: *I am being forced inwards—reduced energy for outer projects keeping me gloomy and quiet. Perhaps I should strengthen myself and attend to home affairs. I have been rising at 5.30 a.m. these past mornings—new rhythms—exercise and speech awareness; singing practice—attention to my voice. A month before our school mid-winter 'do' where I am organizing the music. Are you going to it? Abby has been present for the past three days, giving me life-shocks when she turns away as I approach, culminating in her daughter losing her shoes while I was relieving her class. The subsequent conversation eased the anxiety I had been feeling. But now a candle is burning and a hot salt-pack warms a strained buttock. Two swords lie on the kitchen table and a literary description of St. Michael rests on my lap. But my eyes are heavy and dulled—my guts are jumpy—positive and negative—the mid-point. Flat but striving. More processing required.*
He thanks her for her presence and steadiness—looking for a pillow note after her visit; nodding his head thoughtfully to her sacrifice suggestion. Perhaps there will be a chance to see each other tonight? Or this afternoon? There is something grounding in this slow, sticky churn he struggles with—slowing and steadying—facing fears—feeling fears—their weight—new resolutions that acknowledge the weight—the chores—the responsibilities—attending—

Mouse: *She has missed his messages—their intrigue—the insights. The Laird will be present in the white Ute when he comes to The Festival. Yes—I would like to see you later when I am free. Looks like I have a whole 24 hours alone! Book time? Do you have any spare minutes?*

160

The sun is glorious today. The dog and I could have swum at Pillans Beach if we had had time this morning. I did manage a quick dip in the indoor pools. I changed into my festival clothes and joined the school in front of Class 1 and 2 for the St. Michael Pageant this afternoon—a Holy and reverent performance it was too. Adrian had scattered autumn leaves across the concrete and 'borrowed' a few potted ferns to complete the stage. The new sword was removed from its glass case and laid on a blue velvet cloth surrounded by candles and a dusting of autumn leaves. Saint Michael, robed in gold and white silk and flanked by his Angelic Host, raised the sword and carried it out of the library to the waiting school community. How special that was; a new ritual in an already well-established pageant. Spectators are asked not to clap after festivals; the children offer the pageants as a gift. The silence afterwards cements the spiritual intention.

I helped clear away the costumes and props when everyone had gone. The Laird is away on a course about sexuality and marriage; a course for teachers—oops—and the children are with friends for the night. Thank you St. Michael; Lord Swallow and I can claim a few hours.

Early P.m. Mouse: *Hi there, My Friend, I am free until hockey tomorrow—yippee! Are you free at all? I am just running the Bog-Brush at Tui Park.*

Adrian: *I have a meeting about the Community Village at 3p.m—then free. How is the permission? Questions? Suspicion?*

Mouse: *Should I come to the meeting? Are people coming back to school? I decided not to ask permission—it only causes more trouble. Perhaps I will just go home. Let me know about the meeting—*

Adrian: *Hi—with Fin right now at school. Come up—teachers here now, but no worries.*

I park behind school and walk up through the long grass to the top meadow where I spy two men surveying the school land; one of them most familiar, the other is Fin, the friendly man from the local Hot Pools who has offered Adrian his farming expertise. He doesn't appear to remember me when I say hello. Together we look over the fence at the handful of residential building sites under construction. "I've already had a neighbour complain about the growing farm," Adrian tells us. Oh dear. We climb through the fence to survey the land for sale beyond the farm. "This is my place," he announces. "Yes, an architect-designed eco-village; the views aren't the best but the position is great; positive in so many ways. Yep, I can feel it!" My Lover rubs his hands together gleefully; one of his endearing habits. We walk around a pond that collects rainwater from the surrounding hills; the water drains away through the strip of conservation wetland that borders the school property. "Look at these Choko Vines;" Fin indicates a strange vine climbing in the trees along the path. His wife knows how best to deal with the slippery fruit that resembles a Prickly Pear. Like many Kiwi women Cathy is a great cook, experienced in bottling and preserving.

The evening sun glances through the branches of an old poplar towering above us. For a moment I imagine St. Michael's sword creating a sun dazzle through the leaves. We look for the eel—apparently he has been spied again. There he is! Adrian leans over the water, allowing the timid creature to kiss his precious Greenstone. I enjoy a swing on the children's tyre and then we clamber over the fallen Eucalyptus Tree. Fin leads us through the dark Bamboo Forest as the sun begins to set over the hills; "I've recently met someone who makes all sorts of amazing things with bamboo," he tells us. We cross the stream again; "oh dear—another broken board," Adrian exclaims; "I'm meant to be the Health and Safety Officer."

We all enjoy the brainstorming session; village rental houses on the ridge above the Kindergartens, larger homes bordering the drive and the village centre above the farm. I have a tedious headache but the men are keen to explore further, so we complete our trek around the far bank of the wetland. "Sammy told me that a Kindergarten parent owns the land behind the farm; did you know that?" I ask. "The sections are a good size but very expensive; 1.7 hectares for $700,000!" Fin has always been interested in the eco-village concept. "I'd be keen to get involved," he says before leaving us for the evening.

"Do you want to milk the cows with me?" Adrian appears keen to get back to work. "I hope to plant a strip of herbs for the animals along this edge of the field, so they can self-medicate when they feel the need. All animals do that. Sasha and I have been talking about it recently. I might clear out this shed now—do you mind?" "I think I'll leave you to it," I say. "I need to shift this headache." I leave The Farmer to his creative drive and go back to his lodgings where I self-medicate myself. I often rely on a natural cure, but this headache calls for modern medicine. Adrian arrives home just as I begin to feel better and we tuck into large bowlfuls of the lamb hotpot he prepared earlier. "Hogart," he informs me; "one-year-old lamb—good, eh?" The veranda swing-seat is a comforting place to linger after supper. I laugh; "no hat between us this time?" "Look at this lovely old scythe I found at the garage sale," Adrian reaches for his new tool with pride. "Try the handle; the wood is beautiful. I'll teach you how to use it. The lawn needs cutting—there's still enough light—come on."

We tend to the dogs after my scything lesson. The Bog-brush leaps out of the van with her usual enthusiasm. She is unfriendly with Vonny's dog to begin with but they soon play together. Adrian is so lovely with her; calm yet firm. We have to stop her from bounding off the deck and away down the drive in the dark. And then it is time to turn in, closing the curtains; cosy and content together. Lord Swallow takes matters in hand and gives me a lovely foot and neck massage to relieve the last of the headache. We don't kiss and cuddle but I lie between his legs and lean into him; platonic lovers we are content and happy. He plays me his favourite Counting Crows song; a beautiful little

162

melody although I don't recall the title, and then we sing our own Saint Michael song; the song we wrote several months ago about the soldiers of fire.

"I can't do the kissing thing," Lord Swallow suddenly announces. "It really throws me. I begin to covet you all over again. I can't cope with that. Can you sense my tiredness—in my eyes? I am definitely overloaded. I am really conscious of my heavy eyes." "All I see is our Heavenly Garden Gate and beyond," I admit. He smiles; we are together and as one—deeply in love. "Oh my, oh my," he sighs. "I can feel a tune brewing." Picking up his guitar Adrian plays me some chords and we fiddle about with the melody for a while before he opens up on a deeper level; the level we both crave.

"I've discovered that one of the reasons I've been feeling bad is that I abandon myself—that's what I do; 'abandon' myself. I was an abandoned baby and an abandoned boy; my mother abandoned me twice when I was small. And when I abandon myself I abandon others." I look at the man I love, suddenly realizing the significance of his statement; integral to the spiritual ecstasy I often experience in his company. At last I see him entirely; this is it. "You have revealed the final skeleton," I tell him. "Do you remember us talking about it? You went through guilt, sneaking, scheming and unworthiness until I said to you; *you will reach abandonment eventually.'* And now, a year later, you have arrived. We have been granted these perfect hours together this weekend. Important things are falling into place. Saint Michael has come for us." Our eyes meet and once again I am transported into our Celestial Realm where powerful understanding replaces any need for words.

"I would like to visit The Laird at his Whisky 'Do' in town before I drive home," I tell Adrian. "I'd better go now." We spend a few minutes talking about the negative aspect of alcohol. "I've never seen The Laird drunk," I say. "He made himself very sick as a fifteen-year-old and has never over-indulged since then. I've never been drunk myself—or touched a cigarette; I've never had any interest in such things. My goals have always been higher; Heaven or nothing. I've only slept with one man—oops—two I should say!" Adrian ushers me out of the room, a smirk on his face. "Now you've planted a picture in my mind; you had better go—fast!"

The Laird is very surprised to see me, suspicious even. I think he is rather shocked by my out-of-character appearance. I stay for an hour, enjoying everyone's company and indulging in a second supper. The Mountain is very quiet when I arrive home at ten-thirty. I am the only one here. The dog and cat are both on my bed. I snuggle up to them, feeling sad that I can't sleep with Lord Swallow. Adrian and I have agreed that I can return to his new, and less inviting, Leafy Glade just before dawn.

Late P.m. Adrian: *A lovely evening—restful—calm—sharing—the important catching-up, yum—bridging—rekindling—clarifying. These Mighty friends, how will their destinies weave? She has declared her readiness for whatever is to come—he has uncovered old wounds. Imagine if they were* *allowed—ah—but would they have learnt this much if it were easy? Could be Angel Perfect—*

Mouse: *I'm home now. Had a second meal—and pudding—oops—yum. My headache is gone; thanks. Hope the late milking went well. Sleep well—rest the sore eyes—no kissing.*

Adrian: *How was your fine husband?*

Mouse: *The Laird appeared relaxed and content—happy in his male world with Simon, Andrew, Bernard and Reg. He probably found it odd that I should have gone down to see him. I told him we had been on the farm with Fin. I couldn't ask him if you could collect the metal etc. Too many close ears listening in. I'm home alone now—no Lover—no husband—none to hold me; probably what I deserve.*

Chapter 4 Rekindling

Saturday 19ᵗʰ May 2007

Waking after a disturbed night of too many animals on the bed I make my way down The Mountain, arriving at Adrian's lodgings before dawn. I find Lord Swallow in the cold garden wearing underpants and a woolly jumper. He is studying his star map and eagerly points out Scorpio and Leo to his Lady Love. And then he invites me into his bed; at last we can be close and cosy together. We are both wearing woolly jumpers but our legs are bare. We curl about each other as if we have never been apart, the narrow bed keeping us close. "Let's keep it platonic," Adrian suggests. "This is important for me—as a meditation and a prayer." So, cosy we remain. We don't kiss, but my, oh my, how close we are; how at one, my Swallow Man and I. "Let's imagine an object," he says; "anything at all; one each. Hold it in our minds and give it our complete focus."

I imagine a small wooden jug I have at home, one I found at a garage sale when we first arrived in New Zealand. I like the chunky, organic shape with over-sized, curved lip and comfortable handle. I hold it in my mind's eye, sensing its lightness, even though it looks heavy. The wood can't be very dense. Suddenly I am inside the jug—it has grown huge, {or 'growan' as the Kiwi's say.} I am trapped in a cosy crater. Luckily I have some tools with me and begin chiselling a set of steps in the side of the jug to reach the chunky rim. I look out when I reach the top—hurrah; that didn't take too long. The rim fits perfectly under my arms. I notice the grain of the wood; it is rougher than I thought with little black spots on each scale. I am curious to know if I can circumnavigate the jug with the rim supporting my weight. I achieve my goal, arriving back at the steps and spying Lord Swallow down in the bottom of the crater. I feel as if I am stranded on top of a Mountain; balanced on an arc, or on board a beached boat. But the sea is far away; bizarre. Lord Swallow is busy making an escape ladder; perfect and strong. He waves his assurance from the wooden valley. I climb back down to join him, making a bunk-bed out of the wood beside him. It is cosy, and then I am suddenly transported to my family home in Hampshire. I am standing in my parents' hall, looking out at the Iron-Age Hill Fort that makes the view so spectacular. I am holding the wooden jug and I am crying.

"So, what did you see; what did you choose?" Adrian asks. "What are you feeling?" I tell him all, surprising him, I think. "You were totally subjective in your imagination!? Well!" He then describes his own journey; "I was holding my yellow pencil," Adrian tells me. "I examined it closely, wondering where the wood had come from; what the yellow paint was made of, and the lead. Where does lead come from? I was really interested in the chemistry of the object; the atoms etc. —quite technical. And then I imagined it had 'growan' huge! It stretched all the way to the harbour, and then all the way to Auckland. I was driving along beside it! Crazy! The yellow monster was getting in the way of everything." Together we imagine Adrian's yellow pencil. It wouldn't really bend, would it? Or comply with his wishes or tooling like my wooden jug. A pencil is unyielding, hard-edged and direct. It certainly wouldn't offer any comfort. I compare it with my curvy object. What fun we have, considering the meaning and symbology of our individual meditations.

Adrian checks the flickering candle beyond my shoulder; "don't want the edge of the duvet to catch, eh?" His toes seek mine, his limbs covering me in a semi-platonic gesture of ownership. How close we are. "Are you wearing make-up?" He asks, surprised, tenderly stroking my cheek. "Well—a little," I admit; "only organic powder. I *am* the Lady of The Castle, not the washer woman, you know! It is The Lady who climbs into My Lord Swallow's bed before the dawn breaks." Adrian laughs; "The Washer Woman is just as sexy as The Lady! Can you see my picture of Christ over there?" He points to a corner of the room. The picture is hanging in the shadows, just behind his clothes rail. "I like having it there, not boldly on display above my bed. I can only see it if I look closely from this angle. It is the picture that hangs in all the Christian Community Churches; the one Rudolf Steiner said was the most realistic image of Christ." "Really?" I answer, surprised. "Who is the artist?" "Nobody famous," Adrian tells me. We are quiet for a while, studying the icon image, sensing a benevolence that reaches our cosy huddle. I like the picture, and Adrian's reason for having it partially hidden. This is a significant moment; the first time I have been allowed in the new Leafy Glade bed. Although it is a narrow fit we are perfectly comfortable—of course. "You know the interesting book I have been reading about those who have gone beyond; the importance of The Deceased in our lives? Well, the other day another book fell off Vonny's shelf into my hands. It describes the beginning of the Rosicrucian movement; {the Rosy Cross}, and the twelve that came together. Rudolf Steiner grew out of this important movement with the Theosophists. The book mentions Medieval Alchemists; how they looked at the spirituality behind the process of crystals; dissolving salt, sacrificial flame etc; to gain spiritual insight and wisdom." Adrian reads from the book and I find myself totally present with him on this new voyage of discovery. The early Alchemists are fascinating; I would love to know more. I can identify with the dissolving salt and the liquid, a strange fact as I have always associated myself more with Fire, although I am certainly not drawn to any sacrifice—not willingly.

"I can identify with the salting; the crystals—converting to solid form," Adrian tells me. "You know something? I really want to start a church, alongside our school philosophy. We have spoken about it before. What do you reckon?" How strongly this man reflects the ideas and dreams I have harboured for years. He is bursting with drive and potential—like me. We talk of the good folk accompanying us on our challenging and exciting journey;

166

loving people like Hau and Simon, Cordelia and others. We count those immediately involved; there are **7**. "Are you sure?" Adrian counts them again, "they make up the inner circle," I suggest. "Then there is the outer circle; Big J, Vonny, Martini, Freya, etc," I continue; "so many caring souls holding us carefully." "Could there be twelve in the outer circle?" Adrian asks. "And what about the invitation you found? Should we accept? Perhaps we should drive past the address in town first."

"How would Big J. be with a church alongside school?" I ask Adrian. "She would need to be involved—as the School Principal." "What are we here?" Adrian skirts my question and highlights the real question—'what are we?' "Perhaps we are part of an alchemic process," I answer. "I think we may be nearing the conclusion; our alchemy takes us there spontaneously, naturally, without all the theory. Imagine spending hours teaching a child the theory of achieving a handspring, only to find he/she turns to you and says; 'do you mean like this?' Followed by a perfect example of the handspring. I think we are like that. That doesn't mean we can do away with the theory, but I don't think we need it. Others begin with the theory and find the treasure; our alchemy takes us directly to the treasure, something like that. Together we are so 'alive'—naturally connected to The Spirit. I sense the vitality we encapsulate. It is very exciting; it touches everything we embrace. Have you noticed how things have gone flat since we halted our lovers' bond? The Festival Group has been listless, the teachers tired and Cordelia out of sorts. Could that be a reflection of our state?" "I've been meaning to speak about Cordelia," Adrian answers. "She has been keeping apart; separate. Did she telephone you?"

"Yes, she did," I reply. "We had a good chat. Her life is certainly challenging. I think we have all needed this year to cement our bond and now we can come together again; richer and directed—as community. Our love is central to it all—strange, but I sense it is so." "A Cross then," my Lover announces, "with The Laird at the base like a crucible, holding The Earth, and Cordelia at the top with her calm handling of Fire and direct celestial communion; a sacrifice she can teach us to embrace. You and I stand at the cross part, me on the left holding the salt crystals; The Air, and you on the right with the briny solution; The Water representing pure, unconditional love. You and I are dependent upon each other to release the crystals; the alchemy happens naturally, through the grace of Spirit. We all meet at the central point of The Cross. You pull naturally towards The Fire and I pull to The Earth. We keep The Cross steady and connected. I'd like to suggest a meeting—yes, a meeting with The Laird together with Simon officiating. I will not deny our love, but I will explain its platonic nature. I need them to hear that." "I don't think I can ask The Laird to go there," I admit. "How I wish I could, but he wouldn't cope. As Simon said; 'he will never be able to meet you on your level.'"

"Okay," Adrian gets out of bed, accepting the situation but acknowledging that we have made important headway. "Why don't you cook breakfast while I take a shower?" How wonderful to start the day together like this. We are so happy, even in our platonic state. Singing wafts from the bathroom and singing hums around the stove. "I know that song," Adrian emerges from the shower with a big smile. He is all clean and sparkly. He wraps me up in a big hug and allows me to kiss him gently behind his ear. I have time for a bite of breakfast and then I have to dash away. The children need collecting; Cedric is the first on the list.

Mid-Morning, Mouse: *Saint Michael comes to us—and we, in humble armour bow our heads in thanks. He comes to us openly, lighting the gloomy patch and quelling the draught that tries to dissipate our vibrant Spirits. All have been taken down; the low ebb unwelcome but necessary. Even she is brought to her knees; her female cycle arrives earlier than usual and saps her strength. And then, on the eve of Saint Michael's important festival, a real sacrifice is turned into the soil, marking the foundation of their new school development. These Lovers—they cannot deny the truth—their alchemy, a living entity upon which these new endeavours can grow with swelling potential. Saint Michael sends them agreement—acknowledgement—a village—a farm—a band of 7 strong and 12 firm. And to prove his allegiance to those he has held all year he marks the moment with an upright blade through the shining poplars.*

And for them? The journey is well underway with a new compass and a fresh set of charts; all brand-spanking new. Lord Swallow is in charge at the helm, allowing his Lady to take control occasionally—as long as she realizes she cannot free-wheel at sea. He knows she doesn't need the boundaries, but her fellow crew is uneasy in the direct approach without life-jacket safety. His Lady sighs—The Boat is longing for The Ocean—quietly and with great excitement, despite the restrictions. Her ache must be the sacrifice. She doesn't feel the need, but those close to her demand it is so. A wrenching sob wells up inside her heart but she doesn't let it out. She plunges a stopper into the natural flow of her life-force. There is no other way at present. She hopes her energies will continue without their free-flow. She has given out for so many months now. Her fine men—one who knows he should show love and passion, but cannot in the way she needs, and one who feels all the love and passion she craves—and my, in what massive quantity, but who cannot allow himself to gift it to her.

So—tidy desks and buttoned jackets—loving handshakes and blessed smiles. There is work to be done.

P.s. Flip—just watched 'Shakespeare in Love'—flip again! If you haven't seen it recently I suggest you do—a 'must' for those who sail The Celestial Sea.

The children have had fun; Cedric is tired but more content and The Go-Getter is very pleased because he played hockey with the older class and they won their match. I don't hear from Adrian this afternoon. He is a busy man, abandoning any covetous feelings for me. His plate is overly-full and he needs clarity. I don't mind too much. I must try and let go—in a way—sort of—yes. I am ready for something; whatever. We shall see. The Laird and I continue our difficult conversations. He cannot accept my truth; "the deepest truth I have ever felt," I have to admit. We do not lie to each other, however much I wish I could be kinder to his heart. I take his face in my hands and say; "I don't think you are really in love with me, My Darling; not the kind of love I need." I cook a roast chicken for supper and he retires to the top cabin for the eternal T.V brain blackout. I wish he had more courage. I speak to my parents in England, discussing Cedric's offer from his old school in Hampshire. He would be based with them if he returned home.

Sunday 20th May 2007

Early A.m. Mouse: Do we light a candle this Sunday dawn, Lord Swallow? Are you awake? What is our morning meditation?

Adrian: Good morning, Friend. I hope the drizzly dawn finds you rested, strong and peaceful. The movie sounds important; I remember scenes from it—but not in this new light. There is much news to tell from the village. Shall I start? Or shall I wait? Well, I have just held the children—not all yet—first I wrote their names beautifully with my yellow pencil, then I saw them and projected them forwards into young men and women. What do they bring? Concentration exercise that sharpens another edge; 'holding the class' edge, or eggs if I am juggling life. Perhaps I could bring you into my picture when I hold them. There is much to tell you, but too much for a text. Suffice to say, a crunch day it was—several mistakes, bringing a confrontation with Brendan leading to a deep and open conversation with him on my position with you. Back into the sunlight I go; a useful reflection from a community perspective. Having been so clear in the morning I was able to hear his advice that came from his own similar experience. 'If things will be misunderstood they will be—you cannot be seen to be encouraging the dissolution of the marriage. It has to be her choice completely. It requires thought about each and every meeting—how could this be misconstrued if others observed you? Have a cup of tea on the deck where all can see it to be transparent. A good man would lay down his own needs and would even uphold the marriage—letting her make the decisions. Then, if she separated and stayed here, after a period of time it would be quite acceptable for you to join her.'

Brendan had other such comments that hit the unease in my gut squarely—my gut feeling about the community's perception. And I stood and said 'yes' to all, except the upholding; there I can work more. Simon is on my list to call today. I might even see him—more coals, but purifying. And then I managed to miss an appointment with a milking helper at school. The cows had run out of water and Sasha sent me a text. I saw her and it was good— she is very interested in the church idea; keen. She's been feeling low too, needing the community's help. So, I am ripped open, hurray! Youch. Had a session with Gary Govern; Vonny's dog managed to scratch the new door. Oops—useful though. Busy time.

Mouse: Good morning, My Friend. What a busy day awaited you after our blessed start. I would like to see you to hear more. I'd love you to see the film I mentioned. I really need to—no, I won't go there. Hmm. I hope you are rested? I am lying low with blood loss; purifying; waiting. Cedric's old school has offered a 50% fee reduction—and an offer on our Sussex flat has just come through! Something is opening. Blessings to you, My Fine Sir.

We spend a lazy morning at home on The Mountain. My tum is sore and it rains all day. Even I indulge in some T.V while Cedric tackles his homework. I complete more writing and we wait—wait for what?

Midday, Mouse: A damp day. Time to re-group. Long, restorative sleep for all family members who have been away from the safe haven of 'home.' Strange how exhausting nights away can be. Even she slept for part of the morning, The Bog-Brush draped across her on the sofa, resigned to the quiet. But now it is time for action—children's bedrooms to tidy; how easily a small space becomes chaotic. This is one of her favourite tasks; to bring order after dysfunction; to add a dash of artistry and to hold the space with designed direction. She hasn't done much of that here, on these foreign shores, not really. Other creative forces have been to the fore! She longs to take him into her world of traditional rhythm—set in English history—ancient walls and pewter jugs, wooden vessels and cottage gardens. She knows how much he would love to linger there. She can see him in an honest day's toil amongst the antiquity. But not as a visitor.

She sends him her greeting, knowing how busy he is—not wishing to disturb—not expecting a long, reply message. She likes to send him her thoughts from the laundry basket; {aye—she is the washer-woman today!} She needs to send him her thoughts. No powder on her cheeks—hair in ringlets after a damp dash with The Castle Hound. How is her Fine Sir? Mist hangs over The Mountain top, laden droplets upon each blade of grass. The autumn branches appear nude today.

Adrian: He is a little subdued and serious after yesterday's coals. No illusion. This is a serious business that could easily tidal wave. Being watched is his sense—some ease with it though—not crippling but cautious. Again— attend to your Laird. Simon will phone me later. I am on outreach day—being a friend to Carla and Little J. Dinner invitations for round here, maybe a fire-bath too. Prep and work viewing taking place. Spoke with Cordelia and Sammy. Cool from—

I drive Cedric to Bernard and Felicia's house this afternoon; he is cutting the lawns every week. I shall stay in town until he has finished. I wonder what Adrian's incomplete 'cool from' meant.

P.m. Mouse: I am free for a couple of hours if you would like me to clean house, chop vegs or sleep on your sofa. I am tired. Have just dropped Cedric at Bernard's house. Heading to Tui Park with the dog; understand if it isn't appropriate. No point in going home.

Adrian: A bit jumpy right now—haven't stopped. Might have a cup of tea—maybe not. Feel a bit watched—

Mouse: Okay, My Friend. Have just arrived at Tui Park with a pie for a late lunch and an excited hound. Join me if you feel like it, otherwise I will stay put. Need a kip anyway. Take care.

Adrian: So, My Love—just getting clear and another wallop; makes me think that we have been the subject of discussion—either as a three-some or just Frances and Brendan. It was a clever way to say things are edgy, there are rumours about—watch your step; you are being seen. Or maybe it was just coming straight from him; off the cuff bloke-to-bloke. Maybe—possibly more pre-thought than that. He was very clear and astute. Either way I will graciously concede and ask for your tolerance as I test the water and seek signs and guidance.

Mouse: Sounds fine, My Friend. The bay is beautiful this afternoon—have just taken you on a lovely walk right across the sands—holding hands—our fingers saying 'I love you'—our eyes twinkling at the freedom lapping our toes. We are smiling, jumping over the squelchy bits together—laughing at the bubbles. I'm back in the Leafy Glade on Wheels now—classical music taking me to you—a whole chocolate bar looking tempting—X

Adrian: Perhaps our gifted time this weekend was reassurance; 'yes, things are still unfolding,' and Brendan's talk was a 'but be patient' reminder. So, My Love—limited contact, I'm afraid—back to the cut-back, budget version. Another turn of the stopper on your free-flow; don't explode, something new will be growing; humour perhaps—I am sure—a certain resilience perhaps—tenaciousness of Spirit; a greater appreciation of the wonderful weaving of our loving guides. Probably my learning—how to love but not hold—grip—grasp—smother. How to stay out in the sun and share my prizes with all—generosity—not needing anything—total trust—no fear, yes— no fear. I will play this game. Yes, I will find humour in it. Yes, I will push you back to your husband and say 'work it out'. Look to me as Joyful Friend. Weave no future around me, but dance to the tune playing and maybe that will sweep you into my arms—maybe not. Enjoy it wholeheartedly nonetheless—complete giving yourself to this life and facing squarely what it presents you with.

Thus endeth the sermon. Thus endeth all stress and strain. I wait calmly, lovingly until it is clear. I go fully into what lies before me, trusting that the will of God is at work and our wantings only hinder His plans. So adieu, My Friend, until you are free to see me in whatever form that takes. I will only contact you when it feels right—could be every few minutes, or every few *days. Can you manage? Take me running over the squelchy bits everyday if you want—new energy is in me now. I can concentrate on the task at hand. Good day, Fair Lady—X*

The Park attendant walks over to the van, telling me he is about to lock the gates. It is time to leave. Accompanied by a sombre piece of opera music and the sun setting over Tui Park, I return Adrian's sad message. I am crying:

Mouse: *Good day, My Fine Sir, your loving sermon is where I am at— where I have been for a while. Remember, I have had more barren weeks than you. I am accustomed to the distance—hard as it is. So, I shall manage fine. If you feel me in your arms—in your winged glory—it will be the magic of our alchemy; the liquid of pure love—the reality of solid form in breathtaking crystal. I shall be here if you need me—every minute—every few days, or only occasionally. Adieu, My Smiling Minstrel—Prince of Elves— adieu—X*

Part Four Tally

How long is she to be stranded here—at the bottom of the slipway, touching the water yet not afloat? The Celestial Sea tries to be patient; her friendly dockworker is concerned. Why has she been left there? Like a beached whale she is blocking the natural flow of the Marina's lively traffic. The Harbour Master won't explain and her crew appears undecided.

News of her stranding reaches Lord Swallow as he labours in his valley—shut off and troubled, his work unsatisfying. He reads his Lady's message coldly; the beast wrapped around his mind using her words as further evidence of his own worthlessness, awakening not compassion but self-blame and accusations of weakness and cowardice. He stops. How is the beast overcome? Courage. The Sword. Faith. The Honouring. His Lady—his Companion—has foundered alongside their vessel. Why does he not leap to her side? Race to her aid? His Friend and Lover—she has given him up—the grief and loss she has suffered maintaining their Boat alone, while also tending her own pitching, family vessel, has broken her. She cannot do it alone. He has abandoned her. His demons have driven him into hiding and unhappy seclusion. He watches, wondering what he should do. He is so timid—he hates himself for it, but knows this is not helpful. What action? His failing courage—he decides on a plan; he doesn't think he could carry out a bold one just yet. He will let her walk from The Boat—his Fine Lady—his Soft-Breasted Lover of old—his Lacy Bride. He will let her walk away for he does not want to make promises he is unsure he can keep. He would rather see her stay in one place and tend her grieving soul than be constantly let down by his spurting, fluctuating signals. He has so much work to do. Quietly he slips down to the abandoned Boat. He is not nervous, though if someone were to see him he would probably flee—or would he?

Oh, his farm animals need tending—today he meets Sienna for a performance appraisal—there is little time. He carries a heavy load. He takes an anchor line and secures it to a nearby fixing point; perhaps with the incoming tide he can right The Celestial Sea and bring her to a safer mooring. He could work on her quietly—maybe even be bold enough to sail again. He does not wish to awaken his Lady's hopes though—unsure of himself—seeing how wobbly he is; the merest gust and he is scuttled. He strives to discipline himself. He turns to his books with a backwards glance. Will she be alright? Should he do more? The alarm bells are ringing. He chooses to go; "goodbye dear Boat. I will see you tonight—maybe a slot this afternoon where I could come to check on you."

Chapter 1 Tending

Monday 21ˢᵗ May 2007

A.m. Mouse, {unsent}: *Good morning, Lord Swallow. Your dignity and honour is stronger than mine. Thank you. We shall sail for Northern shores before the year is out. At least it will not be so hard—now that we have said 'adieu'. I wonder how you will find the silence? The distance? I have not abandoned you until now. Do I agree to be yours only when the whim takes you? Or perhaps I should say; only when your fear subsides and you feel clear? The truth? Replacing the initial mind-talk? Our passion reaches a certain build-up—a giant wave if you like—even in our platonic state, and we can take it nowhere. It is doomed to crash upon the shore, until such time as the build-up begins again, for to be sure it will. We cannot halt the ocean in its natural surge and swell. Your Lady can accept the impossibilities—can ride the wave without fear. And you? Yes, perhaps that is what the crash upon the shore is about this time around.*

Re-reading yesterday's message I find your new learning. The attainment of 'no grasp'—'no need for a future'—'no sense of next step'—or 'dead end'—truly—'dipping the crest of each wave as it rolls, pure spirit alive and lighting our way'. A new chapter begins. Are we being prepared for our enormous sacrifice? Our geographical parting—as far apart as we can possibly be; a cruel separation—as tough a call as exists, save death itself—without the income for regular trips to visit each other. Hmm, I am resigned to my fate—our death. Ice encloses my heart; numbing, but I sense the promise of a warm glow. I know not why. I shall allow the free-flow of my tears for now. As silent waves they make their way across an unfamiliar shore—'softly—gently—quietly'—

I spend the day writing. It takes ages to get beyond even one day; there is so much to log. I am writing about the Advent Fair at the end of November 2006; the time I met Adrian's father and step-mother. I am beginning to get a feel for the unfolding storyline, I think, especially for The Boat's fate, although I really need Adrian's input to be sure. I catch a glimpse of Lord Swallow this morning; he is writing up the chalk-board messages on the school driveway: **Evening Meetings—a talk on Parenting—a short Wednesday because of parent/teacher sessions—Pine Cones at $5/bag.** I see him again in the afternoon, supervising children on the see-saws. He is wearing his purple shirt; it is Monday again. Where do the weeks go?

I decide to make sensible lists of ways to move forward, trying to avoid any emotion. I am more prepared for that now. The autumn tree at the end of our drive is a mass of fiery orange; delicate leaves in near neon tone—a feast for homesick eyes. I recall it inspired our Workshop initiative last year. Rinky announces she would rather not continue her riding lessons. I don't know why; "I just don't like it that much," she explains. She is out of sorts generally—perhaps feeling the uncertainty of our future. We hang in a 'no-man's land.' I spend all afternoon on The Book; I enjoy describing the vitality and colour of the Advent Fair, and Adrian's loving input of course. I am transported back to those magical days; those days before our Boat was banished and shackled.

I collect The Laird from Freya and Justin's house at the end of the day. Both men are involved in the school's minefield details over monies and how the fees are collected. There are frustrations on several levels. Big J. is difficult at the best of times, but particularly tricky at present. I fall into bed early. Adrian hasn't been in touch. I don't like the return of the 'budget-cut-back version'. Not at all.

Tuesday 22nd May 2007
A.m. Mouse, {unsent}: Ah—imagine if it were allowed—yes, My Love— I imagine every day—every night. I sometimes wish my imagination wasn't so vivid; so acute. I can taste the glory of us—the delicate brush and silent speech as our lips meet—every time I think of you:

Silk and ripple,
Silver breath,
Come forth unto our quick stream
Where we shall be caught forever as Angels.
Laser sharp energy,
Holy connection denied;
Powerful current,
Scorch the handle,
Yet-held in humble joy it is a hallowed place of rest;
If it is allowed, if—

The dog and I walk a long way together in the gentle sun today. We pass lots of squelchy bits in the low tide, and several interesting homes we haven't seen before. I collect the children from school; one mother asks if her son can come home with The Go-Getter during the parent/teacher meetings tomorrow.

Early P.m. Adrian: —XXXXXX—not forgotten—

Mouse: —Ah—imagine if it were allowed—X

How lovely to hear from my Swallow Man. This is all I really need. A loving hello every now and then is fine, rather than the endless unknown; the desolation of those desperate months between January and March. I sit at the desk and work out the culminating chapters of 'The Celestial Sea.' I am reaching the climax now. It makes me cry—again. Will anyone else find it moving—and glorious? The Laird's ankle is still painful. I take him to the hospital at five p.m. to have the plaster removed. He will have to tread carefully; well, there's an interesting metaphor. Pictures of his impossible mother come to mind; her peculiar character and overweight figure rendering her an invalid towards the end. Her tendency to over-eat, and over-talk, {often accusatory and unkind}, and monopolize every situation hover as unpleasant genetic shadows, threatening our future. Her son's depression is returning. Is this my fate? To carry the negative vibe for eternity? Unstable, depressed husband; sounds too awful.

"Let's make some marzipan—like they do at Thackers; they called it Marchpane." Rinky and I have been reading 'A traveller in Time' by Alison Utley again; our favourite book. "Yes, let's," I agree. "I bought some ground almonds yesterday; you'll find them on the top shelf of the store cupboard." The Go-Getter is particularly lovely today; he is busy in his room playing with Lego. Cedric sent me a nice text message earlier; he and I have begun texting each other when he is away from home. I am keen to build a more positive relationship with him.

Cedric: *I'm sorry I got angry with you this morning.*

Mistress: *That's alright, my gorgeous boy. I will always love you, but it makes it easier when you love me back. Thank you—what a thoughtful message. See you later—X*

We take Cedric shopping after The Laird's plaster is removed. He is tempted by a bright pink pair of canvas shoes; they aren't in the sale, so we purchase a sensible black pair instead. "I'm interested in those stripy jumpers, Ma;" he indicates a row of cotton tops with broad, horizontal stripes. He tries one on and looks approvingly at himself in the mirror. He is a very handsome boy and I am pleased to see him positive. He loves clothes shopping. We collapse on the sofa when we get home. It shall be an early bed for everyone I reckon. The Laird is still in pain. I try to care for him, but I am not being a very good wife, not where it counts. His depression is impossible to shoulder.

Wednesday 23rd May 2007

A.m. Adrian: *Good Morning, My Love. I hope you are well and rested? I have the sniffles. This Sunday is Whitsun—do you need the mystery invitation back? Have you checked out the address? I haven't spoken with Simon yet. I tried to make a time, but we didn't connect. Did you meet with Sammy and Pim about the Community Village? Outcome? I'm free after 11 a.m. Do you want a cup of tea around here?*

Mouse: Good Morning, My Darling—how are you today? Sniffles? Do you feel clearer without the extra burden of me—of 'us'? I am lying on the sofa in the early hours. Wonky has been dispatched to the small hen-house. The Bog-Brush and I lie, entwined. I imagine it is you I lie with—except your breath would be better and you wouldn't fart as badly, {on second thoughts, perhaps you would!} I am clasping the wooden jug I imagined in our recent meditation; interesting to note it is heavier than I envisaged—rougher inside too. Also, the black spots in the grain are faint dark lines running horizontally around the whole. I close my eyes quietly—the wind rattles the cardboard that covers the broken glass in the door. Andy is coming on Saturday morning after hockey to sort out minor repairs before we approach the Real Estate Agents.

The peace and quiet is calming—my gut is sore from eating too much chocolate yesterday. Must try to stick to the diet—hmm. I turn towards you as we exchange lovers' breath. My hand is upon your Greenstone, reminding me of the eel encounter; kissing lips blessing you. My lips do the same as I feel you claiming me—X

P.s That was one for The Book. I wasn't going to bother you with it—but—yes, My Friend—I can see you after 11a.m. today. Free until 1p.m. Cup of tea and catch-up would be grand. What time exactly?

Adrian: I'll text you when I'm home, eh?

Mouse: Fine, My Friend. Meeting with Sammy at 1p.m. Coincidence that the church invite is for Whitsun? Better go check it out. I need the address—

Adrian: Skate Centre 884 C. Rd, 6.30 p.m. Sunday **27th** May 2007.

Mouse: You're on. Got the feeling just you and I are meant to attend? Perhaps reason for no movement on the Simon front. Just a thought; could be wrong. See you later. X

I drive along the main road in the centre of town, eventually finding The Skate Centre; an imposing white building. It doesn't look like a welcoming church. The empty car park is enclosed behind a high fence. I have to walk around the back to find the door where a couple of friendly women tell me that one hundred people attend services twice on Sundays. Why such a huge building for the small numbers? The church smacks of American, Christian fundamentalism. We should check it out on the website details they were happy to provide.

Mid-Morning, Adrian: Heading home now.

Mouse: with you in 5—

Adrian is sniffly when I arrive. He doesn't come to greet me. He doesn't even leave the sink when I walk through the door. He is washing some salad leaves for lunch. Eventually he turns and leads me to a public spot by the

178

sitting room windows where we can be seen, keeping himself honourable and all that. Our connection is colder than usual and somewhat unnatural. I share some of his bitter salad. We chat about the strange church I have just visited; we look it up on the Internet and discover it *is* American and probably fundamentalist. Hmm—perhaps we should leave well alone.

"Little J. is coming over soon," he tells me. "She needs to learn a song for the Mid-Winter Party." We sit down on the sofa and I massage Adrian's feet to help his cold. He isn't feeling his best. "So, you might be back to The U.K then?" He asks a touch indifferently. "I've brought my flashdrive," I inform him. "Can I transfer The Book so far?" "Sure," he replies. "I have some music for you too." Adrian transfers a selection of his favourite songs along with the original piece he has written about The Boat's mythology. We need to discuss the subject more, but he isn't in the mood right now. He needs to rest. We chat about School for a while—and The Community Village ideas. "I wish we could make music together," he says, appreciating the harmony I am humming. "Wish we could curl up together somewhere—hmm." I leave after a short hour. Adrian doesn't even give me a hug goodbye. Poor love, I think he finds it too confusing. He is always so thrown by others' opinions. I wish he wasn't so easily swayed.

* * * * * * *

Early P.m. Adrian: *Thanks for coming over. I do wish it could be different—that I could be free to embrace and celebrate you. Maybe it will come—the battle of the earthly slow pace against the lightening possibility of The Spirit; tortoise and hair? So, my apologies for my lack of true welcome. I do hold you esteemed and valued, and hold warm wishes for you—X*

Mouse: *My Friend—I feel it too—so unnatural for us to be apart; our right-placed, close bond held in check—our Spirits dulled—their potential axed. The driving rain drenches our sparks, alone and untended in their separate cages. Perhaps in time the water will rust the metal and then, if still alight, the sparks will break free and find each other again. I just need to be in your arms X*

P.s. Can I phone you? I am at home with a houseful of children. I have lots I need to share with you about The Community Village. Are you free? Wish I could curl up with you and stroke away your sniffles. X

Sammy and I had an excellent meeting in the pouring rain at lunchtime today. She has a good business head and we soon came up with village housing and extended school plans. Sammy is particularly good on local Government Policies re planning and marketing etc. and the funds that might be available. "There is even a fund for a project manager if the enterprise is big enough," she informed me. What fun we had; she and I are natural, creative partners—like someone else I know.

Early P.m. Adrian: *Up on the farm, then out to the old engineer to get a tool made—maybe—fingers crossed—*

Mouse: *Wish I could care for you by my roaring fire. The children are content; the writing is coming along a treat. Well—what a cracking, sparkling meeting Sammy and I had earlier! We make a dynamic team—watch out! We left nothing out, even got the church idea noted. "Funny about that," Sammy said. "I've been thinking about a church." Anyway, before I forget, here are the things I need to ask: Can you text me the name of the eco-friendly, town council man? I think you said you knew him? And, we need a name for the whole project. Apparently The School is looking for a new name anyway. Shall we discuss it? Any local legends? Whatever is chosen will need to work with the village concept too. Should we write a weekly newsletter to keep everyone up to speed with where we are at? Would you be interested in writing one with me? Or is there no time? Also, we need to practice the songs and seating for our School Whitsun Festival. Friday p.m. any good? Same as last year.*

* * * * * * *

Later, Mouse: *Hi Friend, hope you got your tool made? Oh, My Love—am sitting by the fire—supper is cooking—tears pressing to be released—listening to the music you gave me; 'long, long time'—one for us I think. I keep wondering what you would do if I came to you in the dead of night? Would you turn me away? I keep wondering if we should take every minute we can, in case I have to leave. I keep thinking how we might regret if we don't embrace this gift before it is too late—M—X*

Thursday 24th May 2007

A.m. Adrian: *{the first part of Adrian's message is missing.}*
—her comment is enough to bowl his whole mental constructs of how it could be. There is no way—that he can see anyway. He does not rule out the possibility of something emerging, but right now he feels forced to concede—and further, he must not be seen to be encouraging the dissolution of marriage; even private texting—unseen by her husband—is not allowed. Confusion. How to honour what they have and let it fortify them both, but acting honourably; being fair to—

Mouse: *My morning routine—a cup of tea and canine company in our dawn correspondence. I hope I didn't confuse you yesterday when I sent you my thoughts. Your anxiety over Brendan's words—our halting to keep the perceived peace—even our partial platonic state—these barriers are rigid and Earth-based. How can we explain to others that our bond is not about splitting families—damaging children—undermining community? No, it is not. How can we explain its Holy source? For us, a rich support to each other in our individual, vocational work—a vital backbone to the current and future community projects—and privately—a deep spiritual practice for two souls who together find 'lightning speed' communion with The Holy Truth. So, My Love, this blessed gift can be accepted by others—except for the physical element.*

180

For us, the profundity is only partially experienced without the physical. I keep wondering how far we could go before the earthier urges would take over? I know I could go a long, long way, holding open The Garden Gate— and I sense in you an understanding of this when you call for clarity and integrity before we proceed. Hmm—I feel that in spiritual terms we are allowed this joy if placed in this context—but am I deluding myself? Do I justify our continued desire to be joined in—Holy—what? Matrimony? Yes, if we were able—but as we are not, then Holy—Communion—yes. As my mind tries to find us passage I wonder if this is fair on you. A normal life with a normal wife and family, or a most unconventional partner and support for your vocational journey? You need to decide. Make a decision on what you really want from our love, for now and for a misty idea of some sort of future. I will be asked to make decisions soon and you are too important to me to let it pass without serious consideration. Here endeth the sermon. X

P.s Good Morning, My Love—only half your message came through—the second half. Can you resend? Loving you—X

Adrian: *Oh drat. His sent items folder just emptied itself, losing all 5 texts of the morning that hadn't sent properly. Frustration—anger. It matters little in the scheme. His thoughts must remain his own. He retires, the question unanswered. How to honour what they have whilst still acting honourably? Is it ploughing the grain back into the soil again? How else could we act transparently? Is she good for him? Do they need to learn the iron of self-discipline? Acting honourably? Transparency? No texts. No meetings without approval. That's what it means. Support given in public ways. Cups of tea at school. For him to stand in his integrity he must do this. But what happens to their Love? It appears their Love may not flourish. The sparks need re-caging—the imaginations dismantled. The pipe-dreams dispelled. Flourishing without contact—finding nourishment for their crop from elsewhere. Clairvoyant. The Earthly is locked. Now bow to it and find another way. Lord, guide us here. Do we go deeper into The Moon's realm and kindle a secret, hidden passion—running in the face of outrage—risking our careers and place in society—or something else? Cage it, but use the spark.*

He knows that she has been through this many times already, but now he needs to make it conscious. The obvious way is through The Books. Drop all personal connections from now on—rely on no contact to nourish—seek that from the review of what has been. To this he agrees. Maybe this is what she has been asking of him. He agrees. They will not see each other for reasons other than school-related matters—maintaining transparency—and he will read their history, giving his thoughts but not seeking nourishment through e-mail communication. This he will seek through their shared focus on The Books. The winter outwardly—the warmth of summer inwardly. How does it sound?

Mouse: *She reads his sermon, knowing it will call for greater sacrifice, knowing he is probably right. She sighs—a dulling of her Spirit—a separation* *from the man she loves. She agrees. She cries inside—NO! NO! But she knows she must concede. At last he realizes the true possibility in The Books—their alchemy—unlocking on many levels. And who knows what they may bring? She thanks him for seeing; for responding to her invitation. As for no texting? She is unsure about that. Not every day perhaps, but maybe a couple of times a week—or whatever feels right—to be in touch on a personal level and to continue The Story. And are they allowed no close embrace? No hugs? I will follow whatever you feel to be right on both these matters. I will take your lead. Perhaps I am being disciplined. Perhaps this way I shall be able to board that plane more easily.*

I cry for much of the day—great sobs that I cannot control; most unlike me. Why does it have to be like this? Each time I get close to Adrian he pushes me away. Perhaps I should listen and stop being a burden to him. But that is so hard when I know he needs and wants me as much as I need and want him. I take a long walk across the sands, and an energetic swim in the indoor pool. I shop for a couple of clothing items for Rinky at The Warehouse. And then I return home for lunch. I tidy the house and hang a load of washing on the line—and I write, of course. I collect the children from school and take them for our weekly trip to the library. Then we collect Cedric and come home. It is a normal and rather boring day.

The Laird arrives home late; at least he can drive now. He remains reluctant to love me, saying he doesn't feel anything for his wife, which is understandable. "It looks like Cedric could take his English and maths N.C.E.A. Level One exams in correspondence from New Zealand if he goes back to England in August." I can't wait to tell Cedric his life is about to change. We have made the final decision—Cedric *will* complete his schooling in The U.K. Thank you, Lord. We just need to sell both our Kiwi and our English properties and life should be easier. Our English tenant, {a friend called Nettie}, is making noises about buying the English property. We retire to the top cabin to watch a drama we enjoy; 'Grey's Anatomy.' The heroine almost drowns; all very dramatic. Will she make it next week? I am surprised by a text message from Adrian before the day is over:

P.m. Adrian: *Hello, My Friend. Hope you are well. Sorry to be out of contact for the day. Thinking about my radical plan. Little J. gave me the same suggestion as Brendan today—let you sort out your relationship with The Laird and see what happens. She came here to practise the song for the Mid-Winter 'do'. We were chatting about Martha and her second husband—our situation arose naturally. So, we have a Whitsun Festival song to learn, do we? School practice is tomorrow at 2.30 p.m, so can you get the music to me in the morning? We need to catch up on The Community Village meeting with Sammy too, so I can get a newsletter out. A new Maori mum in my class has put forward a proposal to her Iwi, {Maori tribe}, for an eco-multi-purpose-complex; a residential and commercially-friendly enterprise. She is a clever lady—won Entrepreneur of the Year or something. She's interested in our* *plans too. The list is growing. Shall I write a draught newsletter and beam it through? I'm flat and tired; feeling snotty. Still grotty—attacked by thing—*

Mouse: *My Friend—you have been in my thoughts, but I don't wish to disturb you; rattle you. Nice to receive a message. Thank you. Been torn between tears and thoughts—"I'm selfish—wrong—bad for My Fine Sir—what do I think I'm doing?"—And—"I don't mind what he says in the light of correct behaviour. I shan't deny the Love we both know exists—I'm going to kiss him whether he backs away or not!"*

Hmm—that's all I'm going to say about that. So, yes—festival song—the same one as last year; 'White Bird'. I shall bring it in tomorrow to photocopy; it would be good to have copies for all adults present. The new Maori parent sounds brill! You should see the radical plans Sammy and I have hatched! Can't wait to show you. We need a list of interested parties—need a name for the enterprise—something exciting—need the councillor's name—newsletter to keep community focused and informed; use an interesting colour and clever logo perhaps? Lots to discuss—over a cup of tea—in the window where we can be seen! Glad you chatted to Little J. I'm not sure where we are headed. Big Love—to you—platonically if that feels safer. Speak soon. Look after the sniffles—M—X

Friday 25th May 2011

A.m. Adrian: *Good Morning, Strolling Lady of the Mountains. I too am up and walking—on my way to school to catch up with marking. It is time to break in and discipline my Wild Man in the Pond. Time to take myself on. It is likely that Class 3 will be separated from Class 2 this year—maybe I'll be asked to take them—do I want that? Hmm, better hit the books. Hope you're well. Song? X*

Mouse: *My Fine Sir—strolling to school. I shall not disclose the details of our morning embrace—just to say it was long and—mmm—*

The song will arrive when I do—possibly a little flushed. I shall find you, or pop it in your pigeon hole. So, the whole of Class 3? In your new standing? In your King's state? Your Lady considers—she sends a morning greeting—X

I don't see Adrian at school, but I complete the photocopying as promised. I spy him in the courtyard as I leave. Tui Park is Heavenly today. I spend three hours logging texts, watching the tide come right in.

Midday, Mouse: *I have organized the music, My Friend. Sienna has a copy—also a couple of Michael B's verses for teachers' Morning Prayer around Whitsun. Spoke to Fin just now—he is happy to come along to the next Community Village Meeting. Have a good day. Tui Park for me right now— empty bay—filling up the notebook pages—glorious sunshine and still atmosphere. Blessings on you—on us—X*

P.s. Sudden inspiration—Sammy says we might be awarded funding for a Project Manager; I would be up for it if still in the country. We would need an office—the caravan? Would School allow us to put it beside the woodwork shed if we decorated it beautifully? I would love to do that. Also thought about trying to get a 'sister community or school' involved with us—somewhere in Europe or The U.K. Just writing thoughts down before I forget—X

Adrian: *Hello, My Friend—you—you radical little thing, you. My goodness, what are we to do with you? And with me for that matter? Sounds as if your mind is ticking over pretty fast. Name of Village, eh? How about Mushroom Village? Talk to you later.*

Mouse: *My Partner in Crime—oops—sorry—everything but—see you at 2.30. I'll try not to let on that we are Naughty Angels—X*

The 'White Bird' song goes down well; one I brought from my English Kindergarten, suggesting we sing it with more bounce than the smaller children usually manage. I catch Adrian's eye and we linger in our secret for a while. Eventually I look down, not wanting to give the game away. The Laird takes Rinky and The Go-Getter home after school and Cedric and I go shopping. He needs a few more clothes. We browse in Farmers, {a department store}, and another clothes shop called Postie Plus, {no, not the Post Office!} We come home with the stripy jumpers we spied the other day; all the rage apparently, and some long T-shirts and trousers. Cedric is a happy boy.

Early P.m. Mouse: *'Star Dome Village?'—What do you reckon? It would put us on the map—we would be noticed! Especially if we have an observatory integral to the community—something we have considered. I need to ask if you are going to Zion's farewell party on Saturday? We are just planning our weekend. The Laird might want to go. Would it be a good time for you to meet him? Or steer clear? Do you feel it would be better to meet with Simon first?*

Adrian: *Thought not to go as so much to do this weekend. So, this has made my decision. No, I won't be going. Have to talk later—on a mission—*

Mouse: *—X—We've been in town, just me and Cedric—birthday clothes shopping—very happy fellow! Good luck with the mission. Speak later—X*

* * * * * * *

Later, Mouse {Unsent}: *A good day—full of everything; sunlight, inspiration and plans. A walk in freedom across solitary sands; reverence in Whitsun Waiting, pages of texts logged and revisited, {the lovers' quandary continues, caught between Earthly code of practice and Heavenly homecoming}, then a playful, frisky evening, {just as well she isn't with Lord Swallow, he would have sent her home by now}, followed by a crashing exhaustion that claims her* *with a headache and nausea. She has felt a bit peculiar for two days now. "Must be pregnant," mutters The Laird. "Chance would be a fine thing," she replies under her breath. No husband or lover to lie beside her these days. The exhaustion must be an accumulation of this week's stress—yesterday's tears— her endless giving out with no return—hmm—better catch some rest. Sleep well, My Friend—X*

I don't hear from Adrian tonight. He is being strong and sticking to his 'no communication' agreement, although I thought he said he would be in touch. Never mind.

Saturday 26th May 2007

I wake early. My head is still spinning and the nausea remains. Perhaps I have a bug? I rest on the sofa. I eat—my appetite is okay. I can feel Adrian so close this morning. I write him a message, although I won't send it unless he asks me to.

A.m. Mouse {Unsent}: *Good Morning, My Partner in Quill and Silent Kiss. I lie upon the sofa after a brief stroll in the dark with The Castle Hound. A banana to start the day—don't want the nausea to wash me overboard this morning. I wrote a text message to you last night that I could, or could not send you, depending on whether it is a Red or a Green Flag day. I would appreciate a message saying just that; Red Flag, or Green Flag. If I don't hear anything I might send it anyway; 'just for The Book, Sir, honestly. Read it as if you were deep in a romantic novel. I do.' X*

No squeak from the valley means my message remains 'unsent'. Adrian is trying to keep his distance so I will honour his decision and distract him not. My headache and nausea continue.

Mouse {Unsent}: *His whispers tease the back of her neck, dancing between the dark curls that lie waiting for the touch of his fingers. She is almost naked in his arms—cotton underwear her only shield. She wakes to his pressing desire, wrapping him in silky limbs and shallow breaths of welcome. She needs him, needs him now. With a silent quiver he slides into her—softness meeting strength—Rainbow ripples taking him by surprise as they move in the swell of their private ocean. They are in Heaven—she is open to his spilling. Deep inside her—he lets himself go; they both know she is unprotected. With smiles and delicate kisses they lay themselves open to His will—to the clear path of a potential new life.*

I feel Adrian so close, but I don't hear from him today. I am not sad. Our Love is too deep; too real to be displaced by the barriers we or others erect. The higher the bars, the closer we become. I spend most of the morning on the sofa and then we all leave the house for The Go-Getter's hockey match down by the port. Cedric stays at home. I leave The Laird to hockey duties, hoping he doesn't bump into Adrian. I watch Flo approach him, hopefully to suggest some massage to help heal his painful ankle. The dog and I head for the spectacular long beach that is located on this side of town. The Bog-Brush loves the beach. The sun is gorgeous and the huge expanse of sand a dream. We jump over the waves; I am sorely tempted to swim but I haven't brought a change of clothes. The water is warm. We walk for a good forty minutes following the line of houses behind the steep sand dunes, passing a handful of walkers and joggers as we stroll. We stop just short of a giant crane at work on a new building site. The roof is covered in red and blue plastic billowing in the sea breeze. We pass several dogs. The Bog-Brush is out of season so I let her say hello. She snarls a few times but then plays happily. Turning back towards the van a woman from College calls out a friendly hello. I stop to chat; her husband is a good friend of The Laird's. She has a summer house on the beach and a farm house in the hills behind town. She is walking two dogs, one a Scottie Dog she keeps tethered. "He's not good with other dogs."

Mid-Morning, Mouse: *Morning, My Friend—just a quick message to say we are not going to Zion's leaving party after hockey. Hope you are okay?*

{Marie and Louis, the French boat-builders, are returning to France with their family next week. We shall miss them.}

The Go-Getter's team is receiving a thrashing when I arrive back at The Hockey Centre. The game is nearly over. Despite his depression The Laird hopes to improve his fitness, so I deliver him to the large indoor pool close to the beach when the hockey ends. I displease my husband further by suggesting his whisky drinking isn't helping matters. He has been more unsettled since he resumed his regular interest. The Go-Getter has gone out with a friend; they are off to watch a basketball match and then a film; 'Pirates of the Caribbean 3.' Rinky decides to swim with Daddy and a German classmate that we meet at the pools.

"I watched three hawks circling the land below the cabins, Ma." Cedric is alight with interest when I get home. I am touched—so pleased that he is beginning to notice special things like that. The swimmers are having great fun together in the pool when I drive back down The Mountain to collect them at two o'clock, (always so much driving!) The wave machine is on today. Poor Rinky nearly gets stuck in the large swell. Members of an English family recently arrived in the country are swimming with The Laird and the children. "This is great," they exclaim. "It's just like the beach! You can tell we are English—you too? We haven't been here long. We couldn't wait to escape the London crowds. My husband's a carpenter," the friendly woman divulges. "We've bought a house further along the coast. We have a fifteen-year-old; he's very happy with his new life."

Rinky's German friend comes home with us and I cook spaghetti bolognaise for a late lunch. Cedric and The Laird disappear to the top cabin for the T.V. and I get down to some serious writing. By four o'clock I am driving back down The Mountain to deliver Rinky and her friend to Sonya's daughter's birthday party in a local Reserve; an extensive park with stunning trees and wooden board-walks over meandering wet land. The cabbage trees and ferns are spectacular. I love the groups of deciduous trees here; a rare sight in this part of New Zealand. The autumn display is wonderful and the children play in the crispy leaf piles. Sonya has an interesting group of friends from The Coromandel that always come to her parties. I leave them half-way through the celebration.

Mouse: Hi Friend. Are you home? Business only—need to ask a couple of things—

Adrian: At school on the farm—come on up. Sean is here.

Mouse: Might do—just dropped Rinky and Johanna at Amelia's party in Jason Reserve. I am free until 6p.m. I'm not feeling that well, so I might drop in and ask a couple of things briefly.

I arrive at school. There is no sign of life. Where are the men? Their cars are here. I follow my ears, eventually tracking them down in The Bush. Adrian is standing on a tree trunk with Sean and his daughter. They have been working on the pig-pen and have come in search of more timber. We chat for a while. "My pig, Molly, is coming to live in the new palace, so I have a vested interest," I tell Sean. "My supposed lawn needs rescuing!" The new pen is indeed magnificent—and huge! I am most impressed. "Hi there," Adrian warms to me, sidling up close as we meander across the land, discussing more of our village ideas. Sean is interested. We have a growing number of keen community members. Sasha also joins us; she too is interested in our plans, especially the extended farm. She and Sonya would be a great team—as well as a potter, Sonya is an expert gardener. Adrian and I chat over the roof of the car before I depart. We speak about The Laird's continuing gloom; we chat about our relationship—all above board with others around but not too near. "I keep thinking how life is so short that we should overcome our fears and accept this gift," I tell him. "Yes, I know," he replies. "I have had those thoughts too. But then," he adds, "I have to weigh it up against the loneliness of being ostracized by the community." Hmm—we smile at each other, knowing there isn't any way we can be together right now; not really. "Tomorrow then— are you going to that church service? With The Laird?" "No," I reply. "Not with The Laird. Perhaps you and I should go. Could you look into the web details more thoroughly? I haven't had a chance to do so. Thanks." "I've been reading more of our Book," Adrian tells me. "I'm not sure where to begin with it all. I've been wondering—wondering if I shall follow you back to England—if you are to lead me there." Adrian's announcement surprises me. "Perhaps," I respond. "I have considered it; take you home to your original roots."

A trailer-load of long yew branches stands in the car park, waiting to be removed from school. "Rolf gave them to me; he's a Tree Surgeon; kind, eh?" Adrian starts chewing a twig until I warn him off; "I wouldn't do that if I were you. The tree is very poisonous, and spiritually significant. I have a wonderful book you must borrow; a dictionary of Tree Wisdom. The Yew features heavily." "Oops—better away," Adrian hastily spits out the twig before driving off with his magnificent and toxic load.

Collecting Rinky from the party I find myself enjoying an interesting chat with Hau and a lovely man called Cory—a professional theatre technician. He designed the lighting in the new Wellington theatre. His twin daughters are in the same class as The Go-Getter. Hau joins in the conversation, adding his expertise on orchard growing. He and Abby work so hard on their section; a large piece of land with lots of trees and vegetables. "We do struggle to keep it going on our own," he admits. I haven't been feeling that well all day. I am very tired by the time I reach home. The Laird has gone to collect The Go-Getter from the cinema. He has expressed upset at my writing and retires to the top cabin when he returns. I don't hear from Adrian. I miss his presence.

P.m. Mouse: Hi Friend—nice to see you earlier. As far as The Book goes; best to read the file marked 'Correspondence' first. It gives more of an outline and where you might apply some of your creativity. I would suggest placing your lovely Boat Mythology at the beginning of each part; after the Picture Title and the initial poem. I hope you can make sense of it all—X

Chapter 2 Title

Sunday 27ᵗʰ May 2007

The wind is cold. I wake early. I imagine Lord Swallow beside me; he is strongly present. The Laird leaves the cabin early to read at the eight o'clock church service in town. The whole house is asleep. I talked to him before he left, mentioning our original Celtic Project idea and how we might apply our interest and expertise to the Community Village ideas here, in New Zealand. We spoke of his potential Priest training; an Inter Faith Ministry he has looked into recently. "Perhaps we could have a base in The U.K with a Kiwi project as well." I didn't overplay the potential.

A.m. Mouse: Are you awake, My Friend? I am free for a chat if you would like that. The Laird has gone to church and all the sweet kinder slumber still—

Adrian: Sorry, My Love—off to a hockey coaching course. I've just sent you another e-mail. I've put a large casserole into the slow cook pot so we can have tea at School with Lois as witness to our platonic-ness and have a jolly good chat about it all—The Community Village Project that is. I've decided to grow a beard, to mark the beginning of my voyage into The Mystic. I wonder what the N.Z equivalent of Yew is? Makes me think of Maori spirituality. Four Maori boys are joining my class soon—new friendships? Journey into Shamanism—

Adrian: My Dear Friend, I just found this interview whilst searching for the background on Yew Trees. Felt very right to be storing all these branches away this evening. Found a good piece that fitted my hand so nicely and was weighted perfectly as a light club— waiting to see what that is for. The Yew has symbolism—magic about connection with ancestors. Funny that in my evening eurythmy session I made a prayerful offering of my day's experience to my ancestors. I had a connection to the thoughts and work of this writer. Druids eh? Pagan aren't they. Shamanism, omen reading, earth magic—hmm—quite attractive. This writer puts it in a living way— down to earth magic, not all New-Age waffle, though I do get a bit iffy about it—getting sucked in—losing myself, but no, I don't think so. Thinking about The Laird and him maybe needing to go through this—thinking that he has lost everything—so that he is forced to find his strength. Anyway, check this out. Yews are poisonous actually.

They used to put poison on their arrows made from Yew. Eek. There I was nibbling a twig! Thanks for the warning. Shall I send you the details of Community Village interested parties? Okay, sleep well. Good night.
Your friend—X

Mouse: Dearest Friend—Thank-you for your lovely e-mail. I have missed the lighting up of my screen, so it was really good to find you just now, albeit in a more formal medium. Yes, please do get the details of those interested, and if you know a land agent, then a chat would help too. STAR DOME VILLAGE! —with an observatory in the centre; sounds good! Simon said we would have to look into the feasibility of light pollution etc. One of the first phone calls next week I think. Need to find an expert—someone in Auckland, or wherever there is a stargazing gallery—someone who has designed one before. Here we go!

I had a very good chat with Cory at Sonya's party. He was fairly involved when the last 'Village' idea was launched. He would like to offer his expertise on the professional execution of a theatrical hall. We thought it should be good enough to hire out in the holidays/weekends etc. It could be part of the enterprise. I did a fair amount of conceptual work on my own design project several years ago when I looked into sustainable living within an ancient, Celtic Village model. Celtic Christianity is alive and well, and definitely one for us. The Laird & I have been very interested in it for a long time; we have a certain amount of knowledge about it all. Funny that The Yew wood has triggered that world for you too. I agree with you about some New-Age stuff, but going in through The Church's interpretation of earth-based spirituality and reverence towards our natural environment is truly eye-opening. It all goes back to an outcome at the Synod of Whitby in six hundred and something, {not sure of the exact date}, but a decision was made to follow the Roman form of Christianity which did not place God as central inside the living earth, but external to its matter. They rejected Celtic Christianity as too 'pantheistic'—a serious mistake in my opinion. If you are as interested as we are, {silly question}, then there should be a lot of information at the Celtic Christian Centre on the Island of Iona in Scotland. Not sure of the web details, but there will be some. They have truly beautiful verses, prayers and music. The Laird visited fairly recently. I notice that Michael B. uses one of the prayers in the front of his book that holds the daily verses we like to say.

I haven't brought the drawings of our Celtic Village concept to New Zealand. A rough outline would be to describe an authentic Celtic Homestead with earthwork dips and hollows, palisade walkways, long houses with thatched roofs, or probably an impression of thatch, standing stones, a grass amphitheatre for outdoor theatre, wood-chip paths, no cars, the sounds of authentic, ancient crafts such as wood turning, a forge, weavery etc, and happy, free children running between the pig-pens and the wood shavings. It's all there in my plan—has been sitting waiting for nearly 10 years! How perfect is that?! And the perfect Man? Well, My Friend—running out of space. See you later—M—X

Adrian: Dear Friend, thanks for your reply. Amazing if you could weave your work of 10 years ago into this project! Cory sounds useful. Star Dome concerns were mine also—usually observatories are built on mountain tops far from city lights, yet there is one in Dunedin in the city, on a hilltop and very popular too. More study done on The Yew. Wow! The Yew has been thought to be the archetypal 'Tree of Life' from paradise by ancient peoples. The very story I just told and the children have written about! A Yew stave behind the door used to ward off evil—sprigs put into coffins to help people on their way to the otherworld—branches waved on Palm Sunday. Protection above springs and wells. Ygdrasill, the Nordic tree of life, is thought to be a Yew not an Ash. World's oldest tree too. Has property of regenerating even when it has been dead and dormant for years. Good handles for tools. We now have a huge pile of clippings on the burn pile; quite a responsibility—one little nibble is enough to kill a horse! A bit more will do away a cow, even dried and withered! Blimey. Don't want the children using it either, even the sawdust is poisonous. A tree to be truly respected! And here I am sampling the bark! Hmm. Perhaps a wake up to cautionary tastings. So, a huge pile of Yew staves stored under my house and a great pile of sacred clippings; too important to just be burned. I need a sacred space. Looks like I am heading into the realm of magic; Christian Magic. Guess I have been preparing for this for a long time. Teachings of Don Juan by Carlos Castaneda being my entrance at 18. Astronomy, Biodynamics, Music, Christ, Anthroposophy, Alchemy, Old Testament, Mystic Lover, Druidic Priestess, Herbs, Tree-Lore, Ancient Crafts, Healing, Understanding of the Mind Games, T.V. free, Alcohol/Drug free—ready for new direction, childless, well physical, earthly child at least, 37 years, free. Now what? Better get to hockey thing—late already.

Mouse: Goodness Me, My Lord Swallow—sounds like you are off on a trip! I shall appear by your side if you need some brakes! I have wondered about the relevance of the Celtic impulse with Maori spirituality. I saw a programme recently that linked the Northern Celtic era with the Southern Hemisphere. How about this for an idea—we base our impulse for The Star Dome Enterprise on the earliest origins of Pakea, {white Kiwi citizens}, and Maori? Really investigate those ancient lines and come up with a totally new concept. This is becoming really exciting.
The Laird was easier when I got home yesterday. He and Cedric had

*cleared out the van and found long-lost items; namely the missing vacuum tube! I have broached the subject of a new beginning. I like what you have written—love parts of the Yew Tree missive—deep possibilities—mmm—so exciting—as long as our base-line is solid and we recognize our limits. I spoke to The Laird of the possibilities ahead—priesthood training—a base here and in The U.K; all the stuff we have spoken of. Perhaps if I can be a Project Manager I might be able to stay. Gentle presentation of our possible future; no over-excitement—trying to be low-key. Enjoy your hockey course. I am about to read to Rinky—logging tests right now, even the 'unsent' ones. Phew! Just as well I didn't send **that** one to My Lord Swallow; he would have banned me instantly! —X*

The dog and I enjoy a big walk to the top of our Mountain road this morning. Blue skies, bright green ferns, dusty road and high winds; we can see for miles. I feel so 'alive'—vibrant and ready for whatever life throws at me. I cook everyone a good lunch and then I am away to School to help Lois and Cordelia decorate one of the larger classrooms for Whitsun. I drop Cedric with Bernard and Felicia en route. He mows their lawns most weeks. I am a little late for the decorating, but there is still heaps to complete. The room is draped in white muslin; swoops and folds making a Heavenly cocoon in the now-empty space. It takes a long time to drape the metres of fabric, but the eventual effect is so beautiful. We staple a hooped net to the ceiling this year, hanging twelve doves from the gauzy centre to drift in a pretty swirl above the circular table holding the twelve candles; one for each apostle. The younger children have all made a dove and we hang the surplus around the walls. Lois decides we should use the flame ribbons from a previous festival-"let's hang them on top of the muslin to symbolize the flame of The Holy Spirit." So we do, and the effect is stunning. Adrian appears towards the end of the afternoon. He has been looking after Cordelia's two children. "Anyone hungry? I've brought a stew to share."

Both Lois and Cordelia have to leave, so Adrian and I sit together in his car, enjoying the hot stew alone. Adrian is out of sorts—again. Poor love, he is upset by something Joni said. We chat about the caravan; might it come to school? "Big J. hates caravans; could you talk to Lois about us doing it up? For a project office?" I agree to do so. "And my teaching career, should I consider taking on the whole of Class 3?" We mention Adrian's interest in the mystical material he is reading. "I need to find my truth again," he admits. "I am so easily knocked, and then I abandon our love when anyone questions me about 'us'—I don't know." "But," I add; "you stood so strong and undaunted when you were dragged ever the coals for us in December. Perhaps I am being unfair. I should leave for The U.K. and then life would be easier for you." My frustrated Lover is cross with himself, banging the steering wheel in an attempt to move beyond. "Why can't I get clear?" He exclaims. "I want to be firm—to find a new reason and move—somewhere. I was so buoyed up earlier," he tells me. "You were beside me—my Druidic Priestess. I'm sorry I can't get clear, My Love." He takes my hand, adding;

192

"I imagine you want to kiss and cuddle; I know I do, but I am so on edge. We could be caught at any time. I don't know—even being here like this is not okay." "I haven't lied to The Laird," I reassure him, stroking his chest with the back of my hand. I tell him that I love him. "I haven't denied our truth."

I leave Adrian to his guilt and his milking. I send The Laird a message, saying I am on my way home. He finds it hard to believe me, I know. "It would probably have been easier if you had just left," he says when I walk through the door. Hmm—both my men are frazzled. I am clear for me, but not for them. What should I do? And why has nothing come from the mystery invitation? Perhaps we are meant to appreciate the picture of Christ and nothing more. The evening passes in a blur of writing. The only interruption is my Ma who is amused that our missing vacuum part has been found in the van! We talk about The Laird; "he needs a sabbatical," I suggest. Said gentleman is in the top cabin, his usual residence these days. I retire to bed relatively early.

P.m. Mouse: *She sends him her blessing, beyond all worry and anxiety. Love stands proud and will not cower to others' judgement. It needs no unkind wrestle. She will not have their gift become a source of restless concern, for in truth it is an oasis of tranquillity where she soothes his brow and he takes her bearing unto his own—X*

Monday 28th May 2007

Adrian: *Thanks for your beautiful message, My Friend. A tone of forgiveness and seeing. On my way early this morning. Big process—phew! Shower, breakfast and away. Blessings on your home and day—your sleeping family. Peace. X*

Mouse: *My Love—go gently in your Kingly strength. It is ever the truth of you—X*

The morning passes in a normal fashion. I complete the sad, sad ending to 'The Celestial sea'. I arrive at school on time for The Whitsun Festival. I am holding the tune for the singing. Twelve speakers from the parent body speak the Biblical Whitsun verse in twelve different languages, the new Maori mother and a Spanish mother included. Twelve robed pupils from Class **7** collect a candle each—lighting them from the central flame and standing beside their appointed adult speaker. The younger pupils sit on the floor in wedge-shaped rows around the room. Everyone is dressed in white. This Festival is our holiest ritual. The reverence dances silently with the doves that move gently in the candles' heat.

I pass Adrian briefly as we leave the quiet room. "I'm well today," he whispers. "I'm glad," I reply. The dog and I hike right across the bay at Tui Park this morning, reaching the far bank with ease. The tide is completely out.

We haven't ever done that before. I am still tired and my legs ache after yesterday's ladder work. I am hungry when I reach home. A large lunch sets me up for a couple of hours of uninterrupted writing time. I edit the final paragraphs of 'The Celestial Sea.' I am happy with the ending, if 'happy' is the right expression. I still haven't tackled any of Part Three; that I must memorize and relay as best I can. It is a beautiful yet tragic task, one I adore. I long to create the magic on screen; it is all I want to do—for hours at a time. I let my mind drift for a while; The Laird has three choices: to let me go because he cannot live with me if I am not there for him 100%; take me back to England and pretend I am there for him 100%, even though he knows I am not; or agree to let me go, but travel home himself to pursue his vocation, coming and going as he does right now.

It is time for my afternoon routine. I drive, deliver to the riding stables, recycle and shop, listening to music as I go, thinking about Adrian, of course. I am feeling dry and sad inside. I have been giving out and holding on for almost six months to the day—for little return. I am tired. I am cracked up inside. I am in need of some strong, real love. Both my men folk are in turmoil; neither is able to give me what I need. Do I have to make another decision? Either one way, or the other? I cannot run to my Lord Swallow while he is attached to School, yet can I unseat him by taking him away? He needs the stable framework of a solid community. He needs the personal standing. Hmm—I can only choose one way—and in a way I am living it right now, except that I cannot deny my love for Adrian and I cannot give myself wholeheartedly to The Laird. An impasse; uncomfortable or okay? Here we are, all three, none of us happy or fulfilled in our love lives. Two of us could be, and yet we deny ourselves. I must look at the three choices again. I don't contact Adrian today. I am feeling too sad.

* * * * * * *

P.m. Adrian: *Hi Friend—lovely festival. Have you made contact with Lois about the caravan?*

Mouse: *Have asked Lois—not a positive response, I'm afraid. Not sure why? She didn't really say, except that she doesn't think it worth the trouble. Better to put up a shed or something. What do you reckon? Is it really so unsound? We could perhaps have it up here until we move—or I wondered if it might be worth asking the Waikite Bay Caravan Hire people for their advice. They might even buy it. Glad you liked the festival.*

Adrian: *Thanks. Will check with Fin too. Good idea. Rick, Vonny's ex-partner, is here. Quite nice to have company. Hope you're well.*

I don't reply. I should keep my distance. I have given out so much and my Lover cannot tell me that he loves me in return. I am drained by the one-sidedness. I know it cannot be any other way, but there it is.

Early P.m. Mistress to The Laird: *Darling—hope the day is going well. Festival was lovely. Simon and Felicia both had speaking parts. All was Holy and beautiful. Can I ask your permission for Adrian to come up this week to collect the baths and metal etc? He will only come if you say it is okay. The items will be used on the School Farm. We need them moved—X*

Tuesday 29th May 2007

A.m. Adrian: *Check e-mail.*

I don't reply. I am feeling sad today. I will keep my distance from both The Laird and Lord Swallow. I am run dry. I don't know what Adrian means by 'check e-mail.' Perhaps he is referring to the one about the metal. I do manage some positivity with Stephanie in the School Car Park though. She is interested in The Laird's alternative schooling ideas; very interested. She has two boys who could do with his vocational input. She will put the ideas to the School Board; as a trustee she has some clout.

Andy arrives to mend the broken glass in our front door, as well as a few other things that need attention. The Land Agent arrives too. Things are moving ahead at last. A rough-looking fellow drives up in a black four-wheel drive to remove our rented caravan; not an easy task on The Mountain. The Maori driver is covered in tattoos and wears a black vest top over black jeans. He grins with a pirate's smirk as he bumps down the drive. He has several teeth missing. I shop in the afternoon; the dog and I notice the smell of cigarettes as we enter the park—cigarette smoke in old carpet—that smell. How strange. It reminds me of my Grandmother who used to smoke; her house always smelled like that. Is she with me on this adventure? It makes me wonder. I do recall her appreciative remarks during a film we saw together years ago; two children were shipwrecked and grew up on an island together, eventually discovering each other as sexual, loving partners. "Such beautiful young bodies," I remember her saying. And then there was that time when a strong smell of lilies filled my house in Sussex. It was peculiar as no flower was in sight. I later learnt that my Grandmother had fallen badly in Dorset that same afternoon.

Early P.m. Mouse: *Our caravan was taken away this morning—the company certainly buys old wrecks. Phone Kerry on 5541523. As for the teaching, have you considered taking Class 3 until the end of this year? And then starting with a new Class 1? Just some thoughts—keeping your skills at the end of the School you prefer. Anyway, say welcome home to Vonny and family.*

Mistress to The Laird: *Darling—are you coming back at the normal time? If later, Rinky is at Freya and Justin's and needs collecting. Thanks—X—Just let me know.*

Oops—I sent The Laird's message to Adrian by mistake.

Mouse: *Sorry Friend—just sent you a message meant for The Laird by mistake. Better that way around.*

Adrian: *Only just starting to milk now. Lovely girls. Thanks for messages today. Nice that you call The Laird, Darling. It's hard to find the magic at the moment—true gratitude escapes me—life through a screen is how it seems—crisis management. Maybe having Vonny home will change that. Not much company lately, though usually my lows come through not getting on top of challenges—letting people down—guilt—must seek that old familiar place—strong, wobbly—strong, wobbly—X*

Mouse: *She has stalled on the slipway—The Boat is grounded. She has been stranded for 6 months, relying on the strength of her personal reserve, until some movement, but she has come to a standstill again—quite suddenly. She has been searching the coastline for a new harbour—for a possible safe berth to rescue her flagging Spirit, but none has appeared. With dampened heart she abandons their stricken vessel. The Boat lies on her side on the hard concrete, making it easy to climb overboard—and away. Lord Swallow's Lady has no choice. She cannot continue alone. She runs her hand along the familiar, exposed keel—sadly—yet no tears will come. Her well is empty. She walks away—where to? Who knows? The Boat may well be claimed by the approaching winter weather. She supposes she had better inform The Captain, as well as The Harbour Master who has a vested interest, although he has never sailed her.*
A lonely silence follows her retreating steps. The sand is cold between her toes this unwelcome dusk; 'oh myriad of strange intention, shower me with Lovers' balm, for I have run a-ground after many barren months. In lapping wavelet and pretty birdsong—I am spent.'

I climb the stairs to my waiting bed, tired yet unable to switch off. The Laird and I are both weary. Rinky wakes several times during the night with another infected mosquito bite. Monty the cat disturbs us too. I desert the bedroom for a couple of hours between two and four a.m. to write some more. The Laird is cosy and warm when I return, holding me tenderly which is a pleasant change. He is in a positive mood because an English contact, a high profile actress we know from Hampshire, has been in touch about his alternative school ideas. So, our Boat is stranded but The Laird's vocational calling is rallying. I appreciate his honesty; "what are we going to do?" He asks. "You can't move forward, can you?" I talk again about the picture I hold—and he again tells me he can't imagine us being apart. "I can be a business partner to you, in the background. Perhaps you need to find someone new in your life too." This is his chance to 'go for it'—strike out and grab his vocational calling in every way. "But that means I would have to share you, doesn't it?" He asks again. "You are so stubborn. Once you have an idea you just won't budge." I assure him that I love him—that I could love him more if I was freed up. "We could become globe trotters," I smile. "Everything will work out fine, just wait and see. The Angels are holding us." The Laird rolls over but sleep continues to avoid me.

Wednesday 30th May 2007

A.m. Adrian: *News of her stranding reaches him as he labours in his valley—shut off and troubled—his work unsatisfying. He reads her message coldly—the beast wrapped around his mind using her words as further evidence of his own worthlessness, awakening not compassion but self-blame and accusations of weakness and cowardice. He stops. How is the beast overcome? Courage; The Sword—faith; the honouring. His Lady—his companion—has foundered. Why does he not leap to her side? Race to her aid? His Friend and Lover—she has given him up—the grief and loss she has suffered maintaining their Boat alone, while also tending her own pitching, family vessel, has broken her. She cannot do it alone. He has abandoned her. His demons have driven him into hiding and unhappy seclusion. He watches, wondering what he should do. He is so timid—he hates himself for it, but knows this is not helpful. What action? His failing courage—*

he decides on a plan; he doesn't think he could carry out a bold one just yet. He will let her walk from The Boat—his Fine Lady—his soft-breasted Lover of old—his Lacy Bride. He will let her walk away for he does not want to make promises he is unsure he can keep. He would rather see her stay in one place and tend her grieving soul than be constantly let down by his spurting, fluctuating signals. He has so much work to do. Quietly he slips down to the foundered Boat; he is not nervous, though if someone were to see him he would probably flee—or would he?

Oh, his farm animals need tending—today he meets Sienna for a performance appraisal—there is little time. He has much to do. He takes an anchor line and secures it to a nearby fixing point—perhaps with the incoming tide he can right The Boat and bring her to a safer mooring. He could work on her quietly, maybe even be bold enough to sail again. He does not wish to awaken his Lady's hopes though—unsure of himself—seeing how wobbly he is; the merest gust and he is scuttled. He strives to discipline himself. He turns to his books with a backwards glance. Will she be alright? Should he do more? The alarm bells are ringing. He chooses to go; goodbye dear Boat. I will see you tonight—maybe a slot this afternoon where I could come to check on you.

Mouse: *She spent a restless night out in the cold marina—a small shed giving her little shelter. The Harbour Master finds her in dull distress; "you cannot let go, can you? Do you cry every morning?" "No," she replies. "I am dry inside; the tears left weeks ago. I am trying to let go, but it isn't working." She leaves the uncomfortable ground, braving the strong wind that has picked up since her stranding. She cannot abandon their Boat; it is part of her now. Perhaps it is the same for Lord Swallow. She is flat—lifeless—but she will make* *sure their vessel is safe, albeit it in a breached, distressed state.*

The Harbour Master gave signals of resignation last night—well—a glimpse anyway—her continuing argument not leaving their marriage challenge. She wants him to take a strong stand—to strike out alone, knowing that he is cared for while she holds their foundation. Is she deluded? Even in her distress the truth she shares with her Lover is the greater force. She watches the retreating figure of a tall, slim man; he has been working on their Boat! She hurries to the slipway; did she really walk all the way from The Mountain last night? She stands beside their stranded vessel again. The Boat looks so sad, her potential cruelly thwarted. But—she has been strongly secured by a skilled and determined hand, the type of knot immediately recognizable. It is he— her Lord Swallow—her Prince—her King—in whose arms she found herself this cold, unfriendly dawn, despite her barren Spirit. She raises a hand to his retreating dignity. She would rather he kept clear; he has so much to hold. She will not be an extra burden to him. In her idealism she aches for his steady presence within their love—hopes they can rise above the huge waves to find at last a safe harbour where integrity and truth lie as content bedfellows giving each other support and nurture. She blesses him for his salvage—in many ways they are on course. Perhaps it is time for them to recharge their batteries before they duck back into the dance on land. A six month time frame was always held as important. She has completed the final pages of their first Book; perhaps another reason for her sadness.

She blows him a kiss—go gently, My Love. I shall try to keep strong—X

Rinky's mosquito bites are really troubling her. I won't take her to school today. "Pray for me," The Laird says as he leaves for College. "I really can't face work at the moment." I watch him leave, sensing a new impulse in his step. I deliver The Go-Getter to his class and stop to chat with Lisa, Andy's wife. She is excited by our Star Dome Village ideas; "push it big time," she enthuses, indicating Sharon who is approaching, another potentially interested party. "I reckon we should start singing—as a community," Sharon announces her grand idea with positivity. "Soul Mothers or something! Can you sing? Could you lead us?" "When you know what plans we have cooking you will be so excited," I tell her; "singing and all. Do you have five minutes?" "Ooo— more mothers' groups?" She asks. "No, more thrilling than that," we laugh. "We are talking International Corporation!" Lisa hoots with laughter over my description of The Laird in his red underpants trying to ward off the chick-killing pig with a hockey stick! Here we go then—full steam ahead.

Mid-Morning, Adrian: *Hi, My Love. Mid pig-pen. Think it would be good to send a weekly note about Community Village idea; take out question marks from heading. Small update. Newsletter coming.*

Mouse: *My Lovely Friend—great idea—am speaking about project to individuals as I meet them; quietly and tentatively. Lisa today, and Sharon; very supportive. Rinky is off school with bad mosquito bites—been to John*

Goodfellow the homoeopath who advised vitamin B6 internally and applied directly to bites! Patient is now drawing in the car while I walk the dog in Monument Park—nice memories of a Seaweed Heart. Happy pig-penning. Good luck with the appraisal. Take care M X

Rinky and I drive home to meet Andy who is coming once more to finish the odd jobs. He should be here soon. The autumn sun is glorious. I sit on the deck and feel the autumn sun-burn potential, even through my trousers. Rinky relaxes on the sofa with her books and a good lunch. I smile as I recall my recent chat with Andy—about our pig Molly. "She'll be part 'Captain Cooker' with her ginger colouring," he told me. "Captain Cook had livestock on board his ship when he arrived in New Zealand; ginger pigs with black spots. Several wild herds run free across the country. I had a friend whose young lambs were all eaten by wild pigs!" Andy went on to tell me how Aucklanders are selling up and moving to this region where they can purchase property with land, leaving them capital to spend. "And then they complain if any business or industry ruins their view. The School would meet lots of opposition if it tried to move elsewhere. The rural communities are growing; deluxe properties cropping up everywhere, especially with these coastal views. I recently met a local builder with an office in Auckland. He's doing really well."

P.m. Adrian: *Pooped, but the best day for ages. Felt really relaxed—strong—having faced fears—meeting with Sienna very good. Had identified in my morning writing all the developmental points she had loaded up for me—made our meeting very smooth. Daily plans and daily objectives, reviewed at end of day to assist planning for next day. Sienna to check me and keep me on track—fully aware of my challenges; supportive. Molly's new home took a step forward with the Class doing a good couple of hour's work; slow but they're learning to work together; great learning, in fact. Should speed up over the next few days. Powerful experience—more than I realized—perseverance—cooperation—stamina. And then—to continue my download—wondering how your day went too.*

Teaching The Go-Getter's Class which was like old times—no wobble at all. Really good fun and not drained by the end, even meeting with Hau and having a valuable teaching moment about honesty. Was it your love wrapping around me that gave my teaching wings? Hmm—then an extraordinary guitar lesson with Kevin. Then to Vonny who gave me both barrels about what made her cross; me taking over her house, not feeling like it's her place, things that need to change which I was extremely shocked by but handled bloody well—nodding and clarifying—defending myself where needed, conceding to some accusations and ending clearer and with an understanding that she does want me to stay. Clarity will come, but she acknowledges my willingness to make it work. Pretty big crash landing—she is giving up smoking and is jet-lagged too—yikes! Anyway, still have my hair on and staying cool. Change is remarkable—feel so much stronger. Is it full moon? So, do share your news, Sweatpea. Love to hear. Thanks for being my listening post. I can breathe again. About to milk, then off to 'More to Life' meeting. Home late. Hear from you soon, I hope. X

Late P.m. Mouse: *My darling Friend—I reached for my phone several times just minutes before your blessed shower of news greeted my hopeful eyes. An understanding today of how psychically linked we are—that huge crash as much a reflection of your position as my spent Spirit. So—we need each other—my day as fresh and clear as yours in its hope and holding—the union with our Boat last night and this morning, so important—one of those build-up waves that eventually has to crash upon the shore. It was an especially heavy crash-landing this time round. Why? Our lesson? How much clearer I feel now—how easily I could—mmm—let's leave it there. I am delighted that all has gone so well, except for taking over Vonny's house, hmm—I did wonder; My Fine Sir and his creativity! Better write us a best seller and line our own nest, speaking of which, I have just been editing the part where we are licking our fingers after our chicken supper in Maketu. Now re-wording our time as we sat on the private sand—our 8 dollar finale. So, My Love—my hand is in yours—my thoughts with you at your meeting. Big love— your Lady—less stranded this evening. Thank you—X*

We all sleep better tonight, thank goodness. What a relief! Sleep is so vital; 'the most important vitamin,' as J.J. advocates.

200

Chapter 3 Thoughts

Thursday 31ˢᵗ May 2007

A.m. Mouse: We walk under a full moon, the dog and I. So busy looking at its glow and feeling your hand in mine that I lose my footing on the skiddy gravel and crash right over! I smile at the hound's surprise. I smile at the bright, welcome light. I'm still looking at the moon. It is a happy crash this morning. This private intimacy we share every dawn is a treasure from Heaven. I feel you so close—can sense you beside me. I love to share my soul with my Man— to know he is with me—possibly sharing the same secrets of the early skies. If you ever want one of those—you know—especially close messages—just send me a text saying: —'Mmm'——and you might get a nice surprise! Only when the time feels right and clear, of course. Do you think our Boat is affected by the moon's waxing and waning? I have wondered. Let's watch it this month.
And how are you this fine dawn?

Adrian: His candle flaming high last night gave out much light to others and was reluctant to dim. A late night reaching out—it leaves him tired again today, with questions on how he can use his time and energy. He knows that after a high he can drop quickly. He chooses to take precautions against this by really watching his time and energy output. Keeping to his list-ticking and to his disciplines; noting life-shocks, facing the little fears as they arise, attending and not cruising now that the pressure has released him somewhat, but keeping some internal pressure. There is still so much to do. When he has confessed his difficulties to someone the relief is huge and he can be fooled into thinking that it is time to relax. Not so. He has made this mistake again and again. So, back to the notebook and the planning he goes; back within to seek humour— where he can laugh at his falls and his dog's expression. For him he chooses to use the processing tools. A great support to keep clarity—staying steady— available. Without it he drifts into choppy seas that eventually swamp him. Processing is like navigation—establishing position—correcting drift—the effect of tide and wind—charting new courses—planning ahead, perhaps only to the next headland or around the next point, but sometimes a look to where we are heading in a bigger sense—new lands. Better get the charts out. X

Mouse: Good morning, My Friend. Thank you for your message. Hope the processing is going well—X

I spend the day cleaning the house and walking the dog—and going over much of The Book, of course, re-editing like a painter who can't quite finish the composition. Ian the Real Estate Agent came for another look around and to talk about the property value. "You don't know anyone looking for a Pointer dog?" I ask, in case we need to find The Bog-Brush a new home. I mention that School might be looking for land—does he have any suggestions? The Laird texts me, asking if I can collect Cedric from College. Our tetchy, almost sixteen-year-old has discovered our plans to take him and two friends out for his birthday dinner. He isn't too pleased about it. Oops.

Mistress to The Laird: *I can certainly collect Cedric, My Lovely. Ian has just been up here taking pictures. Loving you—exciting futures. God bless; Angels smiling X*

* * * * * * *

P.m. Adrian: *It's been a busy day and his evening rest saw him fall asleep before milking. He sets off, buckets in hand, dog trotting happily beside him, awaiting her chance to dash off and crap— the full moon gleaming and lighting his way. Every Thursday is like this—the sense of the week being done—the heavier duties behind him; the compression easing. Feels like a holiday—and this is exactly when he needs/chooses to dig it in—find his discipline—continue the list-ticking.*

Mouse, Unsent until later: *Hello, My Farming Friend, high on the pasture. Good to hear your news—you have felt distant today. I have been cleaning the house; Ian from Cavendish Real Estate arrived to take photos this afternoon. The Mountain will be on the market next week! Here we go! Not sure where to, but movement. I shall send you my writing from this morning if you like? Hope it isn't too long-winded. I send my love and blessings—your Lady in rubber gloves—M—X*

P.s {Thoughts from this morning}: A receding tide—a taste of real winter in the damp chill and the need of a warm hat when the sun is caught behind grey cloud. There is a promise of warmth though—the bright sky is dappled. The water is mirror-flat; The Bog-Brush leaps and bounds, sploshing happily. Two duck rise lazily off the glassy surface, the town's morning rumble more noticeable today. The autumn colours are dulled. She spies bare branches amongst the native evergreen, a deciduous link with home, sort of, the work of keen horticulturists of decades past who tried to claim and tame these vibrant shores. The Tui Birds are spectacular above us as we wander into the back of the small Reserve. A chorus of bird-song gains in volume as we approach The Bush. I wish I could capture the magical sounds for our Books. In fact, between Adrian's drawings and the music we have shared I imagine another element to our story; a C.D. accompaniment and a native icon on the spine of each volume?

I wonder how he is—My Fine Sir? So much to tell when we are apart. Was my friendly message of this morning too much? I hope he can move beyond the unfounded worry that too much warmth will give me the wrong message. I must wait for his dawn text before I send mine, that way I won't throw him by being too—too whatever. My mood is pretty steady. I shall have to get used to the yo-yo flips of his. It certainly makes for an interesting ride, but only if it is a two-sided nurture. It becomes unsustainable when the balance is lop-sided, as we have discovered in our stranded Boat lying unhappily upon her side. The concrete is cold. Yes, I must choose my words and timing with care. I will not send this message until I know he is less burdened with work and nervous baggage.

I wonder what he would make of the e-mail The Laird received yesterday—a message of high excitement from the actress friend who would like to sponsor The Laird's alternative school initiative for her son. She speaks of introducing The Laird to all sorts of high-profile, influential people, from the Shadow Education Minister to Richard Branson! There is talk about making a film about the whole thing too. The Laird is quietly excited, but he will not get overly enthused without the backbone his wife always provides. He cannot imagine any plan happening without her solid energy and input, not her background presence alone, especially if she has another in her life. So—is she faced with two thrilling projects in two hemispheres? Both of them feeding off her life-force? Both with central men who share her energy and focus to drive them to fruition? Hmm—an interesting quandary for a Thursday morning; trans-global—fuelled by powerful, True Love—paths appearing on all sides. And should the projects be linked in some way? My goodness—better get fit; stop eating biscuits and chocolate! She might need super amounts of stamina! She yawns, just thinking about it makes her sleepy, her over-indulgent breakfast taking its toll. Perhaps she and Lord Swallow should just sail away somewhere quietly; how she would love to spend time with him—in silent prayer—in ocean swell and rhythmic dance. But, this would not be 'ploughing the harvest back into the soil'. Is their sacrifice pay-back really this enormous? Or does she have to choose? X

Adrian: He thinks of her—her clever mind—her effusive imagination leaping and swinging—her ordered, systematic intelligence planning and working—strong will achieving much—awakening eye noticing and drinking in the colour and change; the artist heart stirring into creative movement. How is she?

Mouse: Thank you for your beautiful, kind words. I am peaceful—sleep well—X

Late P.m. Adrian: Good night, Old Friend—thinking warm thoughts for you—actually very warm! X

Friday 1ˢᵗ June 2007

A.m. Mouse: I am up early—the bright moon calling me downstairs. Hope this doesn't wake you. I am lying on the sofa with one hound draped over me and one cat curled up on the rocking chair. Oh—before I forget—The Laird says you can come up anytime to collect the metal etc, as long as he is away. His refusal to accept and my refusal to concede continue—stale-mate with the likely outcome of a return to England. Who knows—am waiting for divine inspiration—am still feeling pretty flat, caught between two flight paths, an unclaimed bride at the airport, waiting for the notice-board to announce her flight number. Hmm, anyway—back to The Book I go; at least I am claimed there; you are just undressing me slowly as the sun sinks behind that spectacular golden rain and upright Rainbow in Maketu. On with the edit—X

P.s—Mmm—warm thoughts too; thank you. They mean a lot. Nice to see The Boat righted again. I walked past just now—my, but she is a stayer, isn't she?! Appears to be okay—resigned to her upright position on the concrete, but in good shape considering. Good morning Old Friend—are you rested and processed? I was pleased to hear you recognize the false holiday feeling; I would like to work on that discipline too—keep me off the chocolate for one thing! X

Adrian: Peaceful awakening. Still heart and an easy merge from dream to thought. I dreamt about Sinead O'Connor making a song over a beautiful estuary in a helicopter with a weather balloon attached—bizarre but lovely—

And My Lady—is she walking her dog? He arises for a loo visit—listens to the neighbourhood rooster and watches his hungry cat stalking the guinea pigs—must get her some food quickly! His plan of attack for the pig-pen seems to be secure; Class 4 joining them today and two parents coming to help; the first part of the roof on, the children's enthusiasm growing. Looking forward to a chance to see her—maybe an opportunity this weekend? He re-reads her morning message.

Mouse: Lovely, happy text. I love to hear you at peace. I sit at the computer, still re-editing our final night on the beach, especially your outburst in the morning—your hasty retreat clutching notebook—my tears and demands; "you will cry with me—please, it is important." Hmm, not sure you want to hear that right now. Sorry. Hope you liked my morning greeting. A weekend session would be good. Sammy has suggested tea on Saturday afternoon to discuss The Community Village. "Oh, I'll invite Adrian as well," she innocently suggested! "Then we can really get going!" Are you about this weekend? I told The Laird about the invite—but not that you might be there. As you can imagine, he is unsure about my motive for wishing to be involved. I'm not sure he wants to go. I also had Freya on the phone—wanting me to team up with you to sing at the Mid-Winter 'do;' children too—open brazier, old ballads? I've had one or two ideas; love to share them with you. Help! We keep being put together! It is so right for us to be there. But now it is in front of others and The Laird needs to face the truth. Help again! Is it time to make an honest choice? Hope this isn't loading you, My Friend. My issues—will work on them. Just need you to know. Loving you—if that is allowed—M—X

Adrian: I'm completely free this weekend. Ask The Laird when I can come and collect the metal. Go well. Exciting movements. Maybe all The Laird needs to shift out of his low; selling house and new prospects. Just lean back over us—we are being looked after. I think we trust—X

Mouse: thank you, My Friend. Am at school now, waiting for Cordelia. Exciting plans for the Winter Spiral to work on. Am feeling anxious this morning—maybe a walk will help. How are you? I could be free for an hour or two at 4p.m. X

Adrian: Check out the nerves before we meet. If you feel alright I'm good to see you after school.

Mouse: thanks—we are nearing some sort of new level. Maybe see you later if it feels okay—X

Mistress to The Laird: Table booked for 6.30p.m. for Cedric's birthday. Lovely French proprietress. Kinder booked in to stay with friends; Phil, Freya and Justin. They'll need collecting by 9.30p.m. Galaxy chocolate bar kindly bought at English shop on The Go-Getter's instructions for his brother. Loving you, despite what you might think; exciting avenues appearing on all sides. Are we brave enough to walk them? Oh, gorgeous Earth Companion of mine, tread firmly and seize the day. This is your chance, My Darling. I will always be here—X

I log all our recent text messages once I am home. We are writing so much—all the time. I bought a magazine in the supermarket this morning because it had an article about one of my favourite films; 'Dirty Dancing'. I always wondered why it made me leap from my seat. The article says it was unplanned; the soul connection just happened. The magic was real.

Mistress to The Laird: Hi there—birthday cake cooked. Filling and trimmings can wait for tomorrow. Need a bath and hair-wash. Hope you are okay? You are very precious to me. I'll stay in town after school collections; walk the dog and deliver children to respective friends. See you at the restaurant; 4th Street. Big love—X

I deliver the children and walk the dog at Tui Park. I am looking forward to seeing Adrian, platonically. He was wearing the faded, pink polo shirt with long sleeves rolled up when I saw him at school earlier; a shirt I recently found for him at the large Opp. Shop on the edge of town.

Mouse: My Fine Sir—anxiety has departed. Am alone and free until 6.30p.m. Are you still free? Love the shirt—who's your supplier? Handsome man—X

Adrian: So, where shall we meet now The Leafy Glade has gone? Strong likelihood of being seen wherever we are? Tired too. Come round here for a cup of tea?

Mouse: My Friend—am enjoying glorious sunshine in Tui Park. Apparently it's a full moon tonight. I'll walk the dog and come over, shall I? Unless you feel like a stroll? There's a lovely little shack on the water line right around the bay that I've been meaning to show you—it has our name on it. If I don't hear I'll presume you are too pooped and you'll see me at Vonny's when I'm done—okay? X

Adrian: Am pooped. I'll have a lie-down and wait for you. I know the shack you mean. Can you pick up a fish and chip order for me? I'll order them by phone. Do you want anything? And what time will you be clear?

Mouse: Can collect food in 15 mins. Don't need anything myself. We are taking Cedric and two friends out for a birthday meal tonight. He's sixteen tomorrow! Have a good rest. See you shortly—X

I find Adrian in bed in a messy room; "come and join me," he lifts up his duvet and invites me into his waiting arms. We lie close and snuggly together. I stroke his chest and we kiss as friends, not lovers. I find the hole in his trouser leg; "Oh—you've found that hole, have you?" He laughs as he strokes my back and holds me close. This is so easy; like an old married couple done with a sexual connection we are content. Strangely, Adrian has no mind-talk to take us deep into our lovers' realm. We disengage reluctantly, rising to put more of The Book into his laptop files. He holds me on his knee while we work. I kiss the back of his neck, bestowing my adoration. "The Laird's Wife," he sighs. "I like to touch your breasts—mm—my soft-breasted Lady."

Fish and chips washed down with tea beside Vonny's crackling wood-burning stove are a treat, even though I refrain from eating much. I leave Adrian with a new bottle of Supergreens and a smile, having so enjoyed the partially platonic intimacy we have allowed ourselves this evening. I must get to 4th Street and he has the cows to milk.

The Birthday boy and friends arrive on time and we enjoy our evening at The French Restaurant; it wasn't as bad as he had imagined! I tell The Laird that I visited Adrian. He appears okay about it, but on reflection he probably isn't.

P.m. Mouse: Happy boys—truthful wife—accepting Laird, {?}, pretty, ex-college waitress—Cedric smiling in his new stripy jumper—yummy salad and pizza—tight trousers—oops. Lovely snuggle with you. Hope the milking went well. On our way home now in two cars. Loving you—X

Adrian: Sterilized a squad of bottles. Had a cup of tea to keep awake but fell fast asleep. Just milking now—poor bursting cows. They are officially T.B free; results just in. Found that I have a nagging, unprocessed life-shock from school about over-working the children and being too zealous in my own selfish desire to complete pig-sty. Useless teacher self-accusation. Totally false! This is where my navigation skills kick in—sailing out of choppy waters back into the clear.

The Laird came to bed late and stroked my forehead. "Kind girl," he said quietly.

Saturday 2nd June 2007 Cedric's 16th birthday
A.m. Mouse: Old Friends—has it only been one year that they have been moving at the centre of each other's lives? She fits inside his embrace with cosy familiarity. They manage to bypass the need to turn each other inside out, although they both know it is but the blink of an eyelid away. They didn't have the time or inclination to reach the hallowed, sacred ground. That is their magic—but not yesterday. Yesterday was a time of happy hello, in a gentle caress, lingering momentarily in a hip suggestion as they made a cup of tea. For once he was calm—immediately centred—different. They have grown accustomed to the processing; to centre their coupling. But yesterday they were more normal. She likes him in his pink polo shirt; a sailing shirt for sure. The vibrant, faded colour suits his good looks and wind-swept demeanour; Lord Swallow at the helm—yes. She approves. Good morning, My Fine Sir. And how are you? X

Adrian: A nice perspective on their easy catch-up of yesterday eve. Unbeknown to him a torrent of negative mind-talk was beneath the surface. Luckily he noticed it before it swept him onto the rocks, but it has still tipped him off-course and he must be mindful of today's holding. A yoga session—youch—to start the day. Now off to do errands before returning to Supergreens and breakfast. He is loving her more, now he has his ship under some control.

Mouse: Hello, Fine Sir. Hope the mind-talk has abated. It was strangely absent yesterday; an Old Friend—a familiar gateway to our inner sanctuary. Hmm—well, it is drizzly up here on The Mountain. I am about to get in the bath. More writing completed. Tweaking the end before I return to the beginning. I will try to e-mail you a more complete breakdown of the chapters; my weekend task. I'll let you know about Sammy's invite later on—X
P.s. Loving you—X

Adrian: Thank you, My Friend. Just heading into my room for a clean-up and a lie down before I meet with Vonny.

Mouse: Happy tidy up—always makes one feel clear. My boys are in town.

I had some lovely calls from home; Mizzie and my brother Wilf whom you met; both phoning for Cedric's birthday. Both asking about The Book! Gulp—better get a move on—X

Later, Adrian: *Hi Friend—my meeting with Vonny went very well. Even-footing—air cleared—understandings. Really good news. Lots of jobs to do, however! Better get to it. Thinking of you, Adrian.*

Mouse: *Darling Friend—so glad all is clear with Vonny—and that you still have a roof over your head; a bit vital on this wet, wet day! The Laird has decided last minute that he will accompany me to Sammy's house this evening. Sounds as if you have enough on your plate anyway. What jobs do you have to do? Keep in touch—lovely to know you are with me in my pocket all the time. I'll let you know how the business side of our evening goes. Big Love—M—X*

The boys return from town and settle in the top cabin for the rest of the day. There isn't much to do on a rainy Mountain.

Early P.m. Mouse: *The rain it batters us so. Your Lady sighs, wishing she were tucked up with you; reading—planning—singing—touching—mmm. Sport is on the T.V. Ho hum—X*

Adrian: *He feels like a Storm-Trooper—completely encased in heavy weather protection; big oil-skin just like the one his Lady lent him, but more fitting, coupled with the finest over-pants The Warehouse could provide. Yes, a well-equipped farmer he now is. The yearling herd next door come to see what's going on—the most interesting event for days, reminding him of the Kindy Kids watching the school children through the fence. All is well—the cows run to the—*

The Laird and I drive in pouring rain to Sammy and Bruce's section behind Mallory Falls. We enjoy a cooked meal and easy chats about the Community Village idea, although The Laird and I are ill-at-ease in each other's company, even though he feigns interest, being kind to his enthusiastic wife. The children watch 'Pirates of the Caribbean' in the sitting room. We have left Cedric at home with his birthday presents. Sammy and Bruce are both interested in the school philosophy; they attended meetings in Auckland before they moved further south. "Bruce was meant to teach at school, but Big J. gave his job to Martini and forgot to inform us!" Sammy disclosed; "we wouldn't have moved here if we had been told the position wasn't secure."

P.m. Mouse: *My Darling Adrian—we are back home and very tired after a quiet day and pleasant evening out. I'm not sure why we are so exhausted? Reckon we might be more stressed than we realize. The Laird is back in the grumps after my honest disclosure of our catch-up and tea meeting at Vonny's* *yesterday. Doesn't bode too well for his eventual acceptance. Perhaps the house sale and Cedric's schooling change will make things clearer. Meeting with Sammy went well—a few things to explore—*

Adrian: *Goodnight, Dear friend. He has been reading The Book—a little at least. It does indeed read well. It inspired him to put pen to paper and a little more about The Boat construction spilled out; a little. Lots of computer time—sometimes a waste—printing out song sheets—not wasted. So strange to visit my full-bodied leap into our relationship again after this long period of holding back. Goodness me—the light of Love in our eye—-real? I feel such a grump—heavy in the face—compressing myself—trying to fit—to master this new ocean with my own ungainly vessel; teaching, structure, longing for release from it—tired of the squash—a life of holiday—freedom. Light the pipe, he says. Dream on. But somewhere in him lives a spark of hope that a miraculous unfolding is going to happen—an opening—*

Mouse: *She watches him, her Friend. He holds their Story in his hands, plunging back into their celestial world of exquisite love. She imagines the shock; his indrawn breath; what slip-stream did they find? How did they maintain the sails' tension to maximise the cutting edge? Was it true? Is it true? She considers—are they Story-Book Lovers only? Existing in their imaginative creativity? Will it remain an impossibility to merge their mystical life with their mundane routines? Would the magic leave them if they ever achieved this near-impossible task? Hmm—Earthly love takes many knocks; it puts aside all personal desire; it bends to the heavy weight of selflessness and commitment— so hard to keep the magic, unless the couple possesses a key—a Key to a Gate—and knowledge of a path accessed swiftly—snatched moments for regular walks to replenish the life-force; to combat the drudgery of every day.*

She wonders on—having found his message at 3a.m. she is alert; her skills at finding their private world honed and polished after so many months. She can access its sustenance any time—across land—across ocean—across hemisphere. 'True?' He asks. Well—what is true? The truth for her lies in mundane washing-up bowl as well as in communion with The Spirit. Hmm— she has to admit to a preference for The Spirit over the soap suds, but knows she cannot escape the latter, and neither can he. The two worlds in tandem work well for her. She wishes she could exist under the same roof as her Lover, but perhaps that wouldn't work. All she can be certain about is the true line of their perfect vessel—the exact match of his Key in her Gate and their joint ability to enter Heaven whenever they feel the need; the desire. Is the multi-layered way a female thing? Is it unfair to ask him to dwell there with her? To relive their history in the knowledge that it lives on can be sustenance—continuing to be written as they speak. Is this an unfair and unreal request? To keep their Boat afloat wherever they are?

She sighs into the dark night, wishing they were walking through The Gate right now. The real challenge is to hone the nourishment they gain from dancing with The Spirit into a fine and manageable tool to transform the washing-up into a vehicle for service and prayer, knowing that just beyond The Garden Gate, and central to them, lies 'The Way, The Truth and The Life.'

Good Morning, Lord Swallow; how are you this fine dawn? Our quandary continues. Church at 9a.m. Join me there in your mind perhaps? X

The Priest is wearing a spectacular robe today; bright white with a pretty over-detail like Broiderie Anglaise; a shining picture of Christ upon his chest. We enjoy the service, followed by a stroll in Monument Park. Lots of families are enjoying the sunshine today; the little train is chugging around the green. We are missing home; missing all our friends and family who are part of our regular lives. It is time to leave. I walk the dog on the shore while The Laird keeps an eye on the children.

Mid-Morning, Mouse: *She strolls alone at Monument Park with the dog— the service finished. The children are enjoying the Pitch-and-Put. Some interesting thoughts during church—things to say. No message today, My Friend? Are you okay?*

Adrian: *Waking up way-laid with negative mind-talk. Wonder if it is just me? Maybe I'm being attacked—getting paranoid. Thought Vonny was cross with me again this morning after my milk activities last night when she was in bed. I went through the list of things I did wrong—got so jumpy—really anxious. Decided to face her. Went down and got a helmet, ear-muffs and two swords, then asked if she wanted to talk. Turned out she was just shitty over other things and missing her cigarettes. But what a reaction on my part. Yikes—these are treacherous waters, or so it appears. I'm sure it's fine. Poor Laird; he just wants me to back off—leave you alone—leave him to repair things. Sorry Laird. Brendan's advice on the noble man's stance keeps coming back. Don't want to! Question; should I just back off? Give your marriage a chance to work it out fairly? While I am sensitive—knocked back so often. Youch—it's a knife-edge—or is it? May be quite fine when viewed from the right place. But my old guilty conscience and lack of self-discipline makes me a sitting-duck for mind-talk. Help.*

Mouse: *She worries that she is suggesting too much—an intoxicating and sticky web? Is this how he feels? She must let go—blow the delicate yet powerfully strong threads away—set him free—hmm—perhaps this is what he is asking of her. She will ponder on it. Like him, she doesn't want to go there. It is Holy Trinity Sunday. The young, impassioned Priest spoke boldly on the interdependence of God the Father, God the Son and God the Holy Spirit. "The Holy Spirit is poured into each and every one of us by God. The aliveness of The Trinity—The Cross—inside us all from Baptism. Say goodbye to flaky notions—the reality of this living presence is beyond compare!"*

I consider—a Trinity—I bless the two, beautiful men in my life—wondering what it all means—what we are being asked to do—to become. I imagine making the sign of the cross with my thumb upon each brow, and then in

reverent blessing I receive the same. A picture of a new church; a vision of our beautiful Boat changed in a golden shimmer into—what? That was not disclosed, but it was truly wondrous—a split-second vision of its destiny. And hands held in Love. And so, My Friend, I'm sorry to send so many confusing messages but I sense it is important you know the pictures that come to me on Sunday. I wish I could be with you to help combat the mind-talk; that Old Familiar Friend. I send you a deep, loving smile. There has to be a reason for all this.

P.m. Adrian: Milking is done. Poor Esmeralda's teat is so puckered and sore. 5 days of salicylic acid applications to combat the cowpox had a dramatic effect—certainly a powerful substance; looks like it may have wounded her good skin too. I'm always experimenting; poor girls. He is lighter this evening—a nagging task dealt with—sorting out the over-payment he received earlier this year. Took a great deal of focus—like tax—put off for ages. And his communication with her—his question of whether he should back-off remains unanswered in his mind; not quite so pressing now that some pressure has eased in him, but still requiring thought. Perhaps every time I want to text you I could turn to The Book; maybe it's a request that we make our link more in The Spiritual——not that I want to. Just seems to stir up the hornets' nest each time we are together, and if our level of texting was revealed it wouldn't look—well, it would look like a very close friendship being maintained—outside of the marriage vows—encouragement. Does it matter? Brendan—those coals glow in his mind—youch. Unfortunately how others view his action is important to him. He wishes it were not so—his weakness—being liked—unsafe if disapproval of others is present; hypersensitive—but would the relief from that really be worth their loss of connection? He will ponder on.

Mouse: My Lovely Adrian—this is your Lady Mouse here. So nice to receive your thoughts and intuitions. Now—about those relentless waves that keep breaking over our heads onto the shore; how are we to utilize them, rather than let them knock us off our feet? That is the question. Like you, I don't like our Boat to remain stranded upon the concrete. Hmm—but equally, I don't want the treasure to produce further worry for your already-overloaded mind-talk challenge. Let's be really honest—an important question—were you less burdened during those barren months? What did my continuing texts between January and Easter mean to you? I need to know if they are a hindrance rather than a helping-hand. Are you unnerved about having pushed our Boat down the slipway, albeit it in a clumsy, undecided fashion? My Darling, I am happy to do whatever feels right—responding if and when you give me the nod—when tension eases—when the wind fills our sails—when our whispers dance easily on the breeze between Mountain and Forest, or at times only between the pages of our Books. Perhaps we are being prepared for the ultimate separation across hemispheres. I wonder. Let's see. We have music to make, a pig to move, metal and old baths to shift and an eager editor awaiting our Story. Let's use our precious gift, not let it use us. I love you. I am not afraid to admit that I do, for we both know the source to be pure. Sleep held and cherished—M—X

Adrian: *They are best friends. He enjoys her company—she his. They unwind together so easily—love to share news, ideas and Angel dustings. She makes his life more exciting and richer—even in this thwarted form. Could he be without it? Yes—of course. He would reach out more—Carla—Vonny—Andy. Good people, yet not the safety of acceptance. He would have to make new friends—or be alone with his work duties and the children in his care. He could easily manage—maybe even new things—a church; much prefer to do it with her. But—he scratches his head. The sensible way is to acknowledge his Love and let her married relationship naturally change, and after a year if she had decided to break, then none would think twice about them being together. But this way she has far too much to lose. No, in this case it doesn't work like that.*

Everyone is standing by, amazed that she feels so strongly that she would consider breaking apart the family. She has gone to the edge of the family land—pushed as far as she can—for him—for them. Her belief so strong—her invitation so activated. Could she be wrong? This is what baffles them all. How can she hold so strongly to something so impossible? Clinging on tenaciously—like those cliff-hugging plants; exposed, vulnerable and tough. How he could shut off from commitment like that. He is so honoured by her. It is all he can do to return her gift. How could he be cowardly in the face of her courage? Or craziness? And if The Laird did give in, what would that look like? 'She's yours while I'm away'?! Could he even accept it then? The eyes of the community—the staff's raised eye-brows—Martha's raised eyebrows—Big J's frown—Martini's reserve. 'Have you considered the impact on the children?' They would say—and yet, if there were no scandal there would be nothing to see; she would be staying behind to continue the children's education and maintain a base. Hmm—pipe dreams.

So, the question as to whether we stay in contact, in the face of what The Laird has already tolerated, is not so bad. I would be interested to know what The Laird thought of our texting; whether he could accept it. How much would he consider acceptable? None? Once or twice a week? Business only? Poor man—two cheeky friends unashamedly continuing a friendship. I suppose that if you lost interest I would not pursue you. So in a way it is your doing that maintains a relationship between us. My faltering heart would not have had the courage to push through to you—over the castle walls. You breached them and invited me in. And continue to do so. Poor Laird. How bewildering. So, My Friend, I would seek to know if The Laird is troubled by our continued contact, or whether he could tolerate it. Then I would set boundaries for myself so that our contact did not interfere with my Class holding. Perhaps this is our last communication—perhaps not. I don't know how you would go about finding out, but will leave that to your good thinking. Maybe that decision is mine to take anyway—whether I risk it or not, taking all that I know into account. Insight would be useful but not essential.

Good night then, My Fine Friend. Peaceful dreams. X

I don't respond to Adrian's clear-thinking message. I am feeling flat again. I see the reality of our situation—and Adrian's nerves are raw. Strange how unsteady The Boat is out of the water. I am sure we shall have to fly home with our tails between our legs. There is no other answer. The Laird is distant when he comes to bed.

Chapter 4 Tails

Monday 4ᵗʰ June 2007

I wake early and compose a text message to Adrian that I don't send. I shall wait and see if he contacts me first. He does.

A.m. Adrian: *The Medieval Alchemist saw the phenomena of combustion and meditated upon its reflection within him. He saw flame as a sacrifice; lesser gods sacrificing themselves to higher gods and he pondered in what way he could do likewise. Contemplating an imaginary candle I consider its make-up; a thing of fibre and wax. I wonder what in me would be fibre—what is the wax. Surely my feeling-life is the wax—its molten gold—and the fibre, my will—my earnest desire to serve; to know truth. The seeking part of me; Christ in me—and may He fill thy Spirit. The Father God be in me, The Son God be in me, The Spirit God enlighten me. And the flame—Holy Passion— Spiritual Touch—Fire of Love—Deep Burning Reverence—Wonder and Awe—Gratitude. I have some way to go to achieve this rich experience, but my goals are being set; a practise tentatively established. I have a mind to ask Cordelia for guidance, perhaps to share an evening meditation once a week? Our eyes met at Whitsun, briefly, but held for that second and seen— great openness—strength—yes, she could be a Master—I wonder.*

And so, new enlivening thoughts—grounded in a list of tasks to do today, but brighter than I have had for a while. Disciplined inner practise and disciplined outer work. Meeting my commitments fully; yes. This is my task. And other thoughts—perhaps you must return to England—maybe I go there too, taking my woodcraft, farming and teaching experience and musical skills and offering them to a similar school to ours. We are not limited. Blessings on your day, My Friend. How fare you?

P.s My Priestess

Mouse: *Lord Swallow's beautiful words and intentions come to her as powder dust on the breeze—only she can read into the separate particles. She can taste the potential. She does not know how she feels this morning. His honest message last night—her reality check and split worlds. Perhaps it is time to let go; time to go home. She knows he is there but his admirable nobility and restraint means their magic can only breathe in The Books. To know her presence in his life is probably more damaging than life-giving; to hear his pain and be unable to soothe and bond with him as a natural couple, this distance evokes a dead, cold light of Earthly reality. **Of course** it could* *never work. What on **EARTH** was she thinking? How in **HEAVEN**—hmm.*

*They shall return home at Christmas—for good. Lord Swallow and his Lady shall take flight between the covers of their Books—and whatever future The Angels have planned. Should she send **this** message of Earthly image, or **that** one to make his loins sing with his soul? Perhaps neither—just her blessings for his day; her hopes for his peace of mind—X*

The family is grotty—The Laird's depression raging and Cedric's foul moods horrible. I insist on a bike-ride for all, despite their brooding disapproval. We reach Pillans Beach Reserve and it starts to rain; "there—what did we tell you?" "It will be okay," I try to be positive. And it is—sort of. We enjoy ourselves as best we can. It is good to be out and about, even Cedric appears lighter. The Go-Getter and I challenge each other to a race which ends in a crash, and then I am nearly dragged into the sea by a big wave when we run the dog along the shore. We stop at the shopping Plaza before coming home. An afternoon of rain and sand, eventual sunshine and exercise. I wish it wasn't so hard to instigate. How I long for a positive family atmosphere. At least my writing is positive; positive sadness if such a thing exists. I am worried about The Laird. I don't think he has it in him to take up any new initiative. He can hardly get out of bed at the moment. I grew up surrounded by continuous positive energy. I don't know how to deal with depression. I HATE it. My life has taken a turn for the worse:

1   Depressed husband.
2   Poisonous teenager
3   Nervous lover with little chance of permitted union
4   No family support and few friends
5   Financial troubles
6   Unstable marriage
7   Unknown future

Oh well—it doesn't appear to get me down. I don't really dwell on The Earth, so I am not overly affected by its grim side. A chicken laid an egg in the hat box this evening; how lovely! Eggs for supper. I am working on The Book's chapter and part divisions for Adrian, so he can be clear about the position of The Boat's mythology.

P.m. Mouse: *—'And the flame', {he wrote}; 'Holy Passion, Spiritual Touch, Fire of Love, deep Burning Reverence, Wonder and Awe—Gratitude.' This is what they access when they allow themselves—this is the central mast of their beautiful Boat. She wonders if it is the same for him. To date—she has tasted three, powerful religious experiences through their connection— her thirst quenched by a draught of this sacred elixir. And he—and those others who cannot understand why she holds on so tenaciously—perhaps they would understand if they knew. To own a Key and a Gate into Heaven—to have searched so long for the key-holder—well. BUT—as she has said before,* *it is only worth hanging on if The Key-Holder feels the same way. So—a time of discipline, yes? Of order and routine. This is the week for some answers about their family movements. Hello, My Friend. Hope you are well? —M—X*

Adrian: *Hello, my Lovely Friend, Best Mate, nudge, nudge. This Key-Holder is in fine spirits; order, agreements, communication, achievements, tolerance and understandings; indeed a fruitful day. He has touched The Druid in him once more, putting aside The Yew branches—The Sacred Tree of Life; laid aside for the mid-winter fire; a more fitting place to use their crackling glory than the school rubbish fire. He is down there now, warmed by the mound of glowing embers. Fire—sacrifice—he had not really stopped during the burning to consider his thought of the morning—this enormous combustion—his face singed by the fierce heat. But now, stopped as he is, what can he take from this experience? Ash is all that is left; smoke heat and light beforehand, kindled by a single match—prepared over time for this moment—gathered materials—sun-dried—tended—watched—monitored— enjoyed—fire—bonfire—special moment—RARE; awaited. So, what is on his fire pile? What is to be offered? Himself—his desires—his wants—his achievements; up it goes, nothing held back. Hmm, he says, but does not connect with it. The cows go slowly up the field.*

I find Adrian's bonfire message late. I don't reply. The Laird comes to bed at midnight.

Tuesday 5th June 2007

Adrian: *A new goal—a robust outward personality that is warm, bright and responsive, steady, reliable and strong—light but with depth behind it. He sets to work, crafting a new front; The Boat's hull strengthened. The structure behind it is strongly rhythmic. He has discovered this form only recently; the framework alters little as the days proceed. Steady and enriching, he uses his time wisely. With a safe outer he knows that his inner can flourish—he is brushing it more every day; glimpses of deep potential bound up with his Good Friend, but alongside. He realizes that one of his first significant books was a mystery knowledge book by Don Juan. He has been a potential initiative for a long time. He is now ready to begin his training—his rhythm is beginning to support him—and through this their Love will flourish also, in whatever form that must take; close or distant, here or there. He knows that they are bound—seekers together—beyond intimacy—flaming.*

Mouse: *They are up early—sharing rhythms even now. Their early morning embrace at 3a.m becoming a regular in her life these days. His presence was particularly strong this morning. She would like to send him her writings from these times—but—that would be unfair, unless she told him they were for The Book only. Honour and integrity prevent him for requesting them, she knows. Perhaps she should just send them anyway, but knowing he* *wouldn't receive them until he is up and out of his bed makes her hesitate. This is 'Bed-Time' reading only. Hmm—she likes the new model; Kingly. Perhaps they could start routines together; prayer, meditation, diet, exercise, writing, love-making, {in whatever form}. What say you, oh Druid Alchemist of mine? Methinks you would be very at home in the ancient land of your forebears—X*

P.s. Good morning, My Darling Friend. I am coming to assembly this morning to sing the new song—the one for the Winter Spiral Festival. Cordelia is hoping to be there but may not make it on time. Can you give me a note or two and join in? It's an easy tune. Thank you. Loving you—platonically of course, nudge, nudge! —M—X

My day—a cold and hurried walk in Tui Park where I watch the wind rustle the orange-tipped reeds as if they are alive like wild beats. A single Pukeko bird struts along the edge of the treeline, looking lonely and determined; rather like me, I decide. The tide is right in, so we dash around the grass instead of the sands; twenty minutes only. I fill the van with diesel before swimming in the local indoor pool. I am too cold for the regular pool and swim for twenty-five minutes in the adjoining hot pool. That is a treat, although not so good for exercising. And then I am back at School for assembly, singing a song for the pupils; Martha at the piano with me singing one line at a time for them to follow. I enjoy that challenge. Singing comes naturally to me. Adrian helped with the words and then spoke to the children about the Maori festival of 'Matariki'; New Year. We shall be celebrating our Winter Spiral as part of the cultural impulse.

I work for two hours on The Book after lunch before collecting the children from school this afternoon.

Early P.m. Mouse: *Hi Friend—are you about? Sammy and I are meeting re The Community Village at 3.15 p.m. X*

A group of American students is visiting school today; part of a large-scale wetland planting project. The older pupils have been helping out; The Go-Getter's class included. I bump into Adrian in the school car park at three p.m; he is working with the students, his gum-boots evidence of a busy day. We manage a quick hello—"are you okay?" I ask. He looks a touch hassled.

* * * * * * *

The Laird comes home late, grotty and depressed again. Perhaps he needs a new partner as much as I do. I'd better get him home to The U.K—I don't want to go anywhere just yet, but *he* needs a new horizon. The chicken lays another egg inside; sensible bird! Monty gets tangled up in my chlorine-drenched togs, {kiwi term for swimwear}, and then proceeds to chase the terrified Bog-Brush around the room which makes the children hoot with laughter; a much needed moment of hilarity, although The Laird can't see the humour in it.

Late P.m. Mouse: *Are you okay, My Friend??*

Adrian: *Hi Friend—an unexpected day of teaching. Busy—up to my ankles in water with my boots and jeans. Great day's planting though. Children working hard. Came home after guitar and crashed out. Milking and then a 'More to Life' meeting. I must have been pretty wicked—no rest—phew! Very lovely, courageous singing from you this morning. Strange way to teach it, wasn't it? A bit too stilted. I'd better keep moving—speak to you later. Michele the grounds woman stormed off the job today—not sure why. Might have been about spades being left out all muddy. Huge over-reaction if it was. Sienna seems to know something about long-running frustrations that weren't about me. Not a nice way to lose her though. Don't like the rifts that creep into the staffroom either—people holding resentments; not healthy. I met Trinny from Rotorua; Theresa's mum. She's on the list of those interested in The Community Village. We need to hold a meeting with everyone. What about Friday? Lay out ideas and have a walkabout. Notice in the newsletter tomorrow, eh? Let me know about your conversation with Sammy. Okay, talk soon. X*

Mouse: *Well, My Friend—we are getting good at the double-life thing, aren't we! As close as two peas in a pod—but not in an unacceptable way. Hurrah! The planting sounded fun; wish I could have been there. The Go-Getter is full of beans about the day with the young Americans. He came home clutching an American $1 note and a 1 cent coin, happy as Larry. As for Michele—well—some people have issues—best not to be affected by them; try to support where possible. We all have our challenges.*
You sound busy, My Love. I feel like a snuggle and catch-up. Hmm. I have had an ordered day; fitness, diet, walk and a good meeting with Sammy. We are about to draw up initial plans. I have various people to phone tomorrow. Something in the newsletter would be good. A walk over the land—yes. Friday after school? Sounds good. Can you give the notice to the office, or shall I? Have a good evening. I'm with you—still singing—M—X

My brother Jonathan has sent an e-mail, suggesting he might come to New Zealand on business soon. How wonderful! He should be with us for our Mid-Winter School 'do'.

Late P.m. Mouse: *To have found a way into Heaven—the path she always knew she could reach—to move in such exquisite grace with him—to know that they belong—these are the reasons she clings on—like a stubborn cliff-face plant. Hmm. Crazy? Selfish? She knows it is a matter of her Celestial dwelling verses her Earth dwelling. She has always known—*

Wednesday 6ᵗʰ June 2007

A.m. Mouse: A time of sanctuary—her moment to be still with him is here at last. Curled up with dog and cat and soothing tea, she turns to him and greets the day. It is early; inspired by Lord Swallow's call to discipline, she is set to achieve again today. She has completed the recent edit of the final part of their Book. A content of the chapters and their breakdown is almost done— an e-mail on that to follow. The dog only wants to amble a short distance these dark mornings; just enough to do her business and greet the pig. Our porcine friend runs beside us every dawn—what a racket she makes! She appears genuinely pleased to see us and loves a scratch between her ears before the obligatory dive into the 'shid' for some piggy tucker.

And how is My Friend this morning? I am cuddled up beside him as the wind howls outside. A short meditation right now would be good, followed by some stretching, then work.

May waves of blessing break upon our shore—Love you—X

Adrian: His teeth have been clenched in some way during his short sleep and he wakes to his alarm, wishing for more rest. Having had little time to sift through his yesterday, he knows that he must take care of himself today—gentle and thoughtful—seeking the good. That mental demolition team is hungry for work. He has to make repairs to the events of yesterday or down they'll come. No time to lose. He clutches his warm Supergreens, dons hat and scarf and returns to bed, pen poised above his notebook page. A whirl of child and adult faces before him—and the sound of his own voice—his reprimands and his reaction—phewee! This is tough work, but his heart becomes submerged if he doesn't go there. The Boat will be swamped—dangerous, choppy water. Yikes! X

P.s. Hi Friend—can you speak to the office about tomorrow's newsletter notice? I'm in a rush today.

Mouse: Will do—oh Rushing Friend—

Pretty little song-birds trill away in the trees at the park today. I sit in the van after our walk, logging all our copious text messaging. I have given the notice to Shirley in the school office: 'Interest is growing in The Community Village potential. Meeting on Friday after school by the top classrooms.' Good—Sammy and I shall speak later. My tummy rumbles. I am trying not to eat until lunch. "The music teacher's husband, Ned, is a keen astronomist. He is interested in the Star Dome concept," Lois told us at our recent Festival meeting. Well—that is very exciting news. This project is gaining pace. "You should consider taking over the Head of Kindergarten when Kitty leaves," Sharon suggested this morning. "I don't have the full training," I replied. And that is true. Also, I don't really want such a responsible role. The Laird arrives home late after a long school meeting. He remains cross and grumpy—and negative over our community enterprise. Sammy is very interested in our English plans around a Celtic Homestead; very interested indeed. "The ideas remind me of 'the Song of Waitaha', a legend about an ancient people; more ancient than Maori. We should get the book out of the library."

I can't wait to send Adrian the detailed chapters' breakdown; it feels like an age since we last saw each other and my work on our story is shaping up nicely.

P.m. Adrian: *A mighty busy day—more class relieving—not so controlled this time. A battle to achieve a quiet painting class. Old familiar issues. Not pleasant but something I'm keen to master now. I want to keep it up—push myself to steady The Class; staying present and loving—keeping my warmth so strong. Yeeha—I'm up for it. Sienna is not well—poor thing—soldiering on. I took the morning circle for her. I was well-prepared for my mentor meeting this morning. I did well and offered to relieve for her—a Friend I've been. She reckons I haven't found my true calling—still to come—something about teaching, but not exactly. Vonny's ex-partner helped me put the cross-beams on the milking shed roof—not too far off being finished but need permission first. Just arrived to find the cows already in their milking stalls—better go milk them—can't deny readiness like that—X*

Mouse: *a good day of order and routine—she takes her lead from The High Priest in training—seeking that deeper knowledge too; The Flame igniting—into—white ash—a deceptive make-up. She watches the embers with him as winter creeps into their homes. He is so busy. She thinks of him while he milks—feeling him near, yet distant. The house is quiet—supper finished—computer work in progress and bedtime stories to read.*

After supper The Laird speaks seriously to Cedric about his option to take A-Levels back in England. He will have a large amount of work—a shock after the more laid-back Kiwi education. Does he really understand what is involved? He assures his father that he is up for it—and that he wants to keep with his year group rather than drop a year. Here we go! The property sales are next on the list. Unfortunately, The Laird is unhappy about my involvement with The Star Dome project. Shame.

Late P.m. Mouse: *Tired Mouse—expect you are more so. Very exciting day on Star Dome enquiries—interested party from Wellington—and an astronomical society looking for a new observatory site; much to tell you. Lois said they were thrilled when she suggested our school land! Can you believe that? Anyway, My Friend—more to say, I'm sure. Hope to catch up soon. Blessings to you this eve—X*

Thursday 7ᵗʰ June 2007
Adrian's morning greeting arrives later than usual.

A.m. Adrian: *He finishes his new regime and sips his green health drink—thoughtfully. He thinks of her—his Friend—his Accomplice—his Companion.*

He recalls her suggestion to mix the powder with vegetable juice; she told him twice, her subtle encouragement to share her discovery. He decides to try it, initially balking at the extra cost; goodness, he has become miserly with his debts mounting, but really, this is an investment in health. He admires her forwardness in this—not holding back on the things that are important. He needs this boldness in his life. He will take lessons from her. Money is beginning to flow again; the milk brings in a regular thirty/forty dollars a week. His thigh muscles quiver as he practices his sinking stand; Tai-Chi instruction from long ago as he strives to repair his hip imbalance that has been paining him. He goes back to bed—things feel easier this morning. He has ticked off quite a few things and his new stance of attending promptly helps enormously with his self-worth. He can be a reliable person. Yes, the discipline he so easily casts away—there's no escaping it. He steers his ship into tranquil waters where love can flow more readily. He feels so much more open when he is keeping up—and sleeping earlier. He sends her a—

Mouse: A poem:

Crinkle eye-lids seek union,
Wafer thin barrier to Heaven; denying all,
Clear pool ripple with cry-me-blur,
Abounding pace beside us
As refrain transforms to happening.
Druid, Priestess—Alchemy—to kind and waiting ash.
A hand held, an eye-lid crinkle,
Desire in Holy Communion fortifies the wait.
The ache is ever-present,
Morning herald in absent breath.

Good morning, My Darling Friend. I am with you in crinkle eye-lid and hands held. Have a lovely day. Got to dash—X

The spanking wind gives me an earache this morning. The water is disturbed—everywhere. And regiments of Red-Hot Pokers sway under established trees. A lady wearing a dressing-gown with a yappy dog says hello. We are the only ones in the Park. Hasn't she bothered getting dressed? I sometimes see Maori youth in their pyjamas in the supermarket, but not older ladies in the park.

I wander along the coastline; Garry Govern shouts another funny greeting from the house he is refurbishing; "keep that dog under control!" I shout a friendly reply. My mind runs through Sammy's idea to build a Senior School as a continuum from our primary school. I consider The Laird and his irritability over any plans I make—and with my writing. I loathe the negative block. I pray we may find a way through it all. My positive mind plays out the best scenario; for The Laird to try out his alternative schooling idea with the current senior class in our school, establishing the curriculum he is keen to explore when pupils are fourteen; 'Experiential Learning'—a classroom on the go—teaching subjects while kayaking the Kiwi Rivers. He has always wanted to do that. Once the schooling is established he could hand it over to a colleague and return to The U.K. to establish a similar group, with the support of his actress friend; the idea being to bring the group to New Zealand for part of the year to join in the established sessions. We could travel back and forth, with Adrian holding the N.Z side of things perhaps. I would ask The Laird to accept Adrian and me as lovers. I cannot deny that we desire and need that. And Little Arthur? Hmm—the potential thrills me. If The Laird could accept that he isn't in love with his wife—and that his vocational calling is the greater force—we might actually make the dream happen. Hmm—pipe dreams. But I am very excited about Sammy and me working together. Perhaps we could be the site managers, sharing any income—perhaps extend our business acumen to property development in the long run. The possibilities are endless. I am really excited by them. I so want The Laird to fly; to find his wings and take off, leaving behind his deathly depression. I could love him more if he was free.

It is the **7**th today—our number. Go, go go—

Andy comes up to The Mountain for the final time this afternoon. The repairs are almost complete. He is a gentle, held-back sort of chap, but insightful if you listen carefully. Like his wife, Lisa, he is interested in our plans for the land, suggesting the local Polytech's eco-farming programme might want to get involved. He tells me he has had a difficult year with a bad back and limited contact with the community. "I have felt ostracized. I'd like to get involved with your ideas."

P.m. Mouse: Thursday evening—she hopes he feels relaxed—the week almost done; a time to tentatively breathe out; a time to be together. She sends him a cosy embrace, hoping he is well. She hopes their separation has helped his work—his peace of mind. She has one or two things to share with him—her Friend—her Companion—her Accomplice. Hmm—where to start? The Laird's irritation with her involvement with The Community Project? Or the Holy balm that fell across her path as she drove to the indoor swimming pool? The avenue she took led her straight to a simple cross on the side of a church, heralding strong waves of blessed holding. Or the new friend in one of the pool's Life Guards? A jolly, older Maori fellow called Terry; very chatty. They spoke about needing a bigger clock for the swimmers; problems with maintaining the mechanism where chlorine clogs the workings. All little things, really, but nice to dwell on. She blows him a—

The Laird isn't very friendly this evening. We watch the T.V. together and then collapse into bed. He rarely turns to me for a cuddle. I know he cares, but I need my man to adore and cherish me. He does neither.

Friday 8th June 2007

Very Early A.m. Adrian: I keep wondering about careers other than teaching. All this stern holding and minute preparation—useful but consuming. I watched Sienna teaching yesterday—her well-constructed programme; the children challenged and succeeding; satisfied. Is this where I want to put my life-force? Is it? And if not, where would I put it? Do I cast myself back into the stream of possibility and see where I wash up? I am nearly light enough to do so, though financially heavy. My ties feel light—no strong connections to anyone, bar one. Is it a character flaw that keeps me separate? Or a life purpose? A painful gift to be revered and used in solitary work for the good of The Community, or a weakness needing strengthening? My morning thought is that perhaps I was a strongly developed person in a previous life—this time thwarted by early abandonment to keep my potential arrogance in check. But perhaps I am simply feeling the winter load; inwards, but still working hard outwardly—in the dark. So, to work I go—morning planning pages still blank. Distant, yes—but awaiting the good coming. X

Mouse: My Friend—my Spirit aches for yours so strongly this wild and windy morn. We stand together in the face of quandary as the high gusts batter The Mountain—thwarting our need to hold each other. Another thought that came to me yesterday—your Priesthood calling—a new avenue of study? Lighter load at school—possible grant? Working with that spirituality for The Community, but taking on a specific charitable element; i.e. working with the disabled on the land, like they do in the 'Camphill Villages' in Europe. Learning more. Just some thoughts—hmm—

The wood-burning stove is lit—no smoke blown back down the chimney into the cabin, yet. The computer is switched on. I drink my tea with the dog as company, my Swallow Man's love and companionship contentedly wrapping me. My morning's task is to send the breakdown details of the chapter content—by e-mail. I may be free in the early evening; not sure as yet. Do you want a visit from your Lady? Or would you rather stay clear? My arms around you. I don't care if it is inappropriate. Loving you—M—X

The Bog-Brush points as she watches the bird life over the fast-moving, incoming tide. The wind is wild today—huge and eerie. The cold southerly blows the water into creeping fingers that claw at the sand, swish and flurry, maintaining and gaining momentum. We are blown along as we walk, no different from the beach debris scattered and bowled along the shore. The open end of the bay is filling fast. The South island is receiving a battering, so the radio informs me. I write. The dog looks out of the van window after our dash, used to this regular routine. I spoke to Lois in the wind at school earlier—talking more about The Community Development Plan. Lois is a reserved person; difficult to know what she thinks. I hope I wasn't over-enthusiastic. I might have been. I also went into the office to book our family table at the up-coming Mid-Winter Feast. Rinky tested our parental patience this morning—and we were strict with her, determined not to have another moody, selfish teenager on our hands. Thankfully she responded well.

Midday, Adrian: Hello, My Friend. Would love to see you for a cup of tea. What time are you free, and how will you answer questions?

Mouse: My Friend—are you coming to the 'walk the land' meeting this afternoon? I am free for thirty minutes before I take the children to a party. I might be free later—not sure. Would love to see you if time. Might be too wet for a walk-about? X

At the end of the day Adrian dashes up to school to meet prospective, interested parties for the proposed Community Village. The car park is busy with the usual Friday exodus from school. Only one Maori parent appears. Adrian takes her for a brief walk-about, although the wind is so cold that they don't stay out for long. The children and I have an afternoon party invite, so we drive out of town along the coast to Karen's house, leaving Adrian to his farm duties. The party-goers are playing with two woolly lambs in the paddock when we arrive. We are getting used to many Kiwi families 'growing their own lamb.' No wonder it isn't so obviously available on the supermarket shelves!

P.m. Mouse: My Lovely Adrian—my plans for a free hour have been scuppered, I'm afraid—unless you would like to share ten minutes at the Everglades at 6.30ish? Not a popular choice, I'm sure. I might be free at some other time, but I couldn't say when. I would like to meet you under the stars somewhere—hate this distance—hmm. How was the walk? I have sent you the e-mail with the chapter details. Keep in touch—X

Adrian: Hi Friend—just sent you a text but it got lost—flat-out weekend ahead—floor to ceiling. Will be milking at 6p.m. both nights, then my course finishes at 8p.m. on Sunday. Let's see what The Angels have planned. Wonder what my Druid and your revelation flash will be. An Anthroposophical Conference during the holidays looks interesting; the focus on Biodynamic Farming. So, My Friend—more distance—diverging paths. Stay close. See you when The Angels allow—X

P.m. Mouse: Thanks, My Love—have a really good weekend. I will try and get straight; more work on The Book. I am feeling flat. Keep me posted. Angels nearby, I'm sure—X

Adrian: She needs replenishing—he can imagine her soul—irritation and frustration around her, and the calm she longs for inaccessible; impending decisions and pressure mounting. He wonders what it is all about. Something deeper. The Holy Grail Book is interesting—he wants to speak with her and share. There is so much going on that a text message just can't do it justice. But the time seems to come at divinely appointed moments. We face a clear break—patience.

Mouse: —X—

***** * * *

Later, Adrian: *Milking complete; the girls very chilled out. Gave them both a nice back scratch. Off to Gary for a treatment on my left hip. Might be able to stand stronger this time with my new regime of sinking. We'll see. Wind must be a-howling up on The Mountain tonight. A nice woodwork lesson with Class **7** today. They were pretty chilled out—all working well; two spinning tops finished; some experimenters making flying toys—helicopter things—pretty successful. I spoke to them about my difficulty with something they were doing; that I had a struggle to justify. They've been whinging about having to make stupid toys and why couldn't they use normal wood instead of having to cut it from branches themselves—and some boys rushed ahead and made toys out of timber on the burn pile. So, after some thought this morning, I realised that the pre-cut uses only the mind and the will. Whereas the harvested branch requires an artist's eye; feeling.*

I told them my thoughts and asked them to tolerate my whims—silence! No complaint or argument! Wow—respect. Consciousness. Children pick up so much when the adult has them in mind. Off to Garry.

Mouse: *Nice to hear your day's happenings my clever Woodsman/ Teacher/Friend. Am just parking in Grille Street for a College Staff 'do'. Might be okay; not quite our crew, but kind and pleasant people—always some nice surprises. Speak at bedtime. Love—M—X*

Adrian: *Enjoy the night out. Wish I was there. We would have a whale of a time.*

The evening at 'The Plaice' was fun. In the centre of town, an attractively-planted garden led us into the up-market venue. A good number of people was present. I had a nice welcome from Krista—I haven't seen her since the end of our Workshop sessions on The Mountain, so we had lots to talk about. We spoke about the Christian Fundamentalist families who joined a few of our Mountain sessions; Krista was horrified when I told her about the suspect pamphlets they had pushed into our hands. In fact, she and her family were involved in a Fundamentalist Church in Auckland until they left; "we didn't like it in the end." I was pleased to hear Krista waxing lyrical about our alternative schooling philosophy. One of the women at our table was keen to hear more. I also met a friendly man and his wife; College Trustees from a region further north. I enjoyed chatting with them.

Late P.m. Mouse: *All home and buoyed up; wish you had been there too—in your smart jacket and Lord Swallow dignity. Your Lady undertook a subtle, but infiltrating sales pitch for our School and Community ideas—backed by the lovely Krista who sat next to me, proving to be an out-and-out convert! "When can we have another gathering with our Workshop Group?" She asked.*

"We really miss the special environment, especially the seasonal elements. My goodness, is it the Saint Michael Festival again? How one year flies. And Adrian has cows, you say? My boys would love to go milking." One of the dinner guests was interested in learning more about School for her artistic eight-year-old son, and another who said she wanted to visit the Kindergarten. And then the Principal's wife stopped me on the way out, saying she had recently read about a prize-winning vine-yard that used the organic Biodynamic preparations; burying the cow horns etc., and wasn't that linked with our School Philosophy? I even heard The Laird asking a local town planner about The Star Dome Project! Things appear to be marching ahead. Well, well. Yes. Lord Swallow and his Lady would certainly make a dashing marketing team, with The Laird gunning as well. We would have the town knocking at our door in no time. The College fraternity is certainly raising its head!

So, My Love, I expect you are in bed. Thanks for lovely texts. The wind it howleth something wild up here! Are you away early in the morning? X

The Laird and I are feeling more positive when we climb into our cold bed. I am tentatively excited, although I don't think I can ever expect him to jump wholeheartedly into the alchemist's brew.

Part Five Halyards

She waits on the cold concrete, exposed and vulnerable. The wild wind tears and laughs at the stranded vessel's plight. Sometimes the coastal gusts are friendly and exciting, begging The Celestial Sea to set sail, but not this wind; a malevolent, heartless bully it shows no mercy, hoping to knock The Boat clean off the wooden wheeled dollies that hold her tight. The Craftsman watches, anxious but somehow content. The story is on track. Perhaps he will help a little—directing the powerful elements to loosen Lord Swallow's anchor line. He knows The Captain means well—his effort to keep her safe embroiled in his personal struggle between duty and freedom.

Lord Swallow holds his Lady, anxious not to incite her passion, but moving with the tide; the natural free-flow of their Spirit—and The Boat slips quickly and quietly further down the ramp towards the water; not far, but a movement for sure. Should they pull her back in? Rope her more securely to the stanchion? They are ready for a short voyage, perhaps they even need it to refuel and determine the new course. Their desire to be together abates not. Even through the toughest separation over months the caged sparks are still on fire. In fact, they begin to burn their way out of containment. "Open the lid, for pity's sake!" They cry again and again; "let us breathe for a short while, please!" The couple ponders; they know what effect the oxygen fix will have on their inflammable embers.

The Boat needs to sail again, there is no turning back. The Craftsman kisses her hull, delivering a message from Lady Thumbelina who hopes Lord Swallow will find it one day:

"The Hull stands for him; strengthened, new, shining.
Her sails are safe— soft rippling folds held aloft and free.
Together they are invincible; The Angels make sure of it.
She loves him-across oceans and hemisphere divide—she loves him."

Chapter 1 Hoist

Saturday 9th June 2007

Very Early A.m. Adrian: *His face is heavy this morning, but he arose at his new regime time, the urge to pee drawing him out of bed and into Supergreens prep and exercise programme. Back to bed to consume cooling drink, then the processing notebook. Why so glum and tight-chested? Negative mind-talk—lots of little incidents; no single big life-shock but underlying it all he finds lack of self-love. Lots out there—lots of work but not much fun and nurture. He snuggles down, soothing himself—fully clothed he realizes it has been ages since he cherished his body. He removes his clothes; nice to feel his skin and slow arousal. He stops to text his Friend—should he run outside to find a signal so his message will reach her now? Yes—naked into the cold he dashes.*

Mouse: *She is wrapped up with him this early morn. She should be rising and starting her regime but she needs to lie entwined with him a while longer. They have been free and fun in their lovemaking—playing and teasing—earthy and consuming. She strokes him all over—he wraps his long legs around her satisfied form. He is loved—she is beside him—X*
{I wrote this message before Adrian's sensual text reached me. My, my— we are so in tune.}

Adrian: *Poor Laird—an intruder in his house. She holds herself back for him—saving her best for him. For The Laird, it is as though his wife's lover stands between them, his presence maintained by her study and focus of the extra-marital events of the last year. He has lost her. She is his; she belongs to her lover. What does The Laird do now? He knows she pines. He loves her—has built his dreams around her—his steady rock has been turned in the tide. Where does he find himself now? He is set adrift; in danger of drifting right away. It is mighty uncomfortable—and scary. And no respite from it for this other man is often there—manifested by his wife's powerful imagination.*
Said Lover, Friend—consider this revelation. If he is present, should your Swallow Man step into caring for his family—in consciousness at least—loving them—relating to them. Maybe he will try. Meanwhile, he needs a photo of a child to take with him on his course. He is wondering about Little Arthur, now aged 15 if he had been granted life. Could he share this with a large group? Is it right? A question he will carry. Perhaps he will ask the trainers' advice.

*Best away—he is on duty from **7**.30! He has had a soft, remembered cuddle this morning—finding her lacy top still with her scent—peace.*

Mouse: *Go well, My Love. Thank you. My unconditional love does not exclude The Laird—but—the spiritual, deep connection is ours alone. I have never had it met before. The Laird and I share something different. I know I should back down—it is unfair on you, and unkind to him. I will try. I will try harder. I don't want to hurt anyone. Keep me posted on the course. I can't recall the subject? Big X*

Adrian: *'Effective Parenting'—a weekend of navel-gazing—could be deep. Nice to know you're there to report to. Your dinner sounded fun. I see how you are replenished by connecting each day—to stop and be sensual with yourself is nourishing. Go well, My Love.*

Cedric asks me to take him mountain-boarding at a local bike-track this afternoon. We enjoy some private time which he always appreciates. His siblings have been playing hockey and are spending the afternoon with friends. I wish The Laird would pick up. I am bored by his lack of passion; *"passion is what got us into this mess in the first place!"* He exclaimed last week. I walk the dog over the sands at Monument Park to Tat Island before supper; a favourite place when the tide is low. Together we enjoy the pampas grass, the silence and the bird song. We crunch over piles of sharp shells and ooze our way through soft sand. The island's edges crumble onto the beach; orange sandstone with exposed tree roots. Several trees have toppled over in the winter storms.

The Laird collects the children from town, bringing their friends home to play. He returns to the top cabin as usual. I cook for everyone and achieve some more writing.

P.m. Mouse: *She wonders—is he home and milking? Does he return to the weekend course once farming duties are complete? And how has his day been? She has been thinking of him, warmed by his early morning message of self-nurture and time spent with her in their private, shared domain—a world none can take from them. Mmm, did he realize that their early morning messages crossed? She felt his sensual touch. Her day has been full; lovely dog walk in the sunshine. The bay was like silky chocolate today; a silent ripple with extra ingredients. They walked past Dragon-Fly Cove, strolling right around Tat Island. She likes its private, separate life inhabited only by gulls and secret hollows. Have you seen the Pampas Grass out there? Or perhaps it is the Native variety; Toitoi? She imagines being there with him; a reverent escape they would enjoy—so much. She knows he would embrace the treat in the same, listening way; 'well, hello, Little Island—how fares thy secret life? May we linger a while with thee?' X*

Adrian must be busy. He doesn't respond to my evening missive. He is probably stuck into his course; engaged and engrossed. Justin and Freya collect Lucia at six p.m. They stay for a cup of tea. Phil has already collected Matthew.

P.m. Mouse: *Hello, My Love—a good day—apart from continued bewilderment from one husband. Your earlier assumptions were correct, hmm—yes—he longs for me to back down; to lie. Once his future falls into place and he knows where he is headed all will be settled. He hates the unknown. He is always tetchy without exciting new agendas; he thinks they hinge on me, but I am a background figure in his psyche, even though he thinks I am central. I wish he could see that. His insecurities increase with age, I fear. I have managed to get him off the whisky for the moment. I am sure his mood has worsened since the golden liquor became such a firm companion. Sleep well, My Fine Sir. I am here. X*

Sunday 10th June 2007

A.m. Mouse: *She is up later than usual. A fire is lit—the animals have received their regular greetings—scratch and tickle. Will it rain? The washing waits to be hung out to dry, the basket left outside when she ran out of time yesterday. She thinks of him—her Friend—how engrossed he must be. Just blowing him a good morning kiss—X*

Adrian: *I, Adrian, undertake to seek connection at all times. I seek to embody The Holy Spirit, the connecting of Spirit and the Spirit of connection. May my music soothe, my toys delight, my manner heal and uplift, my steadiness reassure, my humility pacify, my faith give peace and may my selfless service maintain my modest needs and give me enough to assist those in need. Lord—I'm into this life, holding nothing back—total connection—no fear—taking the knocks and set-backs with interest and curiosity about what they are to teach me. I am enjoying my life—every last bit of it—learning and growing and taking myself on wherever life points my attention. So, right now it is to be reliable—give my word with weight and keep it—be conscious of the money I create and where I owe it—rising to a Good Shepherd of all that is in my care.*
My Friend, as you can tell, I am propelled by a surge of energy today. I am going to surf it. Racing to catch up with you ahead of me on the wave-face—smiling and waving—you Little Sweetie, you. So, here we go, deciding to attend to my affairs joyfully and to drop the heaviness and worry—heading for The Light—lightening my load. On that note, I lent The Go-Getter a C.D. I think—ages ago—called 'Eight Orange Orchard'; a picture of a crusty old van on the front. Could you—

Mouse: *Lovely messages, My Friend. Have you followed up Cordelia's e-mail yet? It was good to hear her sounding uplifted again; back to her usual self. I need some of that draught for The Laird—hmm. Big, happy flourish from the wave—oxygen-fuelled—your ever-excited surfer—X*

Adrian: *I haven't received Cordelia's e-mail yet. What have you got up your sleeve for The Laird? Any ideas for replenishing him? Warmth—Hot Pool soak—hot chocolates and marshmallows—something yummy. Enjoy church.*

Mouse: *Funny—I just came down to complete a special 'holding' for The Laird, only to find your question; 'what are you going to do for him?' Well, after my earlier start I went back to bed to hold said man; to give him some attention and care. He was happier—and more open—muttering as he drifted into sleep. 'What are you saying?' I asked. 'Just trying to find a safe place in my mind,' he replied. A thought came to me then—a strong desire to invoke The Holy Spirit into his sleeping form. I found myself imagining I was pushing from his feet upwards—wondering—surely The Holy Spirit would start at the head and work down the body. But no—feet to head felt right; a need to push The Light beyond and above his head to form a protective layer all around him. I found the task was too heavy and loaded with something I couldn't explain or triumph over on my own. Ah, of course, my Fine Friend was beside me; his added strength was all I needed and—we managed! The final 'pop' of the barrier happened as I sat in front of the fire, imagining our work on The Laird's sleeping form upstairs. The dog accompanied us. I am naked; called down by a phone call. We made it! It is done! Phew! Where it will lead I cannot say.*

'It's all about having faith—and letting go,' she reassured her confused husband. 'Come fly with me,' she told him; 'it's very exciting.' 'Hmm, I'm sure it is,' he replied, drifting into sleep again. She wonders on—opening her womanhood to the warmth of the flames—deeply comfortable, lying on the hearth rug. Just as well it is only the animals watching! Wonky has just climbed through the cat flap. Go well, My Love—X

Adrian: *Yum——*

Mouse: *—Love you too—X*

I have returned to the beginning of 'The Celestial Sea'—before Adrian and I ever met. Will I manage to write enthusiastically without the constant passion? Our lives were more measured at the beginning of our tale. I don't have any recorded material either. I'll take it a step at a time and see what transpires. The Go-Getter does well in his hockey rep matches this morning; he and his mates are trying out for the more advanced level of the sport he enjoys. They achieve the second round of the trial; he is chuffed to bits. Cedric and I stay put on The Mountain, cleaning and tidying because potential buyers are supposedly coming to view our property. Unfortunately they cancel because of the bad weather. Never mind—at least the house is spanking clean. Despite my holding, The Laird's mood is even worse today. He is horribly depressed and can't seem to settle at his work; he goes into College to try and concentrate, but eventually comes home without having achieved anything. The printer goes mad and spits out pages and pages of my Book index that make him even more furious. Oops.

Monday 11ᵗʰ June 2007

A.m. Mouse: Good Morning, My Friend—I wonder if you are up early today? I imagine you must be over-tired; I wish you didn't have to dash outside to receive my messages. Did you get a new battery? Would a different phone get better reception? Mine received a message while I was in your chamber the other day. Perhaps that was just a one-off. Anyway—how goes My Noble Lord? Uplifted and inspired? I look forward to receiving your pearls of wisdom in the realm of Effective Parenting; goodness—we could all use some of that! The fire, it roareth—the household slumbers on and your Lady is still and quiet with you as a new week begins. Take care—X

Adrian: Good Morning, Friend. I am well—thoughtful and steady. Focussed on school, so won't talk. Love to you through that. Porridge making—

Porridge is bubbling, bubbling hot,
Stir it round and round in the pot.
The bubbles go plip and the bubbles go plop,
It's ready to eat, all bubbly hot.
(Couldn't resist adding a Kindergarten rhyme here! :)

Mouse: Keep stirring—keep steady—X

I am especially tired today. I don't know why. I have to catch another snooze on the sofa before waking the family. I attend a school meeting early on, talking to a couple of mothers about the Star Dome Enterprise. They are all ears, I am pleased to say. I just wish we had some money to kick-start our ideas. The Laird's schooling plans are discussed; might he take over the top year at our school? That would be interesting; several families have suggested the idea. They don't see his negative side. The upcoming Mid-Winter 'do' is also hotting up; input required from more people. Cordelia is present, looking peaky. Should I reach out to her more?

It is time to walk The Bog-Brush—later than usual in Tui Park. Calm water, wet socks and incoming tide; we stroll along the right-hand shore today. A rusted range kettle is lying on the wet sand; I wonder where that came from? A cluster of new buildings is popping up—like all Kiwi building progress is rapid, rather like the plant life in the fertile ground of Aotearoa.

Adrian telephones me late; he has been very busy all day, working in class and adsorbing the weekend's course. The Laird is due home at ten p.m. from a College meeting. I suspect he will be grumpy.

P.m. Adrian: Mellow day, but he is tired. Weekend catching up on him. Late to milk again—just sitting down to the teat now. Better relations with Vonny makes life easier. He spent an hour in the woodwork shed, making a spoon—a spoon he had been thinking of for a long time; a twisty, turny, goblin spoon—deeply satisfying. Yes, but now the guilt over such self-indulgence;

the creative drive that powers through sensible priorities and more important tasks. It drains his energy with guilt—stolen moments—he has such a policeman on board who tells on him for any misdemeanour; then he gets grounded. But, as he learnt this weekend, there is a way of understanding children's behaviour so that they can be left free—not judged or condemned. Guided or educated it doesn't have to be harsh. So, maybe this is about learning to be a loving, understanding parent to my own inner child—and Little Arthur.

Mouse: My day began with a tired flop—unusual for me—had to kip on the sofa once I was up. An interesting meeting at school today; the Mid-Winter Feast needs more input—you and I to meet with Felicia on Wednesday at 9a.m. about the music? I stayed behind afterwards to chat to Sharon and others about The Community village ideas; they were full of useful comments. Cordelia came in towards the end and I caught up with her later, asking for her participation as 'Sacred Holder' of the project—The Angelic presence behind the impulse. She was interested—said she would give it some thought.

I like the sound of the Goblin Spoon—much needed creative nurture after your non-stop few days, I'm sure. Our Story-Telling Goblin on the Seasonal Table would covet it. Poga sits in a rocking chair and watches the brass kettle bubbling over his fire every winter—yes; he would love your spoon. My mind travels back to my Hampshire Kindergarten Seasonal Shelf; a large piece of unfinished wood that made a special feature in our huge kitchen. Lots of people came in to see the displays; how I enjoyed sharing the magic. The children greeted Poga the Goblin with a combination of delight and hesitation; he is odd-looking; a little weird. His dangling legs almost twitch as I tell the seasonal tales. Our friend, the local vicar, was always keen to know what was happening in the stories.

Hmm—how good to hear from you—X

Did I say I found a rusted kettle on the beach today? Perhaps it belonged to Poga in a time long ago.

Tuesday 12th June 2007

A.m. Adrian: This young man—this boy— is learning to be gentle on himself; a good parent—a wise, compassionate parent—tolerating mistakes and seeing them as opportunities to learn—more and more. Staying soft and connected psychically and on a heart level. The parenting course was for me! This parent—this new and uncertain parent didn't realize he was one! This parent looks back on his son's life with interest and compassion, seeking to understand, not judge; to stand beside his son in the tricky moments—not criticizing or turning away—right there, lending him strength—a proud father; a strong father, guiding his boy towards light, not dark—love, not fear—joy, not pain—connection, not separation—strength over weakness—truth—telling the truth—standing for truth. 'I'm scared, I doubt, I worry'—reminding him at *every crossroads that he is worthwhile; a fundamentally worthwhile person—nothing will diminish that; encouraging him. EN COURAGE-ing him by letting the truth penetrate the cloak of fear—shredding it so that the light and warmth of truth may reach him again and pierce the icy shield around his heart—deep into it—melting—reminding him that his own heart's strength can meet any ice—break any bond—light any dark. Yes, his father will help him light his candle of warm thoughts; thoughts that are light-filled, turning him towards The Light until he does it by himself.*

How nice it would be to see her and really talk—so much water under the bridge—so many leagues sailed single-handed and many adventures unmarked. Yes, the celebration of life and experience is what he misses. But so it is—until all rests well in The Family, and The Castle is happy once more they patiently wait—putting their Love into their families and endeavours—and themselves—speaking of—

Mouse: *Beautiful message from you, this star-spangled dawn. What a lovely picture—the father caring for his son; Little Arthur is there somewhere too. A happy e-mail from Deirdre, {home schooling group}, saying her gang would love to sing carols and dish out presents at the Mid-Winter Feast. I have suggested a practice this weekend—not sure if you would like to be involved? It would be fun if you felt so inclined. I also have a meeting this morning with the new Maori parent, Jan, about our project ideas, and then Sammy and I hope to meet at 2p.m. in the library to work on the plans. Might you be free then? Oh, Master Artist and Partner in all permitted activities—as well as all—hmm. Enjoy your warm Supergreens; 'pond weed,' as my English friend, Nettie calls it. My bottle awaits my morning stroll in Tui Park. I'll be there with you—need to re-group with you soon. Need your strength. Loving you, your Cheeky Mousewife—X*

Adrian's moods fluctuate so often, it is hard to know where to tread. Any outing or event knocks him off balance. I can't imagine living with constant instability. But I admire his efforts to be honourable—difficult in the face of the truth we both recognize. I will write but not send another message. I also need to express how I feel.

Mouse {Unsent}: *He is far away. He does not choose to see me. He is honourable and sensible, maintaining his steady stance and dignity, the Goblin Spoon his only permitted, creative outburst. Oh—how I wish that it were allowed—that he would creatively outburst all over me—inside every inch of me—*

The new Maori school mother is an interesting lady. Jan and I enjoy a lively conversation today where she tells me about tribal land further along the coast and her instigation of a whanau community business plan that won a coveted award. {Whanau means 'extended family.'} "It was my Grandfather's dream," she tells me; "I have been holding the project over recent years. The

Government awarded me a scholarship for the initiative. My Father is partnering me in the project. I might have time to be involved with your exciting plans; the enterprise sounds great. Thanks for sharing the ideas." We sit in the school library, discussing the Star Dome Project for a good hour. Dana the school librarian is very interested and joins in our conversation. "I reckon your husband should take over the senior students," she offers. "He has great charisma. In fact, he would make a great principal!"

Hmm—Dana might not be so sure about that if she caught him on a 'down day.'

I walk the dog and then I visit the College students to discuss the Opp. Shop wall mural they are planning. "We are starting a Rosary Group," young Jim Grills enthuses. "Would you like to join us?" I thank him, saying I am honoured to be included but that I can't manage the after-school time with my school run routine. Later on I bump into Sammy and Bruce with their eldest, Isaiah. Bruce's After-School Club, Camellia House, is next to the indoor pool. "Come in for a quick cup of tea after your swim, have you time?" I have twenty minutes spare, so we enjoy another visionary chat about the potential projects at school, especially where The Laird might be involved. "He and I could run the senior programme, eh?" Bruce is a qualified teacher. We speak about Big J. too—several people have expressed concern about her workload. "Perhaps she needs to step down, or find something new within the community." Our Head of Kindergarten, Kitty, is leaving soon, so the school is undergoing a certain amount of change. Adrian and I have talked about extending some spiritual 'holding' around Big J. as the changes settle.

The Laird stays late at College and after our regular library trip I roast a leg of lamb with the Kiwi tradition of baked pumpkin and kumara; {sweet potato}. The Laird cannot turn to me in bed at the end of the day, despite the yummy meal. I think he is sad that he no longer has loving feelings towards me. I would say he hasn't for several years; fondness, yes, but not the mature love a husband and wife should share. I have tasted that with another and we certainly can't claim to invoke enough of the key ingredients, except for a reliable but boring devotion. I sigh, needing that from Adrian so strongly tonight. I miss him. We belong together; I know we do and I know he knows it too.

P.m. Mouse: *Feeling him strongly—sweeping her unexpectedly off her feet this evening. She wonders what triggers this emotion. It is strong and tangible. Are their thoughts synchronized? Do they create the strong sensation? A whisper-love-touch—a thimble full of sweet loving nectar and delectable caress. She blows him a special kiss tonight. Sammy has extended another weekend invitation to Lord Swallow and his Lady—to consolidate ideas and sketch out the whole scheme. Are you free after hockey? To Camellia House? The Angels may bless us thwarted Lovers with some time together if you are up for some singing also. Mmm—sleep well, My Friend. Nice to see you fleetingly today, you handsome man, you—X*

Wednesday 13th June 2007

A.m. Adrian: Hi, My Friend. Battling and racing. Off to meeting with Sienna. Will you put something in the newsletter about The Star Dome Village? I don't want my name to appear this time. I'm not really in the loop. See you when I resurface—

Mouse: Hi there. Are we having a singing meeting at Vonny's with Felicia? How early can I arrive? I have another meeting afterwards. I will do the village notice—X

Adrian: I don't think I can make the meeting; changed plans due to farm building project. I am taking the Class early. Tomorrow would be better. Can you give my apologies to Felicia? Does The Laird know I am playing music at the Mid-Winter Feast? I won't sing carols with Dierdre's group outside the venue—jumpy young man, am I. Talked to Edwin last night—like to tell you about it.

Mouse: Okay, My Friend. The Laird knows you are involved in the music. He has been asked to direct the auction and be the M.C—but like you he is jumpy and unsure. We are persuading him to accept. Simon says he will share the role. Others are beginning to call for his input at school; to take over the senior pupils perhaps. Goodness—what are we all meant to be doing? And what did Edwin have to say, I wonder? Any chance to see each other?

Adrian: Sounds like The Laird and I need to meet. Do you think he would be open to it?

Mouse: Perhaps—with Simon present. I think the time is ripe. Looks like my brother Jonathan will be here on the night. We will need to be warriors with our swords of courage and love to help propel the whole debacle onto a new plateau—X

Our beloved Tui Park is under siege when The Bog-Brush and I arrive for our daily amble. Oh no! The Council is building designated parking spaces with wooden bollards preventing cars from access to the shore; "except in the fine weather," one of the men informs me; "then we'll remove that central bollard over there. The ground is too wet for vehicle access through the winter months." That is a shame; I won't be able to drive right up to the water's edge where I like to sit and log all our copious text messages. I shall have to be content with a concrete parking slot until the return of the fine weather.

I leave the park and meet the Mid-Winter Feast Committee at the posh Golf Club on the edge of town; the venue is perfect. I am in charge of the carol singing and the decoration—we are putting up a Christmas tree and providing individual gifts for each guest which should ensure the festive atmosphere. Christmas in the summer heat is always a let-down, so this winter gathering redresses the balance somewhat. With my brother, The Laird and Adrian all present in the same room the stage is set for a grand dénouement. "Definitely needs white cloths on all the tables," I suggest. The Formica is off-putting. We position the music stage and the auction of promises area, and we count out the number of parties of eight. We speak to the golf Club chef to finalize the menu. Everyone approves of the detailed confirmation I give on various key issues. Yes—we are organized for the big event.

I am home by midday, more than ready to sit and write—and write. 'The Celestial Sea' is speeding along nicely; I can't wait to show the recent passages to Adrian. He shall collect the metal from The Mountain tomorrow.

Early P.m. Adrian: Hello, My Friend. I hope your day is going well? Any news? I just met with Big J. about pay—she was friendly. She asked about you and me after noticing The Laird's more humble manner at the last school meeting. I told her that we had met a couple of times platonically; that you were a good friend and I missed you—a Soul-Mate like Edwin is for her. She got it and agreed that you were indeed a lovely person. She was pleased I had backed off.

Mouse—Hmm—had a strong picture of Big J yesterday—wanted to talk to you about her. I met with two separate instances calling for her stepping down. She looks so tired. I wondered if we should do some holding around her. I also wondered if she wouldn't like to let go of the stress and get involved with something different—like our Star Dome Enterprise, for instance! Just some thoughts. How are you? I have arrived home; time for lunch and Book writing. Chapter 1 almost complete.

P.s. Good that you can collect the metal during the week; The Laird's continuing sombre mood means weekends are proving tricky. I can be out if you prefer—or wear my grotty jumper and promise to look unattractive. I would not bestow adoring looks upon you; the pig would receive all my kisses instead. Just let me know—X

Adrian: Hi Friend. I am organizing a birthday party for Vonny's Thomasina—pays my rent for the week. I may not be able to meet on Saturday after hockey unless I am very organized. I'm thinking of climbing the volcanic hill in the harbour early on Saturday morning to welcome in Matariki. {Maori New Year when the Pleiades constellation appears in the southern skies.} Looking forward to seeing you tomorrow; I'll bring my trailer for the metal.

Mouse: Hello there, thanks for message. Have a good evening. Looking forward to catch-up tomorrow—over the metal! Sleep well—

Late P.m. Mouse {Unsent}: Sometimes he distances himself—yet maintains a tentative hold at the same time. Do I sense a more earthed reality in myself alongside the new school enterprise? But—I never want to lose our

240

magic—our entwined Lovers' idyll; it fuels these powerful passages; our sacrifice to turn the harvest back into the soil. I know I can be with him as a Lover—as a Wife—if he is still in love with me. I think that he is.

My brother Jonathan telephones as the day ends. He confirms that he would like to be a guest at our Mid-Winter Feast. I am looking forward to that.

Chapter 2 Hmm——

Thursday 14ᵗʰ June 2007

   A.m. Adrian: *His shirt is tangled around him—his Greenstone hanging on his back feels unusual—his purring cat looks for a way under the blankets. His mind is as tangled as his shirt but he is in no rush to straighten it. It is often like this, and sometimes taking an outer discipline is the best way to realign. He lets the 'snooze' alarm ring twice, and then gets up to wash out pee bottle, fill the jug and say his first verse. A Salute to the Sun exercise next—more verses and Eurythmy before some Tai-Chi exercises. These are strong, working his hips and knees—striving to balance and open his joints; sinking down so there is no over-stretching—all movement coming from his centre. An exercise for everyday use—moment by moment consciousness. He finishes with a standing pose before boiling the jug and sitting to write his thoughts.*

   *Today he tells his Friend about his morning regime. Now he tells her how he is. Soon he will ask her how she is. He had a nice talk with his step-mum, Pat, last night who sends her love. She turned **70** on Tuesday—said she feels a strange relief; she has made it—three-score-years-and-ten. Now she is not worried—she can leave when she wants—she is complete. He spoke openly and they laughed and laughed—the winter feelings—the humble pie he is eating—the inwardness—the trust—the missing—the wondering—the new flicker of Druid knowledge—his Soul-Mate. A healing conversation indeed— being heard, accepted and loved, he is appreciated—feeling normal—a human being travelling through life.*

   So, My Love—how my ardour flares at times—but how quickly cooled also; simply quenched when I think of you alongside your rightful husband, tending your children. Gone. And this is right, you are not free and attend you must. And he must in smouldering passion languish—placing no demand upon her— expecting nothing—not even waiting. He lives his life; it is like the Tai-Chi—sinking always—centring—no hope flaring—no sanguine dream soaring—pulled in and restrained—closed in and cloaked. Strength-giving it can be also—steadying—mindful—aware but checking action—nothing impulsive—reliable—controlled. Yikes! No wonder he wants to flee his job and become a Woodworking Druid! But—perhaps he is learning Mastery? X

   Mouse: *They pass each other often—knowing their eyes have met— knowing they have been admired for the briefest of seconds; their claim upon each other a reality in both their lives. He directs his enthralled class. She maintains her family and stirs the pots of entrepreneurship—for they reside* *in an alter/world—where music is wrapped in downy silence—where friendly livestock rest their heads—and where time turns crystal somersaults on the waiting sands.*

She bids him Good Morning; his stunning message matching her realistic mood; a mood that tells her to let go. The delicious agony of 'us'—thwarted passion eating her alive this morning. Sometimes he feels it—fighting the magnetic pull—the battle magnificent and terrible, both. She is aching and sad today. She must turn to Northern shores. X

The Bog-brush and I brave the grey, cold weather and walk along the shore opposite Tui Park this morning; a place called Marama Head. The Council is painting the Public Loo block in two shades of aqua-green on the outside and a bold lilac inside! The colours make me laugh. Lilac? Why not? We walk a long way, passing two large landslides where sandstone and chalk have crashed into the bay, uprooting trees and exposing tangled roots. The winter blooms are magnificent; I don't know the names of the plants but some resemble clematis and bougainvillea. A collection of interesting-looking boat sheds stands close to the shore; one boasts an ample deck with table and chairs while another has an old fashioned, red tractor on display. Whirly windmills and a couple of wooden ducks sit astride the bollards delineating one property's boundary. And speaking of ducks, a couple of real ones swim by accompanied by a friendly Kingfisher darting in and out of the bank above my head.

I swim in lane **7** of the indoor pool today. I watch an older couple I have seen before; they perform their regular stretch routine before entering the water. Like a long-established mated pair of water-fowl; bob and tuck, preen and turn they flop into the pool. Nice. I would like to grow old with Adrian.

Midday, Mouse: *Hello, my fellow smoulderer—are you still coming up to The Mountain after school? If so, can you bring your laptop? Lots more to download. Chapter 3 of Part One is underway. I have been swimming, so I shall be most unappealing in my chlorine aroma. Perhaps you should roll in some cow-dung before you drive up! Ha! If only it were funny—X*

Adrian: *Hi Friend—Vonny borrowing car later. Can I come up now?*

Mouse: *Any time—I'm here until 2.40. Do you want lunch?*

Adrian: *Please—will have a bite here too. Thanks. Just had a life-shock. Sent a message to Lorrie, my ex-partner of **7** years, asking if I could send her daughter a present. Short, curt reply from her spun me out, even though I was expecting it. I don't think she holds as much resentment as my mind tried to tell me just then; it could appear so, but I don't know. Nonetheless, a useful reminder to strengthen my sense of self—not to need—*

Mouse: *Okay, My Lovely One—bacon, onion and mushroom on salad?*

Good for seeing off life-shocks. I'm hungry, but will wait until you get here. It smells yummy—drive carefully—X

Adrian: *Picking up trailer—nearly heading off.*

Lord Swallow and his Lady share a blessed reunion on the sunny Mountain this afternoon. He backs the car and trailer towards the cabins before climbing out and welcoming her with his glorious smile. The sound of the gravel crunch; her heart begins to race, even though she knows it shouldn't. He is wearing his orange-checked shirt; of course, it is Thursday; an orange day. She gives him a big hug on the deck; "I need to steer clear of the hugging," he admits, still smiling broadly; "and the hand-holding. Oh—how I want to do both—so much!" He admits to feeling excited as he drove the car up the steep drive, but he knows he cannot be close—why, he would be all over her! They sit together at the kitchen table, enjoying the salad, and each other. She has included some sliced green apples in the dish; an unusual mix but one he enjoys. "You know that I love you," he admits quietly. They have so much to talk about. They flirt outrageously with each other while they chat—about the children, The Laird's heavy depression and Lord Swallow's own career; perhaps he should give up teaching. She suggests he look into The Priesthood; "coupled with your woodwork and land projects, I think you might be very content—as long as you remain within the framework of a school. You need that." He is pleased by her suggestions; "oh—how good it would be to hold you now!" He showers her with his sensational smile and she cannot resist kissing his neck when she gets up to clear the plates. "Edwin says it will be a disaster if you return to England. We would have no future. He can see the situation is wearing you down. *'She should just leave her husband,'* he said. Oops—you didn't hear that from my lips. No encouragement. Come with me to get the trolley," he says, changing the subject rapidly; "I like it when you walk with me."

How they adore each other. There is no escaping the truth. They have such fun together. He is her gallant Lord Swallow and she his Lady Thumbelina who continues to tempt him—in an acceptable and delectable way. He stands firm however, with an amused glint in his appreciating eye. They couldn't be happier; how comfortable they are in each other's company. Together they load the trailer with the trolley, the heavy bath and the metal. There—all tied down and secure. The aggravating clock goes ping; time for the school run and the regular, Thursday Staff Meeting.

* * * * * * *

Early P.m. Adrian: *A tasty meal sitting nicely inside him he roars down the drive, the heavy trailer-load giving weight to his journey—his concern over being late lifts. He recalls their impeccable timing and relaxes. With The Angels' dusting there is no need to worry. He would be fine, he knew it. This meeting was blessed—uninterrupted—humorous—real; their passion acknowledged but held in check. He is satisfied—and she?*

Mouse: Oh yes, Sir—definitely satisfied—The Game at its best. They just need to be together—blessed and vital—their chemistry not dependent upon the physical, even though they would be overjoyed if it were allowed. Loving you—X

I consider this afternoon's conversations; "I'm really enjoying our text messages," Adrian admitted; "are you? And the abstract poem you sent the other day; I loved that. Oh, and the naked message from the fireside; that was special." "I've got a really sexy one for you," I told him. "Shall I send it when the time is right?" "Mmm—yes, do," he agreed. "Am I allowed to kiss you?" I asked cheekily. "You don't have to kiss me back." "No—I shouldn't give or receive," he stood firm. "I must be able to meet The Laird fair and square and say that I haven't broken my promise. I think he and I need to meet soon—with Simon present; yes. He will want to know my intentions. I will say you are My Friend; My Best Friend." "You won't back down this time, will you?" I asked anxiously. "No more harsh promises?" "No," he reassured me. "Not this time. I will telephone Simon soon. I could follow you to England, I suppose. But I would be wobbly surrounded by your world and family. How would I cope? We must complete The Book—I can see how important that is. Perhaps we are only a conversation away from some sort of resolution between me and The Laird."

The Go-Getter is very pleased with a wooden dagger he made earlier this week. He has smeared the blade with strawberry jam which is effective, but sticky. The Bog-brush is his constant companion. She is very interested in the jam session and even keener on the hockey practise that happens in the main cabin room most evenings. She waits by the wood-burning stove and catches the ball between her paws which pleases the budding hockey player no end.

Later, Adrian: How was it really for her? She is so responsive to him that sometimes he wonders if he is seeing a loving reflection of what he wants. She is deep and real at a very strong level, but needs time and safety to let it rise. Perhaps he didn't see her fully today. Oh for that connection—there is so much more. He thanks her for her reassurance and the idea of School Priest. That was useful—pointing me back to School. The management is still considering splitting Class 2 and 3.

Mouse: If he had held her—if his lips had brushed hers in Kingly ownership—stilling her bubble-breath—then maybe—maybe he would have found his little Thumbelina who needs to cry in his Love and let go of the heavy burden for a while—

Adrian: Hi Friend—just sold the drum kit. Forgot the stand today. Could you bring it to School tomorrow? Much more to talk to you about. X

Mouse: Yes, My Love. Will do—can't wait to be with you again. Lovely to catch up. Just let me know when you are free and I will come over. We need to create the remaining Boat passages. Big, forbidden kiss—X

*   *   *   *   *   *   *

Even later, Adrian: *Hi Friend—movement! I spoke with Martini after the staff meeting and asked for his perspective on my teaching, telling him I was on the cusp of either digging it in or changing direction. He gave me some honest reflection, saying that teaching only on strengths without inner work leads to staleness that the children see right through by the time they reach Class 6. He reckons I have bright lights but dark shadows and he and others haven't seen me move on the shadow front for two years now—probably would have asked me to leave if I was a different person. Martini sees me as a specialist teacher; he also suggested I write an article for the Biodynamic magazine about the farm—so altogether a really strong voice for stepping into Priest role as we discussed—woodwork—farm—relieving—attending the pedagogical meetings and loving The School. Promotion too—many ways to contribute. I spoke to Vonny and Sienna as well—such a relief to think of letting it go—and embracing my passions. I could put my training there; my professional development. In music—counselling—practical work and gardening too. I want to leave now—want the school to split the class and employ a new teacher; big time. I can feel energy and excitement again. Best not to raise my hopes too much though; I might be required to teach until the end of the year. No—don't want to. Want to go now! I might text Martha and expose my thoughts. What say you, My Friend? Any advice?*

Mouse: *My Love—sounds right-placed—you have been concentrating on your inner work, heralding something new—your strengths emerging in those fields for the benefit of all. And the staff knows it. Yes—I am with you—X*

Friday 15th June 2007
A.m. Mouse: *It is early—the first morning she has felt able to trust The Bog-Brush to take herself out unaccompanied—success! The hound is growing up. Warm thoughts as she remembers their special afternoon yesterday; how good to be together again on The Mountain. It was ever theirs. The Laird has never claimed it properly—rather as he avoids holding her these days. The fire is lit—'fizzle, clink and pop,' say the chattering flames; they are playful in the early hours. She is wrapped up with him—needing him close this morning. Oh—those waves—how they carry her fast and relentlessly towards him on the waiting shore. She doesn't want him to wait—and yet—of course she does. They are profoundly in love and neither can alter that now. As soon as things are settled, on course, she may be free to take a step. So many depend on her maintained role. She imagines him starting his regular routine, wondering if his career conviction remains as strong this morning. She holds him as he prays and meditates, watching the new doors swing wide. She asks him to*

hold them all in his beautiful consciousness—one thing at a time perhaps? The sale of their U.K. property is paramount—positive thoughts please—she is the only positive Castle Inmate these days. She thanks him for staying close, knowing it is unfair of her to expect him to do so, unless she makes a move towards change.

Good Morning, My Love—and how are you today? X

Adrian: *A ray of hope and promise to their U.K. sale. May the friend and tenant who resides there be free to move; the property going to a new owner.*

Mouse: *Hello there—quick question—shall I drop off drum stand, and the C.D you wanted from The Go-Getter? I could put them in your car if it's at school—or deliver to your chamber if allowed! Just let me know—leaving now—X*

Adrian: *I'm about to have breakfast, so come around if you have time.*

Mouse: *Just at the Waikite Bay roundabout. With you after school drop off—*

Breakfast is in full swing when I walk through Vonny's kitchen door. Vonny chats to us about The Star Dome project before disappearing into the garden. Adrian leads me to his room when the washing up is done, holding me close and admitting that he is out of sorts—again. "Martini is taking part of next year off; a partial sabbatical. He will concentrate on the Wet Land Project; in fact, my ex-partner Lorrie might help out. The air is still unclear between us. Lorrie is good friends with Martini and Nicola. Am I a failure?" He asks dejectedly. "None of my commitments stick. I can drop partners and classes so easily. What is it with me? I look at others; take Martini and Nicola for instance, they each come from steady, Anthroposophical, backgrounds. What did I have? Dodgy, negative, unsound parenting—all the way!" I assure Adrian that what I see is his powerful, spiritual strength; that is the man I know and love. That is why Big J. and the teaching faculty want him on the staff. I think about The Laird; he is so strong on the outside, but weak and confused on the inside. Adrian is the reverse. "The Laird and I have many similarities—and differences, don't we?" Adrian offers, reading my mind. "We are both showmen. We both dislike paperwork and planning; spontaneous teaching suits us best. We both aspire to The Priesthood and community endeavour. Neither of us is dark-haired either." "Funny, that," I offer; "dark haired men have never interested me." "Opposites always attract," Adrian concludes our enlightening conversation. I don't linger, imagining that Martini's chat will have unseated him; always the way after the highlight of attention he both causes and seeks. I see that now. I'll send him a message—our communication is sometimes easier that way.

Mouse: *My love to you, Good Sir. Did Martini's honest words bring about your low patch? The dip before the new impetus? Wish I could have held you close for longer, although I know that is unsteadying when you are life-*

shocked. I am here beside you. I wonder if our blocked text waves had anything to do with the shock—'try later'—my phone kept saying. Why the different instruction this morning? If there is a problem the screen usually just says 'failed'—X—X

So—walking the dog in Tui Park again—I apologize, Dear Reader, this prose must be getting boring. Please be patient, things are unfolding as I type; important things that need to be said. The diaries are bulging and the recorded text is growing. I cannot make head or tail of the story until all is typed and I can view the whole in the clear light of day. I leave the car on the road outside Tui Park and walk into the less-than-tranquil landscaping project. The work is coming along well, but there is a lot of mud. We don't stay long, completing our morning jobs with a stop at the local chemist; sorry, I should call it the pharmacy. Rinky is out of hair slides and The Go-Getter needs a new mouth guard. Apparently Adrian has made contact with Simon about a formal, facilitated meeting with The Laird. I ponder the potential outcome as I tidy the main cabin and change the children's sheets. A satisfactory hour of writing and I am content—as content as any woman can be whose life is either imploding or about to propel her into indescribable bliss.

Early P.m. Adrian: *Relief—he has braved rebuke—ventured into battle, and been turned away before he even had to draw his sword. Even without a meeting the air is clearer—the invitation extended means that—*

Mouse: *My Friend—only part of your message came through; I'm not sure what the battle and invitation relates to? I send you my love. We have a gap student from our old school in Hampshire staying with us for the night— interesting background of strong atheism and early childhood academia. His mother is an Oxford Don, father an engineer and artist. Interesting case for our very different schooling views; he is directly opposed to the philosophy we know and love. The boy is straight up—hard-edged—karate expert, about to study law and business. Anyway, he is experiencing a dose of Mountain domesticity—lamb chops—roaring fire—card games. Happy boys—house vaguely in order. How are you doing, My Fine Sir? Wish I was with you—X*

The Laird chats late into the night with Tim, our English guest. I go to bed early and leave the men to it. It's that time of the month again anyway, so all I want is my bed. Tim pooh-poohed our school philosophy that believes a child's health is compromised if they are forced into academics too early. He actually laughed at the suggestion! I don't suppose he would like me to know he has a bulging bag of asthma medication beside his bed.

Saturday 16ᵗʰ June 2007
A.m. Mouse: *Cold wind rocks The Mountain retreat—she wears thick jumpers, wrestling the logs that need splitting; perhaps the fire will light*

without too much effort; she would rather not use the axe right now. Yes—success—the kindling does an efficient job this morning. She has had a long sleep—early to bed—greeting him in their hallowed place before rising. Still silence; the dead-end is murky. She doesn't understand last night's message from him—has it something to do with The Laird? She knows her husband spoke with Simon, but she wasn't given any details. Did he refuse to meet with Lord Swallow? Perhaps he will tell her this morning.

Dear Friend, I am not sure how you are. Life-shocked? Sleeping in? Meditating? Fed up with your Little Mousewife? Anyway—said Mouse is here as a Friend; whatever is needed. I am heading out for an early morning meeting at Camellia House with Sammy; we have more work to do on the Village plans. Join us if you feel intrepid. I send loving thoughts from the steep Mountain this wild dawn, however hopeless. I hold you still. Take care—X

P.s—Just discovered the van won't start. I'm stuck on The Mountain. Meeting cancelled. Oh well—have a good day.

Adrian: His invitation was refused. Martha has been told in a hurried way about his intention to withdraw from class teaching. He doubts his choice; failure? Weakness? What to? He attends a meal with the team he worked with on The More to Life Course last weekend. Two of them questioned his decision—running away? What is the fear? Then he went into town—happy people everywhere and him so wound up in himself and self-conscious—same teenage nervousness—sees an argument brewing in the supermarket car park—his safe little bubble world revealed—vulnerable. Sore, cracking voice from talking to someone outside a pub—he is so removed from the world—so many life-shocks—yikes! He creeps home—cowed—Vonny is up and stoned! Good to talk to. He flags the Matariki event and sleeps on—he makes a list of all the broken words—the agreements he has carelessly made and not honoured. They pin and cut him—he thinks of the 13 year old girl who challenged him yesterday—he never went through this stage of honouring his identity. He was bullied and withdrawn; a cloak of shame wrapping him instead. Hid—smiled—hid—joked—seeking the rim of the social circle; the pencil line—refining the art of not being noticed; not in, not out—fearing being shunned—fearing being popular—invisible teen—alone—family—lake—work—tennis—bike—alone—some friends—few—nature his companion.

So much work to do—these young ones—finding their place—challenge the missed stages that still shame him. Joy really—gift—how to best use it? He has had the offer of a processing partner—a good one—maybe one to take up. He will continue to push for leaving class teaching but undertake to work on class management and accountability—narrow the focus to train areas of weakness with more chance of success. Then he is not running; then he is taking charge—and caring for himself. He wants to stay close to it all, but in ways where the responsibility is less; a break to see if teaching is where he wants to be. He is aware that he will probably take on other things and become entangled, but perhaps with support and accountability over major decisions he can walk the healing path that will restore his strength, train him *in sound life skills and let his gifts find their place. Is she up for being his Mentor Friend as well?*

Meantime, hockey and a birthday party call me away. It is cold today; not so nice for a party; the price of a winter birth. Lots of love to you, from your Friend in the grinder—X

Mouse: *Darling Friend in the grinder, thank you for being in touch—find myself getting anxious when I don't know how you are. I tend to know when a rough patch strikes; such a load on your shoulders—wish I could help rather than hinder. Yes—I am up for mentoring; we have been there for each other for over a year already. The wind howls, but the sun shines. Good luck with the party. Keep anchored—X*

I don't hear from Adrian again this morning. He is busy and so am I. Another weekend of domestic routine unfolds. The Laird's horrible depression and bad moods discolour the beautiful Mountain, all except for one important and life-changing decision; Cedric and I had a serious conversation as we drove over the main bridge in town this morning, looking down on the pretty marina as we considered his future. He *would* like to take the opportunity before him and return to England for his 6th Form education. Yes! Cedric will leave New Zealand in the middle of August to attend his old school in Hampshire and live with my parents during the holidays. In effect he will be leaving home. My goodness, this is a big decision. The Laird finds it inordinately difficult to agree, knowing it is the right thing for Cedric but unable to make any decisions right now. Eventually I persuade him it is important—for our boy—and he has grudgingly given his consent. I sigh with relief and anxiety both as we drive off the high bridge, a strange and exhilarating sense of being suspended over the water—and over life itself. I have to break the negative vibes in the home and releasing Cedric's frustration will help enormously. He needs to be right away from all of us, especially from his depressed father. Thank you Angels.

P.m. Adrian: *So the day closes—new moon—the darkest night—Matariki risen—the Maori New Year—and he feels he has stepped through a threshold; dark times behind him—suddenly social—talking again—resolutions to sticky issues—new decisions being tested and approved with Sammy and Martini— the birthday a grand success; horse riding, treasure hunt, games; he can see other openings; boys' birthday parties with archery and trolleys where the birthday boy goes home with a bow and quiver of arrows—really exciting blend of Sherwood Forest business and Birthday adventures. I realized today that to be a teacher one's life must be in order; his is not steady but he knows that he can consistently provide rich experiences for children—it is natural and where his passion lies—not endlessly but in six month stints, then quiet, inward, writing work—music—creatings—a new life—new, new, new—and she?*

Mouse: And she—she feels the new—her hand in his; their writing and entwined inspiration making dreams a reality. It is the passion that rises between them—a passion that is all about learning—creating—adventure; a passion that embodies belief—trust—immersion. The richness dwells in its life-giving source—in its divine elixir. Together they form a channel; let's direct it well.

Hello, My Passionate Friend—the party and future plans sound perfect, and not something you would have to do every day; an ideal supplement to your new roles. Private endeavour within a held community—mmm. My day has been good; Poga the Goblin's cave has been embellished with brass trinkets and brown velvet. His cave is strewn with fallen leaves and polished stones; a troop of merry gnomes about to creep past his kettle. I've managed to clean out the kitchen cupboards too. The boys had a good session on the mountain-board at the local bike track and the dog had an exciting walk while they mucked about. Deirdre dived in with her girls this afternoon which was fun; we practised the carols for the Mid-Winter Feast. It was good to catch up; Deirdre is interested in our Kindergarten for her youngest. She took a copy of our school newsletter for general info—she's interested in our Community Village ideas too.

The Laird's near breakdown mood continues; I am trying to keep him achieving—every little job appears impossible. I don't know what I should do for him. We are telephoning Cedric's English school later on to sort out various details—yes, he has decided to take up the U.K. schooling offer! The Laird might just about cope with that, but there are other college issues where he is losing his grip. I have to watch him when he gets like this—I remember his last terrible depression before we left England. He had to have time off work because he began to self-harm; bashing his head and damaging his hands. I need to get him home—or provide him with a new agenda. Once he has decided he wants out, that's it. His whole psyche is single-tracked and he cannot bend. On the surface he is super-sound and strong, but underneath where it matters—whoa—he is frighteningly unstable. The strange thing is that I know someone who is the complete opposite—rocky on the surface but solid and sure with Angel insight where it counts. Let's pray that the Matariki impulse will prove to be a sluice-gate. The phone call to England should help—movement. Can you hold me tonight, My Friend? I am in need of My Angel. Are you free at all tomorrow? I might be able to escape for some Book creation. Lots of special Love to you—well done on the party—X

Sunday 17th June 2007

A.m. Mouse: Her night was disturbed by a restless Laird—a stream of semi-awake questions from him keeping her alert; 'am I supposed to be awake or asleep? Do I try to go back to where I was in my mind before I drifted off, or do I move towards the future? What am I meant to do?' 'Just accept the now,' she replied; 'go with it—try and let go. You are being held; connect with The Holy Spirit deep inside you—it is time to say hello.' He rolled over and eventually slept. He is so frightened, poor man. She holds him, but he no longer feels close to her he admitted earlier, half-heartedly stroking her brow as he told the truth. She is not sad, it has been this way for many years; perhaps he is only realizing it now. She has known for ages. They are no longer lovers—have not been for a long, long time. Companions, certainly—partners in many ways—but that deep and intimate bond—that delight in connecting and turning each other inside out is no longer theirs. It did exist, a long time ago—before she realized that most of the depth she desired and felt was in her imagination only. Her imagination is razor sharp; a friend and foe, both. It deceived her—and The Laird was perfectly happy to go along with the role; it suited his budding ego. In truth he dances to a different tune, although she is unsure if he knows which tune that is.

She watches the flames this morning; they warm her cheek—and the dog's muzzle—dependable—comforting. She blesses the animals; their furry presence sustaining as the battle continues. She hopes Lord Swallow has slept well? And that he remains inspired?

Adrian: I recommit to seeking Paul's example; not I, but Christ in me—sacrifice—candle burn in me—never go out—flame strong—tended— nurtured —sought—softened—acknowledged—thanked—opened to—as a Friend opens to the warmth of a fire—allowed—loved, and enlightened by it. I ask for Christ's help to strengthen the warming heart, as the blind seed seeks The Light, the tree strives for the sun, the candle reaches for the heights, so too, I seek your might and power, clarifying in me channels of pure love, laughter, wisdom and compassion to flow into my work for the good of all. Purify me for service. Make good this broken vessel—yet maybe if I were complete I would claim it—boost my sense of self, instead of letting my achievements be transformed into gratitude and consumed by the sacrificial fire of working. Lord, I thank you for all that has brought me here—the hereditary—the experience—the talents—the teaching and the people. I claim it right now and offer it to you; all that I have been through; Yours—all that lives in these hands; Yours—the memories, the knowledge; Yours. Use it—use me. I am Yours. I accept reminders of my agreement.

My Friend—some of my messages were dumped by my wilful phone before I could resend them. I hope you can make sense of them. Back to bed I go, to send your family loving thoughts—X

Mouse: She thanks him for his beautiful words—his prayer reaching her in near completion—his pure intention and Holy Love shining through. Blessings to you, My Friend. Go well—X

Adrian: Your good husband—wounded child—is overwhelmed; like a tree brought down by strangling vines, the mind-talk blocking any light from entering, quelling any spark of hope. This morning a powerful prayer that sent shivers down his spine—coming against these dark beings feeding off human torment—who revel in despair. I commanded them to 'LOOSE YOUR HOLD' in

Christ's name. Upholding the noble image of man; it is not right to do it all for him, but to push back enough to allow him a glimpse of The Light—to reawaken the spark of hope that would then grow to fullness and allow him to cast them off himself; to claim his human grace. So, a temporary hand; some aid when needed to help him empower his own courage. Does she understand? Can she lend her own weight? It is warfare. Oh Noble Huntress in your fine leather armour, your hair free beneath your silver helm, bow in hand—sword sheathed—quiver full. To battle—

Mouse: *Yes, My Lord Swallow—thank you for the image. I have not thought to acknowledge the presence of the dark forces. How reassuring to know I am not alone in the fight. My image of a mighty push last weekend was correct, I think. I am always filled with the delight of pure love and waiting possibility—those gifts are never far from me, offering constant strength and companionship, for which I give deep thanks and humble gratitude. May I use them wisely according to His Will.*

And so she heads into battle. Her helmet is not so heavy this morn, now that Lord Swallow has re-fashioned it for her. She recognizes his hand at the forge—his artistry in the fine detail, the addition of a pair of small wings, one on either side above her temples aiding the natural warrior in her. She smiles—raising her sword high—a glance at his fine figure beside her she marches forth; her battle cry: 'burning wings of light, soldiers of fire, standing sentry through this ageless night'.

Sunday—a day of battle as the warriors realize the dark enemy of depression and fear. Adrian's words are powerful, and important. I consider the hidden agenda as the day progresses. Do we face a massive task? And if so, what destiny forces have brought us together? It is intriguing and yes, I sense we are ready. I had better take my sword off the top shelf—just in case.

Mid-Morning, Mouse: *Hi there, oh Priestly Lover and Brave Warrior of handsome bearing. Your helmeted Lady shall be setting out for Sammy's at Mallory Falls in half an hour. We hope to put a cohesive plan down on paper. I expect you are busy? But—if not—can we entice you along? Rinky and I can always collect you. The Laird is away with The Go-Getter for the rep hockey trials. Anyway, My Friend, just keeping you in the picture. Sammy says she spoke to you about an artist's impression for the Community Village? She shall present an initial draft to The Board of Trustees tomorrow—X—X—X—X*

Adrian: *Could be free in an hour-and-a-half.*

Mouse: *Why don't you see how you go—join us if you feel like it. Hope you are having a good day? We have people looking at the property later; Mrs Mouse is a vacuum-crazed rodent for the next ten minutes—and then I am away. Cedric can deal with the Estate Agent and possible vendor; good for his growing up skills—X*

254

Sammy and I enjoy our meeting. The Star Dome Plans encompassing Community Village and extension into High School are so exciting. Sammy is clever and organized. We consider the separated divisions of the project and potential names. We move the ideas on a stage, organizing our recent creative sessions into something coherent. Adrian doesn't appear.

P.m. Mouse: *My Friend amongst the bovine ladies and star-spangled sky—WOW—fantastic meeting with Sammy about the enterprise. Sorry not to see you—we really got down to business; planning on paper, zoning departments, naming and listing. Can you give us your urgent thoughts on three constellation star names please? For instance: 'Matariki' we have used for the school impulse. The three other divisions needing appropriate star association are: The Workshop Village, with bakery etc, The Adult Education Centre with facilities for those with Learning Disability, including The Star Dome Observatory, The Farm and The Theatre and finally The Community Villlage. Sammy is presenting the ideas to The Board tomorrow, so ideally we need the constellation names as soon as possible. The individual segments within the whole can be named as individual stars later on. What do you reckon? We decided you would know a lot more about it than we do! Maori names perhaps? Or one other to go with Matariki and the other two Western? To reflect our combined cultures? I shall leave it with you, My Love. I hope you are well—X*

Adrian: *Centaurus, Pegasus, Andromeda—top of the head ideas. Rushing home from Little J's to milk. Meeting sounds fantastic. Poor Laird—you'll be on a buzz like me. Two new openings today—young man at a loose end keen to work for Sherwood Forest—and Little J. keen to sing at the dinner; 2 or 3 songs, probably more if she drinks wine. I'm also aware that you will need a drawing for the proposal—and Boat ideas for the Book Parts; busy. A useful day. Better get my skates on and go a-milking. Might text later if still awake.*

Mouse: *Good to hear of your successful day. Thanks for ideas; will pass them on to Sammy. Drawing for proposal is not immediately required, and The Book can wait until next week. Perhaps we should discuss ideas soon if you have time. Let me know if a free slot appears. The chapters in Part One are short, so I think we need a longish piece about The Boat at the beginning; your original thoughts are good and we could work on those. As the chapters get longer in the subsequent Parts the Boat's mythology could be shorter.*
Little J's singing sounds lovely—think perhaps we will need to steer clear of performing together this year. We only need the guitar for one carol; 'Little Drummer Boy', and we might do this outside under the trees as all the guests arrive. Sleep well, My Friend—from your fellow, buzzy Mousey—X

Adrian: *How about we meet at 11.15 tomorrow and discuss everything— including a drawing for the enterprise?*

Mouse: 11.15 sounds good—let's try and be efficient and get lots done. Big Love—can feel everything revving up this evening! X

'Revved up,' is the phrase—phew—how we spin each other along, time and again. Our creative spark might be too much if we were a permanent couple—if we didn't find the still waters; but we do find them—and how.

Monday 18th June 2007

A.m. Mouse: Good Morning, My Love—I wrote a special bedtime poem last night, but I kept dropping off and found it wiped from my screen. I couldn't recall if I had erased it or sent it by mistake? I must have been tired; did you receive anything? Anyway, my thoughts are with you at the beginning of this busy week. I am in town early on, with dog walking before we meet. Text me when you are home after 11 a.m. and I will come straight over. I'll probably be in Tui Park. Lots of love—X

Adrian: Hello, My Friend—re-writing this message after my wilful phone dumped the last one; great. Looking forward to seeing you; productive morning. Thoughts turning to The Laird—take the pressure of M.C for the Feast off him; it could be too much. Help get his paperwork in order. I suspect that negative core beliefs are buried deep—failure—useless—all surfacing with the impending review and his loss of you. He is being crushed. I wonder if you could drop your projects and help him? Really get on top of his paperwork. It will relieve him so much and give him back his power so he can make decisions more clearly. Poor man—how I recognize the stress he is under. Stand by your man—X

Mouse: I know, My Friend. I am constantly by his side—lots of hand-holding and helping him carry the details of his European trip in September. He is leading a large group from College. He is scared stiff of the load in his depressed state, but deposits are paid and tickets booked. I AM there with him all the time. I placed a ring of protective fire about him this morning, standing guard with you—our swords to the fore. I am aware. I am there. I keep checking the signs—thanks—X

Adrian: Just got your message; thank you. Thought you would be, but worth noting. See you soon.

I park in the new bays at Tui Park; they haven't interfered with the reserve as much I had initially feared. The tide is right up today—as high as it will go. The dog and I stroll for twenty minutes. I log more of our endless text messages; I have fifty to transfer to my diary! Then I drive into town and start my candle hunt for the up-coming Matariki Festival.

Mid-Morning, Adrian: I'm free, My Friend—and in good shape. Come on over. Keep your good husband in mind.

Mouse: My Friend—just about to deliver said husband a loving box of sushi—his favourite. I'll come over as soon as I am free. Have you read the beginning of The Book? It's not long—so glad you are well—X

Fifteen minutes later, Mouse: *All done—a nice surprise on his desk, with a card too. Just at Waikite Bay roundabout—*

The sun is shining through Vonny's kitchen windows when I arrive. Adrian is wearing a thick cotton shirt I found him recently; he looks great in pale blue. He holds me close; for once he is feeling relaxed and easy. We eat salad and sushi in the garden, our hands touching each other's thighs through our jeans. Fingers loving, we are happy together. I run through the complete plans for the Star Dome enterprise. Vonny and her ex-partner are in the house; I make them a cup of tea and thread a needle for Vonny whose eye-sight isn't the best. Adrian is excited by the progress. "Come on—let's download more of The Book." Of course, we end up snuggling in bed—platonically if there is such a thing! We sit up after a while and I lean back against Adrian, reading the beginning of our story with his arms around me. "The beginning part is an introduction," I explain; "an outline of my life before I met you." It takes a while to read and Adrian snoozes lightly. "I like the picture you paint," he says; "the way you describe the photo of me teaching—and the passage about my chalkboard drawing of The Boat that was pinned up in your family kitchen."

I am completely happy in Adrian's company; lying together like this is perfect. I study his bedroom walls, recognizing the familiar flower prints cut out from a 'Weleda' herbal calendar and a couple of prayers I haven't seen before. And the friendly jumble that is him; a recently donated duvet set in yellow and blue does nothing for the room, although his loyal cat doesn't mind. "I'm getting used to holding a woman in my bed he laughs, indicating Tilly who climbs in beside us. Adrian strokes the back of my neck as I read and I melt into him; loving him; needing him. "I had the most amazing orgasm the other night," he whispers. "Were you thinking of me?" I whisper back. "Yes, but don't let that encourage you!" We snuggle closer and his lips brush mine. I kiss his eyes, his brow and his neck, desiring him more than words can describe. "I love you," I admit. "I couldn't be more encouraged. It doesn't matter what you say or don't say." "Did you snooze just now?" "No," I answer; "I was looking at the pictures on your walls. "Mmm, I dropped off," Adrian says. "It was lovely. You are very observant, aren't you? Oh, no! Is that the time? I'd better get to hockey." He leaps up, pulling me to him with beautiful poise. We hold each other close and he lays his head upon my shoulder. "Oops—I've kissed you," he says. "Yes," I agree; "but not sexually; not really." Adrian mentions The Laird; "he is just like me; how I sympathize—poor man."

We are very close today—so nearly reinstated as lovers. It would take but the flick of a switch.

* * * * * * *

Early P.m. Mouse: *Are you teaching guitar, my Love? If not—just to let you know that I am free until 5 p.m. if you wanted to think 'Boat'. Next time I read to you it will be the ending—more interesting than the beginning, although we need to familiarize ourselves with the essence of the first three chapters. I hope they weren't too boring—and don't worry about 'encouraging me'. Tried that—doesn't seem to work.*

The edible treat did the trick. The Laird is certainly less stressed. Perhaps a part of his weekend dip was due to your brave invitation—not being able to face it making him even harder on himself. Hmm, sounds right. So, My Gorgeous Friend, he would definitely rather not know if and when we see each other. He knows I do exactly as I please. I am not changing my tune—so—perhaps he might slowly accept our friendship in a tolerant/intolerant manner. Lord Swallow is steady and strong at the helm today. His Lady can sense a new calm; a new confidence that he can move The Boat off the confines of the concrete. She watches his skill—waves of exquisite desire rushing through her in real physicality as he tells her of a recent sailing trip he took alone, imagining her by his side. She is there again just thinking about it—mmm— they are so in tune. Big hug—lovely session earlier—wanted to hear more of your news. Sleep well, My Love—X

Adrian: *No sleep for this milker—he has cared for his crazed landlady's family; stressed mother, out-of-control daughter who needs such careful holding, boundary-less father who seems to incite his daughter's spins. Trying to harmonize that lot takes a lot of doing, but tonight he attends—staying with them—cleaning up—joke telling—cajoling—then ending with producing the picture of Christ, so helpful to him and possibly useful for the sceptic—always a question; is this a seed for this person? Or is it my own need to feel important in having something worthwhile to say? I hope it is a seed.*

He scratches Daisy's back as she lies contentedly chewing the cud. No matter how tired, this time is always okay—somehow special—away from it all—away from demanding landladies—untidy house. Yes, something tied but free. Does she want to be his relief milker while he is at the conference, he wonders? She—his reader—she who gave him rest today—unexpected—warm beside him—progress—slow—maybe—no hope yet—but glimmer? He had better milk. It is cold tonight. X

Mouse: *A seed, Fine Sir—definitely a seed. They need you amongst their trials; the family you live with. My Angel—My Friend—My fellow Warrior. When is the conference? Is it the one you mentioned; the Biodynamic one this holidays? If so I shall consult the diary and see if we are free for milking. Could I do it earlier in the afternoon? Early evening is the worst time for a mother to abandon her hearth and home. T'would incite The Laird's wrath otherwise. Sleep well—X*

Chapter 3 Hearth and Home

Tuesday 19ᵗʰ June 2007

A.m. Mouse: *The hour of sanctuary—mug of tea and woollen snug on the downstairs sofa. Hairy muzzle on my knee—six layers; cosy heat. The fire is lit and I am yours—in Friends' embrace and Lovers' silence.*

He held her to him—yesterday—anxious not to incite her passion, but moving with the tide; the natural free-flow of their Spirit—and The Boat slips quickly and quietly further down the ramp towards the water; not far, but a movement for sure. Should they pull her back in? Rope her more securely to the stanchion? They are ready for a short voyage, perhaps they even need it to refuel and determine the new course. Their desire to be together abates not—even through the toughest separation over months the caged sparks are still on fire. In fact, they begin to burn their way out of containment. "Open the lid, for pity's sake," they cry again and again; "let us breathe for a short while, please." Lord Swallow and his Lady Thumbelina ponder; they both know what effect the oxygen fix will have on their inflammable embers.

We are 'great' together, My Love—with swords held high and passion checked—we stride forth, loving each other despite the armour—X

I see Adrian briefly in the car park at school drop-off. He tells me that a young man called Gareth is keen to work alongside him on any woodwork projects; "do you know him? We would remain self-employed but share any profits when they arose; best that way." "Are we still going to do the Sherwood Forest idea?" Rinky pipes up eagerly; Mrs Flappy Ears! "Oh, yes—why, are you still keen?" Adrian asks. "Do you want to dress up as an elf—or a little princess?"

* * * * * * *

Mid-Morning, Adrian: *Hi Friend—what are you doing today? Wondering if I'll be free later this afternoon—*

Mouse: *My Fine Sir—what time might you be free? I will be coming down for the school run at the usual time. I could possibly come down earlier, but The Go-Getter isn't too well today and is at home resting. I could leave him alone for an hour-ish. Love to see you.*

The Go-Getter isn't too ill really; just under-the-weather and in need of some quality 'Mummy time' which we have today. He rests on the sofa reading his book, chatting every now and then while I continue to log messages. I cook him a good meal and generally administer love and attention. The Bog-Brush gets a walk too.

Mid Afternoon, Adrian: *Hello, My Friend. Gareth and I have just started making trolleys—will have to wait for mission trip. Sorry. X*
{What does he mean by that? Was he considering coming up to The Mountain?}

P.m. Mouse: *She sits in the dark college car park, waiting for The Laird to complete a task he is struggling over. A van load of logs on board—the College groundsman helping to load them into the boot. One of our school mothers has just been to The Mountain to trim my unruly mop; Terryn is a hairdresser. I am a slightly more presentable Mrs. Mouse for the Mid-Winter 'do', as well as for those who have to look at me every day! Terryn and family are thinking of selling up; she jumped at the Community Village idea! One-to-one selling technique seems to work well. I am back home now—cooking supper. Are you milking? And how was the trolley making? Thinking of you as my pans bubble. Special love—M—X*

Adrian: *Excited and side-tracked down in the shed—trolley number three taking shape quickly. Gareth keen—interesting guy—might just work; we'll see. Two new children for Class 3 today—Maori and Korean girls. Wow. Better plan my lessons and get up to speed.*

Later: *Finally relaxing—still to milk but warming up in bed with a cuppa and some paperwork. Thinking of you; had that old sense of holiday and possibility back again—had a wild suggestion for my two guitar pupils that we should do a concert for the Class, all dressed up in afro wigs and flares, playing 'By the Rivers of Babylon'. Get them fired up singing and playing with gusto. So, all is well here—new energy moving and flowing again. Easy to over-extend, neglect things and wind up stressed again, but will seek the balance—the creative with the constructive—inspiration and perspiration—CHRIST. Pondering on your earlier pondering point also. Blessings to you.*

Later still, Adrian: *The milking is finished—another peaceful ending to a day—the steady crunch of mighty molars on grass keeping a beat—the raucous cry of a Pukeko down in the swamp reaches the hill. He has written a report for Lottie who leaves the school for Hastings these holidays. He loves the little girl and the emerging young woman. He is pleased to write a farewell for her—digging for his perceptions—knowing how appreciated they will be by Frances and Big J.—casting aside Sienna's more regular appraisal that says nothing—and yet she did get it done. He thinks back to Matthew's late call for milk and his offer of 2 acres of land for farming—his appreciation of efforts;*

260

his willingness to pay. Bless these upright people—but why has Freya fallen out with Stephanie? Hmm? Gossip he passes on.

So, it is cold on the hilltop; his toes are nipped. Away home—check the water first, but, must get some native leaves for Esmeralda's teats.

Mouse: *Lovely, chatty messages from My Man tonight. I have slept on the sofa for a while, but am heading to bed now—not quite my usual energy today—a bit off-colour myself. I know all about the Freya/Stephanie thing—I was a shoulder to cry on for Freya. Will tell you more when I see you; just a domestic spat. Feeling you so close, My Friend. Deep longing and pondering on waiting embers—mmm—sleep well. I am snuggling into you.*

My day ends in helping The Laird address College issues he cannot face. Poor darling—the depression is relentless and hopeless; a wrecker on all fronts. I hate to see him so stressed but don't know what I can do to alleviate his troubles. It isn't as simple as stopping any contact with Adrian. The Laird's recurring depression has nothing to do with me, although he will hotly deny the fact. I won't lie to him by telling him he is my one, true love, because he isn't. Adrian keeps me positive and chipper for the family—goodness knows I need his support.

Wednesday 20th June 2007

A.m. Mouse: *They have stood guard all night—their desire for each other being turned instead to the fire of protection around their charge. The Laird was so restless, disturbing her ever-wakeful repose; bemused by his state. He doesn't usually mess with complication. He dislikes this call for deep questioning into his 'other side'. He refuses to go there—he withdrew the drawbridge in his teens to protect himself from his impossible mother; no more emotional connection with family. Luckily he has agreed to see a counsellor. His wife can only do so much. Time and again her imagination turns to her Lovers' longing arms as the night progresses—but time and again they refuse the temptation and raise their swords instead, dipping the tips into the ring of fire. Their deflected passion ignites a mighty wall of flame against the dark. She loves him—she aches for her Lover—oh, how she aches, but this was the right choice last night—X*

Adrian: *Thanks, My Love. "Oh Christ, upon the temple of our body worked through the ages, the servants of God, mighty spiritual creators. This is now my dwelling place but it is darkened by the power of tempters to whom my soul has listened. Oh Christ, against thee the voice of temptation could achieve nothing. Thou art the healer for all our sickness. Work in this body that each of its elements, its warmth and its breath, its quickening blood, the bones which sustain the form which God gave, be hallowed by thee."*

Adam Bittleston; 'Meditative Prayers for Today.' This will be my present to you when I next see you. X

Mouse: *thank you, My Friend—the strength and support from My Angel is a blessed balm—a resting place; my home in him. Just had a lovely surprise phone call from my friend J.J—so good to be able to chat with her about our precious Boat, and know that it makes perfect sense to someone else. My Love to you this day—our swords shining bright for all our tasks. I am ever by your side.Go well—X*

J.J and I had such a good chat. She is very happy with her man, Archie. They have been together for two years now; approximately. Archie runs a pitch and put golf course on the south coast of England. The business is going well and J.J has been helping him with the building of a new club house due to open any day for the summer season. Archie owns property abroad and they have been in France looking at more investments. "France has become expensive," she told me; "we visited some incredible medieval towns. I love France."

J.J. is very understanding about Adrian. I tell her about the extraordinary magic that keeps occurring—the coincidences and our writing. She is interested in my tales of The Boat. "Do you think you have changed?" She asked a question I hadn't considered. "Perhaps?" I wondered. "I am certainly deeply fulfilled as a woman. I can hardly describe the joy in achieving the levels of spiritual/physical intimacy Adrian and I ignite in each other. I don't think I have ever felt so happy." "But how can you reconcile it with your marriage?" She asked. I explained that The Laird and I are no longer a normal couple; my choices have made that clear. I don't think we have been a proper couple for a while now, although we have been kidding ourselves that we are. Thoughts of Adrian rocked me as I told her about him. Am I infatuated? Will it last? Whatever holds me is quite simply—glorious.

The white Ute is leaking oil and off the road; it might need a new gear box—ouch. I had to do all the school and college runs this morning in the van. The Police stopped us about the problem yesterday, pointing out the trouble. That wasn't so good. Rinky was with me and was rather upset. The Ute is generally The Laird's vehicle, but I sometimes drive it, especially when he needs the van to transport students. I would like to send Adrian a message right now, but I don't want to disturb him. However, he beats me to it:

A.m. Adrian: *Where are you, My Love?*

Mouse: *On The Mountain with The Go-Getter—a recovery day—both of us indulging in a wicked breakfast. Nearly called you as I left school; decided I had better not interrupt the week. Are you free at all today? Oh Lover of my heart and soul? —M—X*

I don't hear back from Adrian immediately. I suspect he is busy.

Half an hour later, Mouse: *Sorry, My Friend, should have realized you*

262

may have needed me to do an errand for you. Let me know before 8.30 another time as I can often fit something in—X

Mid-Morning, Adrian: *No, wanted to see you for breakfast—I had a free half hour; nice message from you though. I've finished at school now but am making trolleys again with Gareth. I might be free to come up for another load of metal—alright you think?*

Midday, Mouse: *That would be fine. Need to see you—and we would have our wee chaperone here. A visit to collect stuff would be okay. Love you—X*

The Go-Getter and I are curled up together on the sofa beside the fire, listening to music. We always enjoy our one-to-one time. I especially recall our short walk between home and village school before we left The U.K—how much we both savoured those moments with hands held warmly and school satchel swinging. I continue to be overcome with desire for Adrian despite the domestic bliss; constant, real and wonderful. The sword twists and turns in welcome wounding; the victim mesmerized and unable to move away—her Lover speared likewise under the same magnetic hand of fate.

Early P.m. Adrian: *Running about—new tyres etc—still keen to come up—trailer on board. Might be half an hour—*

Mouse: *Okay, My Love. I have to leave at 2.40ish. Our Go-Getter is busy making some type of contraption at the woodwork bench. Classic! I could always come down early and see you briefly if you run out of time—and hold you close—X*

Adrian: *Might work better, then I can get all my errands done. See you before 3p.m—X*

Mouse: *Okay—what time? Shall I set off now? The Go-Getter is fine on his own for a while.*

Adrian: *I'm still shopping. Let you know when I'm heading home.*

A little later, Adrian: *On my way now.*

Mouse: *On my way too—part way down the hill—see you there—just for fifteen minutes—*

"It's woken up again, hasn't it?" Adrian states the obvious as he holds me close this afternoon. We share some hummus and corn chips while we are wrapped up and happy; "until the next slam, perhaps. I think The Laird's refusal to meet with me sort of means he just doesn't want to know; not a green light but a 'get-on-with-it-if-you-must,' signal." We sigh; we don't have much time together today. I can't leave The Go-Getter for long and Rinky comes out of school in five minutes. With our family vehicular needs reduced to one set of wheels and Adrian's busy timetable we are struggling to re-launch our Boat.

"If things had been easier this week we would have been inside each other's clothes by now." "Speak for yourself!" Adrian smiles. "I have made a gentleman's agreement, remember?!"

I say hello to Gareth on my way out; the young fellow helping Adrian with the trolleys. He is working in the woodwork room beneath the house. His girlfriend is pregnant. She has younger half-brothers at our school. I see Lois and Cordelia in the school office and we try out the sample festival candles I found in town. Unfortunately they are artificially scented so not suitable. We have a festival Meeting on Monday and I need to have the candle issue sorted by then. What with shopping, school runs and cooking I am tired by the end of the day.

P.m. Adrian: *The falling rain blurs his phone screen as once again he sets out for the fields. He hopes his message is readable tonight, for editing is tricky. The water soon finds the hole in his old sneakers and his socks suck up the wet. It is all part of the adventure, trying out this hilariously serious role as farmer. What do people think as this figure with a steaming bucket in each hand looms out of the night as they fly homeward along the Waikite Bay Road? A ghost—an apparition. He has reached the field and greets the ever-hopeful horses who inspect the perpetually disappointing buckets. He takes his gum-boots out of the storage bin and looks at them. Time to round up the lovely cows—his friends. He decides to leave his already soaked shoes on; tied as they are with a double bow. He needs the phone now to shine on the lethal piles of dung awaiting his un-sheathed feet.*

It's been a big afternoon—learning to live with Vonny—the Matriarch of Complaint—bloody whinging poms; that grating voice sending shudders through his body. Somehow they get through and end up laughing and happy. Training of a higher order needed. Tonight he has put the pantry in order—even to the satisfaction of The Matriach—enduring her high-pitched 'suggestions' and 'noticings'. He gives it straight back at her—teasing and pushing—pointing out her inconsistencies.

Right—the bovine girls are settled—off we go.

Mouse: *He spills forth fine prose this wild, wet night. She thinks of him, her Friend—the man she loves—his ever-noticing eyes—his soggy socks. How she enjoys their writing; all the little stories and domestic happenings, and their close, night-time whispers. She is tired. The Laird seems easier. Pancakes and mince—everyone relaxed and ready for bed. She thinks on their day—Lord Swallow and his Lady made a hasty dash to the boat-yard for a five minute check of their vessel. The brass-ware received a light polish—the ropes are sound and they wondered about opening the hatch. Saved by the bell;*

the call to duty sees them remaining dignified and noble, even though they would rather set sail immediately without the endless checks that protocol demands. They say goodbye, wiping hummus from their chins and stealing another corn chip. Hmm—life is indeed short—X

Thursday 21st June 2007

A.m. Mouse: A crashing sound upon the door gives her a fright—the pig expects food—crazy look in her eye—one of the electrical switches has tripped—a big one—affecting the kettle and toaster and all the sockets on one side of the house. Perhaps the driving rain is to blame; the cabin boasts a number of leaks; more expense—and now the Ute. Can the old gear box be repaired? Or do they have to ditch the entire thing? Need to sell the English house soon. She slept from 8ish last night, much to The Laird's dislike, although he was polite enough not to show annoyance when he commented on the fact. Meanwhile—wickedly—she and Lord Swallow have been making glorious love in her imagination, yet again! The rain kept them in bed for longer than usual; so cosy under the warm duvet. Knowing that life is short breaks down all their unwanted barriers; "Oh, My Lord," she giggles, "you are mischievous this morning;" his exploring fingers and gentle kisses arousing in her a shower of cascading Rainbows—X

The dog and I take our morning stroll under a sunshine sky scattered with grey clouds, just reaching home before the rain returns. Winter is here, although it isn't as cold today—no need to light the wood-burning stove. The logs from College don't produce as much heat as the pine off-cuts we have been using to date. The Laird is in a state; the problems inside his head continue to mount. Everything is too much, including the imminent arrival of my brother Jonathan. He is stressed over timings and who is meeting who and when. I just wish I could earn some money to get him off the treadmill. I wish he could relax and let go. Why is he so afraid? But I am not giving up my love for Lord Swallow. He and I belong in some undefined way.

I stop and chat to the Indian shopkeeper at the Waikite Bay Dairy at lunchtime. "We have had three burglaries in three weeks! Can you believe it? One for a single bar of chocolate!" I fill up with petrol and drive on to College. I shall give the pie from the Dairy to The Laird for his lunch. Food seems to mollify him. I meet with some of the College girls from the community project; they are a fun bunch.

Early P.m. Mouse: Hi there, My Lovely One—we have Deirdre and gang arriving at School at three-thirty to look at the Kindergarten and practice carols. Do join us if you are about—big kiss—X

The Laird yells at me when we get home; I haven't paid a phone bill and we cannot access our foreign cheap rates. "I wish you'd stop spending time at that bloody school!" His depression and negativity remain as immoveable features; even the children are commenting on his behaviour. Cedric adds to the negativity of the household with his foul, short temper. I need Adrian—he is quiet today.

P.m. Mouse: *Hi Friend—quiet man today—busy man I expect. Milking? Singing? Hope all's well—don't need a long message—just nice to know you are okay. All well here. The Laird in slightly better spirits after a moody afternoon; he has been out with Bernard and Felicia. The children and I are being blown about up on The Mountain! Love and blessings—M—X*

Adrian: *Landing after a full day—catching up with Vonny over a fatty, slow-cooked stew—yum. Full day teaching with excited children delighted to be let off the leash as Sienna was away. Then a College of Teachers meeting—always a wake-up—accountability. Tired now—but clear. Oops—being attacked by a small child—*

Mouse: *So glad you are well. Hair-washing and massive laundry spread here; sheets etc. all drying about the house. My brother Jonathan—the business wiz from London—arrives tomorrow. I haven't seen him for two years! Big hurly-burly excitement. Are you still on for a breakfast meeting tomorrow? Sleep well, My Friend. Thanks for message—X*

Chapter 4 Hurly Burly Hooray

Friday 22ⁿᵈ June 2007

I rise extra early to have a bath and get ready for our special visitor. I have time to write up more of our story before The Laird stomps downstairs. He is very anxious about the arrangements for Jonathan's arrival; the timing clashes with a local event. He hopes to join his fellow teaching colleagues in 'The Polar Bear Swim,' an annual event where daring folk plunge into the cold sea at midwinter. How will he fit everything in? I should be thankful that he wants to be active; that is more like his usual self, but I find the intense anxiety a real struggle; unnerving too, reminding me of the alarming time he was laid off work in Hampshire.

Adrian: His mind sweeps the classrooms—scanning the children— identifying the one described by teachers as requiring support, remembering the needs mentioned. It awakens a keen response in him; edged and honed. He must be steady—an example for this future of mankind before him; the teacher in him awoken anew. Martini's description of the testing he is undergoing stimulates him further—how The Class relies so heavily on the ego of the teacher in so many ways—to push them and whip their will into action using whatever tool is at hand—cajoling, demand, reward. Mobility is needed and deep thought; his deep thinking gets waylaid into seductive paths, comfort and ease, spiritual bliss, quiet and creative work. He is called back to the forge—back to the heat and sweat and pounding. He is planning a crunch meeting with Class 7 boys today—wanting improvements in their behaviour. It has taken his morning regime time to plan his approach—input is required— the morning in his shed, preparing pieces to streamline their wake-up—leave nothing to their own whim except the shaping and tool work.

He thinks ahead—the conference—biodynamics the focus—the doors have opened to get him there; a lift, a half-price ticket, a place to stay and a relief milker—yes, something is afoot. Perhaps he will see Jules there too—he has not got a lift back yet; perhaps he will hitch. And his Friend? How fares she this morn? Will he be able to see her for a breakfast cup of tea? He is focused on school and thinks he will hold that focus—not break it too much; should be possible, although he sways around, swinging with the tide. It is reassuring to feel her steady position alongside—accommodating his movements—always ready to steady his craft. He knows that she will understand his awakened state—his alert—and patiently wait for his return. He stretches lazily—his sleep-in sadly nearing its end. His throat is sore this morning, although he has not eaten sugar for a week—nor wheat—or dairy—and he has consumed Supergreens. It is both over-use and over-eating that have led to this rawness—late milkings too.

Her bother comes; the one she respects. She awaits his verdict a little anxiously; her moment of accountability. As someone said; it is only with our peers that we really meet ourselves—measure up.

8.30ish then—X

Mouse: *Wind—rain—impending sentence—anxious—pitching—8.30—keep the school focus.*

Our morning is hurried and stressful. I am a prisoner of The Laird's dark cloud. At least I am a happy prisoner; my Swallow Man ensures that I am content and able to cope. I deliver the children to school on time—and then I can be his for a while. I see Adrian crossing the Playground ahead of us. He must have come into school early and is on his way home for breakfast.

Adrian: *Heading home now.*

Rory is a tree surgeon; a jolly, amiable Kiwi with two children at school. He always wears shorts and steel-capped boots. He runs a successful business in the region. I stop to chat in the car park—can he supply us with some pine off-cuts to make our mid-winter spirals for the Matariki Festival this year? "Oh, it's not looking too good for pine right now," he gives me an honest answer. Bother, we might have to spend our weekend lopping branches; not something I had in mind for my brother's visit. I bump into a stressed Martha outside the office; things are tricky with the head of Kindergarten on the move and the new twenty-hour government funding for the under-fives to juggle. She is agitated and asks me to help out in class during Monday's festival. "The planets are all off-kilter at the moment," she tells me. "Explains a lot, eh?"

I reckon we are all a touch anxious and stressed. I arrive at Vonny's house a little after eight-thirty. I kiss my Lover lightly and together we share some porridge outside in the garden. "I'm feeling strong—and good. I can get distracted by long texting though," he admits. "Okay, I'll say goodbye and leave you to your duties." I depart after a short interlude, realizing he is probably unsure about my brother's visit and his potential condemnation of our illicit bond. "We may not see each other for a while, then." He waves me off without disclosing his true feelings. We haven't time for that, besides, unravelling our complicated scenario would disrupt 'the focus'.

Rinky and I shop this afternoon in readiness for Jonathan's arrival. She and I drive in lovely sunshine to the airport, accompanied by the Bog-Brush who sits bolt upright in the passenger seat next to me. She is so funny; a hoot with her bushy eye-brows, straggly beard and quizzical expression. My gorgeous brother walks through the glass doors of our local airport with a delighted smile and big hugs for us both. Just over six feet with stunning blue eyes he is a handsome man. Jonathan keeps his tightly curled hair short and dresses in a classical/continental fashion. Perhaps he has filled out in recent years. His exhausting working life has taken its toll; he does look older. "Well, isn't this lovely—how well you both look. I haven't much luggage. I hope you haven't been waiting long?" We stroll through the arrival lounge, stepping out into the winter sunshine. The airport sits in the middle of the industry, close to the port and the beautiful beach. "We'll drive along the coast; it is so beautiful. Have you had lunch?" The Bog-Brush eyes him suspiciously and grudgingly gives over her seat. Jonathan glances sideways at her, grinning warily at her funny looks while realizing he cannot over-step the mark. She isn't easy with strangers.

Rinky is excited by her uncle's arrival and points out various landmarks as we drive; 'that's where the boys play hockey—and that's where we bought the Ute.' Leaving the industrial region we quickly reach the stunning shoreline with its rows of stately Pahutukawa trees and enticing cafes. "I'd love a stroll on the beach—and then I could take you out for a late lunch, couldn't I?" So, to the dog's delight that is exactly what we do, ending up at a popular café in the heart of the famous resort. I have met the café owners before and they serve us while chatting about this and that. A couple from College walks in through the doors and wave. I hope they don't think I am with my Lover! The savoury Panini are excellent and then we drive east, right along the glorious beach front until we reach the big road and a short cut through to Waikite Bay. "This is the region we call home," I explain, pointing out the orchards with their high wind-breaks, and the residential housing climbing into the green hills. "Most of these orchards are owned by Maori families—and here we are at school."

Dodging the surprising showers that have appeared from nowhere we take Jonathan on a tour of the school grounds surrounded by the extraordinary, volcanic scenery. How we enjoy sharing his delight and interest. I introduce him to several members of staff as the school day ends and then I am brave and take him down to the woodwork shed to meet Adrian. The two men shake hands warmly; "call me Jon," my friendly brother puts Adrian instantly at ease. We admire the spinning tops under construction; one boy is still hard at work, totally engrossed in his project. We chat away about the land—and the pigs— and the inspiring curriculum; plans and general enthusiasm spilling out of us both. "Would you like to see my classroom?" Adrian leads the way, explaining the teaching method to Jonathan while showing his recent chalkboard drawing of Noah's Ark. "The Class 3 children study biblical stories, as well as working the land. Building strong foundations is the important underlying intention; that's why the nine year-old pupils dig and build, plant and harvest. Here's an example of a Main Lesson book." Jonathan is impressed by the colourful lessons drawn by the children; their books are spectacular.

"Would you like to see my classroom?" Rinky leads her uncle away while I say goodbye to Adrian. She has had the afternoon off as a treat; it isn't every day that an uncle arrives in New Zealand. Rory walks past the classrooms as we are winding up; "I've seen a whole heap of pine branches dumped along the Tara road—the stretch just after the petrol station," he informs us. "I'll go and fetch them," Adrian offers; "hitch up the trailer later on this afternoon. We are desperate for branches, eh? When are we laying out the spirals?"

What a star—relief; that is one worry dispatched. I don't need a 'pine branch frenzy' right now. "Thank you," I shoot Adrian an appreciative nod. Now I have to deal with The Laird who is stressing over whether he should, or should not, take the Polar Bear Plunge. He has texted me several times already over the quandary. *'Where are you? Should I do the swim or not?'* He finds decision-making impossible when he is depressed.

Continuing the school run we drive to College to collect Cedric; Jonathan is so pleased to see the boys and they are delighted to have a positive, male member of the family amongst us. "And this is our Mountain," I state proudly as we round the final bend of our drive. I know my brother will be blown away by the spectacle. I smile, recalling the many adventures we shared in our youth—finding extraordinary hideaways with incredible views was always a favourite. "Pretty good, eh?" I grin, assuming the Kiwi inflection. "A veritable 'Withnail' moment!" {A favourite, British film.}

Early P.m. Adrian: The foliage is great—easily accessible along the State Highway. One more trailer load should be enough. Perhaps I'll do it before hockey tomorrow—

Mouse: Well done, My Hero. Exciting chats with my brother—tell you later. Thanks so much—love you—proud to call you 'Special Friend'—X

I take my interested brother for a good stomp around our section of land before finally arriving on top of The Mountain at The Pa Site. Of course I talk about The Laird's depression and my relationship with Adrian. He knows a certain amount from the family back home; I must be causing quite a stir amongst our otherwise calm and orderly family. Jonathan's response surprises me; "You must make sure you are happy—don't sacrifice yourself." He is very understanding when I tell him about the magical chemistry Adrian and I share. "I am a 'Frodo' character and he is definitely my Elven Soul-Mate. I don't know where it will lead, or what I am supposed to do. All I know is that it is screamingly 'right'—Adrian finds I give him a new standing in his position at school. I steady him while he allows me to fly."

My darling brother is a good listener. He can see the issues we face, especially Cedric's difficulties with his father. He talks about his own, high-achieving children who all speak fluent French, Spanish and now they are learning Chinese! He makes me laugh over stories of the Chinese tutor who at the end of every session always asks: *can I have my money now?'* "The children think it is hilarious and quote the phrase with perfect Chinese accents every time her name is mentioned." Jonathan is a wonderful father, often recreating the imaginative games that we used to play as children, usually under my bossy direction. I haven't done much of that with mine. Cedric is totally dismissive of any creative, parental input, so I have been rather put off, and now the impulse has gone. Instead, I apply my creativity to my tapping fingers and Lovers' bond. At least it is appreciated and wanted there. "Valerie and her friends put on a play every year; a play I direct," Jonathan tells me. "I love doing that. It is such fun." My brother would make a superb teacher. I wonder if he has ever considered a change in career. I don't suppose he would appreciate the massive loss of salary; not with an expensive French wife and four supersonic off-spring with their hunger for the ski slopes and foreign adventures. He has come to New Zealand to direct the N.Z Yellow Pages takeover; he heads up the bank lending the huge sum of money for the deal. He is due in Wellington after the weekend. Jonathan is a high flyer—and a wonderful person.

I leave my brother in charge of The Mountain while I make a dash for the hockey ground this evening, driving across the large town for the second time today. I collect both The Laird and The Go-Getter. Our boy has been playing a rep game. Unfortunately the team didn't win. The Laird is delighted to see his brother-in-law and the two men chat over supper. I *did* show Jonathan The Book's synopsis earlier. He especially liked the poetry. He enjoys writing himself; he produced a short poetry collection which he published for charity a few years ago. The wind is wild this evening. I retire early to bed, leaving the boys playing cards. It is wonderful having my brother here with us. Two years is a long time to be parted.

Late P.m. Mouse: *At last—a moment to lie down; the boys all fed and happily playing cards, her brother's steady presence a relief and delight, both. He was her childhood companion, discovering and inventing together. Her active role-play scenarios prepared him well for the high-life; a strong-willed wife and full family taking the place of the row of dolls and stuffed toys in their inventive games. She drops off for a spell—the card game continues with much enjoyment all round. The Laird's leap into the sea with The Polar Bear Club meant they ate late; her chauffeur role a regular these days. Somehow she manages to wrestle the clean sheets on the beds. The fire mumbles on— the new wood burns more slowly, giving out less heat.*

And how is he? She thinks of him, her Friend who sparkles, leading her brother on such a wonderful tour through the heart of The School today. She felt honoured and proud to be able to introduce him; to stand beside him, knowing that her brother would realize who he was. She loves his workmanship; the Gorse Goblin Spoon just as she imagined, only better, made out of such an unusual material—his clever partnership with the pale wood. And then the beautiful chalk-board drawing of Noah's Ark; fantastic—her brother is impressed. He is such a loving man, playing cards with Rinky and now with the boys. His own children benefit greatly from the games he plays with them; all our childhood favourites. He lives a rich and exciting life, making our own appear small and limited in comparison. But there again, he does have the income to make anything possible. She led him on a walk across The Mountain

*before the light failed—speaking honestly about Lord Swallow and his Lady—
and their precious Boat. She awaits the lecture from home—open—no longer
anxious. She tells it straight but the lecture doesn't come. Instead there is
concern that she is not taking her own needs and fulfilment into account, that
this new man in her life is important. She is surprised—she is humbled—he
knows her so well. They discuss The Laird's needs, and Cedric's too. She looks
forward to being close with Lord Swallow soon, then she will tell him more.*

*She sends him her love this eve—an unexpected turn of events—warm
and loving. God bless, My Friend. Sleep well. A huge thank you for collecting
the pine branches. My Hero—X*

Adrian: *The Tour Guide is presently beside the big swing reclining on the
pine needles, protecting his bucket of milk from his escaped cow that is
standing nearby, breathing heavily, puzzled by everything. Daisy took herself
through the fence and into the line of poplars yesterday when her busy owner
hadn't given her enough feed. She was there all day without water, taking
herself off for a wee walk. And I, arriving late at 9.30 p.m, couldn't find any
trace of her. A-tracking I went and finally a hoof mark in the mud—hooray—
up to The Bamboo Forest she went. And then she bellows—up by the
swing—there she stands! How good to see her. She doesn't come when I call,
but heads down with prompting—balking at the bridge—hmm—what now? A
flax rope—yes—no. She won't let me tie that on. Oh well, I could try milking
out here. Success. Tomorrow's job is to get a halter on her and lead her out.
So tired—almost nodding. Very lovely brother I—*

Saturday 23rd June 2007

A.m. Mouse: *—'Side by side with our swords, beside Angels we'll stand;'
lovely revelation swept through me this early morn—thinking about my
brother's favourable reaction to The Book's synopsis and the main poem,
{something he could resonate with}; when we took that photo in blinding
Angel Light on the Pa site we were indeed holding swords, side by side!*

*Good morning, Friend. I enjoyed the hilarious adventure of the bovine
escape artist; made your Lady laugh. Said Lady is alone on The Mountain this
morning, except for Cedric who will lie in a while longer. The others have all
gone down to hockey. They left the house at **7**.45 taking Jonathan with them.
They are going to the big toy shop in Church Street after the match; Uncle
treat in store—you can imagine the excitement. "Well, I haven't sent you any
Christmas or Birthday presents for a while," he announced. If the Ute was on
the road I would drive down to say good morning, but I expect you are busy.
More foliage collecting? I'd like to come with you. Oh well—lots of love—X*

Adrian doesn't text me this morning. His team is also playing hockey. I
busy myself with domestic chores and Mid-Winter Feast phone calls. The 'Do'
is tonight and with the Matariki Festival scheduled for Monday we are busy.
We must lay out the winter spirals before Monday evening.

272

Mid-Morning, Mouse: *Short message—Mid-Winter Feast team at golf club venue from 2p.m, although we can't access the main room until 6. Merry is setting up her music machine at 2.30. Do you need to see the music stage early? Check out the P.A. system there? Bernard and Felicia will be on site all afternoon, setting up the auction in the side room adjoining the dining hall. We shall arrive at 6p.m; the singers are coming at 6.45. Hope the hockey goes well—*

"Okay—time for a team walk!" I cajole the reluctant family out of the cabin this afternoon. Jonathan lightens the mood and everyone obliges. The weather is wild; biting wind and rain showers, but we have fun. Jonathan cannot believe the extraordinary landscape around The Mountain. Hobbit country without a doubt. We spend the remainder of the afternoon getting dressed up and ready for the evening party; Rinky will sing with Deirdre's gang while Cedric keeps The Mountain fires burning and looks after The Go-Getter. Jonathan talks to him about his up-and-coming return to England. He is still keen to accept the offer although The Laird is very concerned about the change to the family dynamic. I am certainly NOT! I have had quite enough negative vibe to last a lifetime. The Laird's gloom deepens this evening. He is concerned about the sociable evening ahead. His depression colours everything. Thank goodness Jonathan is here; he helps The Laird accept his son's decision to leave New Zealand, one of the many reasons he has come to our aid this weekend, I'm sure. Dear Lord, please help us to help The Laird—to show him there is a way through the confusion. Thank you.

Sunday 27ᵗʰ June 2007

A.m. Adrian: *If life is a meal—an endless procession of platters with God as the waitress—then much of the servings are plain; simple but relatively nourishing. Sometimes only a thin gruel—at other times more satisfying. But the best parts are the sweet moments when they meet—sometimes like candy—short rush—other times a long, slow dessert; lemon meringue pie, or a baked apple crumble with fresh cream, when there is time to connect. He longs for a more substantial meal—*

Mouse: *She didn't hear from him all day—and when she saw him briefly last night he said he hadn't received her messages. Unnatural division— separate sides of the dining hall—both men nervous—steering clear, although she saw The Laird acknowledge her Lover with a brief nod. School and social— seasonal fare; take your pick of European dishes; carol singing outside the entrance; Deirdre's gang was wonderful—excited children tumbled and climbed; carol singers in the tree made it different; intrepid explorers in the branches of an old Oak beat the rhythm to the songs with their legs against the trunk. Smiling guests passed underneath, surprised and enchanted as they took their places at The Feast. The driveway lighting created unintentional spotlight; clever. Seasonal cheer and flushed energy rising—a small taste of* *a Northern Hemisphere Yuletide. A group of flaxen-haired damsels from school entertained as a string ensemble accompanied by the spicy aroma of mulled wine; {Freya and Justin's girls}. "This feels 'right'," the Europeans told the Kiwis. "Christmas in the summer never hits the spot." "Well—yes," they agreed, surprised.*

The auction raised funds for a new kindergarten building—her lovely brother interested those he met with tales from London. He treated her to several items from the auction; a free supply of bread for three months from the bakers whose children are at school, and a basket of goodies to take home; herbal teas and bath treats. The Laird undertook some M.C. duties, then slipped upstairs to hide in front of the T.V. —sport viewing a regular distraction. Lord Swallow also took to the stage—but quietly, providing background musical balm. He kept to the edges—did not join their party at any stage. She sought him out before the end, just to say hello and goodbye. She would like him to have joined their table, knowing her brother would have enjoyed speaking with him. The musician's nose is stuffed, he told her—she could not greet him as she would like to have done. The night claimed them all in an unknown future.

Jonathan and I leave The Mountain at ten o'clock this morning to collect Rinky from Deirdre's house where she spent the night; the carol singers left the party at nine-thirty after handing out presents from under the tree. Of course, we speak more about my tricky situation with Adrian and The Laird; our pleasant drive down The Mountain offering perfect confidence sharing time. We travel along the Waikite Bay Road and up another long road into the hills, eventually arriving at our destination. Jonathan appreciates the older-style, colonial villa and chats with Deirdre and her husband. The Kiwi home is friendly and nicely chaotic; a very different environment to Jonathan's expensive, London lifestyle. We chat about this and that; namely about our alternative school and how they are considering sending their youngest to the Kindergarten.

We can't chat openly on the way home—Mrs Flappy Ears never misses anything. "I shall try and keep things in balance," I told my brother earlier. "Once the Laird and Cedric are settled life should find its footing. I don't quite know how, but I am trusting that it will."

Mid-Morning, Mouse: *Hi Friend—what are you up to? We would love to see you up here if you have time to collect another load? The Laird is away for a couple of hours. Don't worry if you are busy.*

P.s Let's go for the lemon meringue pie with lashings of cream next time; slow mouthful by slow mouthful. The plain fare is losing its nourishment, she suggests with a flourish—X

The Laird spends time chatting privately with Jonathan this afternoon. I don't know what is said, but they appear happy enough and head down to the coast alone. Jonathan is meeting an old friend who happens to live in the town; they are driving to Wellington together. We are all sad to wave him goodbye. The Laird has a meeting with College students this afternoon; they are undertaking a charity walk this weekend.

Early P.m. Mouse: *His Lady wonders where he is—what is he busy doing? The Laird has departed with her brother—he is away to Wellington now for his business deal. The Laird will not return until 8 p.m. She wonders if Lord Swallow would like a windy walk or something? The kinder are occupied with their own playtime after the toy shop spree—catching up after an action-packed weekend. Just a thought—X*

Adrian: *He has just arrived home—a full day of work on the pig-sty with a small crew. Big blocked nose—weary—chest getting raw, but spirits good. T.L.C needed. Made bed and now to settle down with cup of tea for planning and gentle catch-up. Are you free? New thought—do you want to borrow my car? My new one, while I get a warrant for my old one? And I'm going away, so you can have it for those days too.*

Mouse: *My Lovely Friend—what a kind offer. I might well take you up on it if ours is condemned. Am free, but at home. Could text catch-up? Wish I was with you—strong need of your balm. When are you off? How long for? X*

Adrian: *Going to Anthroposophical Conference in Wellington this Friday night. 4 days. Biodynamic focus. I'm meant to be there too. I'm tucked up planning new length Main Lesson starting tomorrow. Feeling like a teacher—an unwell teacher—listening to Christy Moore—'The Wind that Shakes the Barley'—haunting. Phew—have to play you that one—Irish political singer/songwriter—pointed—modern. I'm a bit weary to really catch you up on events—Later, eh? Breakfast one day this week?*

Mouse: *Another thought. If all is clear, would you like a phone call?*

Adrian: *Cup of tea, still in bed. Yes, a phone call would be good; whenever you are free—*

At last the house is quiet and Cedric away in the top cabin. The children are asleep and The Laird is out with his students until much later. I dial Adrian's number and we enjoy a cosy chat. "Your brother and I spoke briefly on Saturday night," he divulges. "But I didn't really feel like it, so we couldn't say much. I sense a change in you," he comments. "You are stronger—a new woman." We talk about The Laird, and how we will place a wider ring of protection around him and the house. Is there an issue with The Mountain energy? Should we question it? "You have all the colour at the moment," Lord Swallow says; The Star Dome Enterprise, me in your life etc. What does he have? None of that." Cedric arrives in the kitchen unexpectedly and we have to end our call.

Later P.m. Mouse: Sorry to cut short our lovely chat, My Friend. Thank you for being there—for sharing your solid, unwavering love with me. The ring of fire is filled with a swirling mass of reds and oranges for The Laird. The continued prayer—the warriors on guard. Good night, My Love. Here are the sweet whisperings of our special bond that I would have shared if we hadn't been interrupted—my breath upon your brow—your eye within my soul—our truth alive and held. X

Adrian: Striving to reach them through the barriers of distance, to feel into their issues and edges; facilitating—focusing—seeking the edge—yes, seeking the edge. What is being challenged? And what is on offer here? His people—his family—his people.

Monday 25ᵗʰ June 2007

A.m. Mouse: Driving along Charles road; just dropped The Laird at the church for the next elf of the church walk. Good morning, My Friend—tempted to dive in for a hug, but know it would throw things—X {I amended the typo 'elf' to 'leg', but when I returned to this passage the 'elf' version had been reinstated. Why?}

Adrian: Don't know about that; fairly steady today. Still around—Thank you for everything—consistent and steady Friend. Not a wobble has there been from you through all these trials—a Soul-Mate—so much potential. How will he be with Jules? What if she is warm and receptive; inviting? What then? He will honour his stalwart Friend. There is so much unexplored potential; when is it time to act on this strength that lays waiting? And first to The Laird—tender soul—hurt and damaged but awaiting healing and restoration—anger and grief to move and quiver. And so to the circle of protective, Holy Flame they turn, igniting The Laird's own passion, kindling new fires in his heart. Draw out those accusations that his demons beat him with—expose and verify them. Admit where his mistakes have been and accept that he is a learner. Let them go boys—let them go boys. Forgiveness—ring The Fire—humble—fire the humbling Ring; purifying flame course through him, burning out falsehood; igniting compassion for self—turning that big Heart to Service unto himself, allowing all that is disliked to be seen, to rise like scum to the surface to be skimmed off and discarded—in the smelting crucible—Holy Alchemy—purifying—all the lies—the self-hatred—the blame and accusation—like a piece of ore in the hand of the smelter; so much that is worthwhile in it with only a small fraction of impurity.

Yes. And she; so pure. He loves her; his steadfast Friend and Lover. Sudden thought—help The Laird see that he is in the crucible of purification. How does he want to be? What changes would he make if he were to be refashioned? What personal goals? Where would he improve himself? His is not an outside journey, it is an inner one—use this time when he is free of his old ties which would have held him to his old self. Time to be smelted—to become something new; the best of the old, alloyed with new purpose and direction.

But still, he has not been able to tell her of the sweet taste she can leave with him—the lingering after-taste like nectar; refined and pure and good. Dreams of time spent slowly—unrealistic—the moments are fleeting and perhaps this is just how it is, maybe never to be a long draught—just the tiniest essence stolen through the cracks in a week—maybe—X

Mouse: *I'm nearly home now—your beautiful message arriving as I drive—dark metal road meeting watching eye—lovers' lyric meeting heart and soul. I curl my hungry, naked form about you—X*

Adrian: *Yes—her—her woman needing man—to soften and cherish her—melt her—relieve the grind—store and lighten the everyday—deepen the blue velvet nights—with magic.*

Man needing woman—to strengthen and inspire—order and organize—make sense of the world—review the everyday—refocus the lens of purpose—reveal the wider view—nourish and care—awaken and arouse—hone and channel the wild passions—

Mouse: *His whispers tease the back of her neck—dancing between the dark curls that lie waiting, waiting for the artistry of his touch. She is almost naked in his arms, her cotton underwear maintaining some decorum. She imagines waking to his pressing desire, wrapping him in silky limbs and shallow, welcoming breaths. She needs him—needs him now. With checked ardour and a silent quiver he slides into her—softness meeting strength—a ripple of Rainbows taking him by surprise as they move in the swell of their private ocean. They are in Heaven, she is completely open to his spilling. Deep inside her he lets himself go. They both know she is unprotected. With smiles and delectable kisses they lay themselves open to His Will—to the clear path of a potential new life.*

Adrian: *My Friend—can you come and see me after drop off?*

Mouse: *Just briefly, My Love. Meant to be meeting Cordelia. Love to see you though—5 mins—X*

Adrian: *All clear.*

I park the car and dash in for five minutes, so eager to see Adrian. We lie together on his bed, warm and snuggly. "I love to hold you," he admits. "Can I read you my recent text messages?" How much we enjoy our literary world. I stroke his long legs while he holds me close. "I want to see your nobility," he calls for a serious moment. "As Lovers?" I say. I fix his gaze with a single focus. "What is that?" He asks, slightly taken aback. "It is my nobility standing in front of yours," I reply, running the back of my hand down his cheek. "I love you. It is nice to see you steady." The recent Teacher's Meeting had gone well. Adrian mentions Jules again—"don't let me hold you back," I say, knowing I have nothing to offer in the long run, not really. "I suppose you may be whisked away," he sighs. "You are right—I may be. I would be sad, but we might have no alternative." "I am distracting myself dreadfully this morning," he announces as I take my leave. I have a list of errands to complete before this evening's Matariki Festival.

* * * * * * *

Before the Festival begins I stroll to the top field of the school land; I have half an hour before I am needed in class. I suspect Adrian is milking. He is. We milk the cows together, kissing gently before walking hand-in-hand over the field to set the electric fence. I have borrowed his black rain jacket and walk away with it by mistake. "Oh—my jacket," he calls after me, beckoning me back with a big smile; "another excuse to hold you again." Laughing, he pulls me close for a second time and kisses me so passionately that I can hardly stand straight. "Any other clothes you would like to remove from me?" I ask cheekily. "Why, yes Madam, for sure—your under-garments." "Really Sir! How very forward of you!" "Perhaps it is time to make a stand," Adrian announces, suddenly serious. "I can't imagine another twenty-five years of denying my love. Hmm—"

And so to The Festival—candles in the dusk, reverent whispers with Martha at the piano; one giggling child being escorted outside while I play the lyre. Each child walks the fir branch spiral, collecting a river stone from a central glass jar and placing it in a kete as they leave the Holy path. Vonny has made a flax kete for each class spiral. She is an expert weaver. {A kete is a Maori flax basket.} And then I take the parents out of the class and lead them by torchlight to the Matariki Play organized so beautifully by Lois and Cordelia. The stage on The Green has been transformed into a magical platform for the senior pupils to perform the Maori legend with bare-chested Maori boys appearing suddenly from behind the flood-lit ferns, all to the accompaniment of traditional Maori flutes—hauntingly beautiful.

Te Pito o Watea "The Creation of First Light"
It was Tane who was responsible for the distribution of Te Whanau Marama – the stars. Tane's role as the creator of the night skies is told in a number of stories.
Tane is said to have visited his brother Tangotango to congratulate him on the brilliance of his children – the sun, moon and stars. Tane asked Tangotango if he could take these bright offspring to provide light between their separated parents, Ranginui and Papatuuaanuku. But Tangotango was unsure, allowing only Hinatore (phosphorescent light) to go. Tane placed Hinatore against Ranginui and a silver light

altered the darkness. Tane next asked for and received the stars, and a dim light soon spread from Ranginui and filled our world.

In astronomy, the Pleiades, or 7 **Sisters, is located in the constellation of Taurus. It is among the nearest to Earth and is the cluster most obvious in the night sky. Pleiades has several meanings in different cultures and traditions.** {Taurus is Adrian's star sign.}

I drove to College after the festival to collect The Laird and Cedric before we all came home for the night. The Laird has been biting his inside bottom lip so badly that it is swollen. I must watch him carefully; during his last serious depression he began to self-harm. Thank goodness the holidays are nearly here.

P.m. Mouse: To the accompanying clink of metal milking pails—under the fertile gaze of the Matariki mantle—he takes her to him—their lips speak in longed-for caress and natural homecoming. She loves him. Heavenly Flame of praise and possibility, flicker in our aid—a roaring fire is being stoked by our bonding—please—we pray—meet and match our heat, that we may use its strength wisely, both for ourselves and for those with whom we travel—X

Tuesday 26th June 2007

A.m. Mouse: She has always known that their connection would be as fluent as a perfect duet—a pair of flutes, perhaps, or a dancing couple that glides across the floor of life with arresting grace. But the thought that struck her; the very first thought, in fact, was this: 'If they should ever, against all odds, become lovers—if he should ever deign to brush his lips over hers and linger a while with her in celestial union—then, oh yes—then a thousand stars would burst in the sky.' And—she was right. As Matariki fills their sky this year, and the significance of the night time, Heavenly spangle enters their lives on many levels, she knows that she was right.

Adrian doesn't contact me this morning; I imagine he is busy. I always miss his messages, but I know he will text me soon.

P.m. Adrian: Hi Friend—busy today—needing to put my energy into school again. Teaching Class 1 this afternoon. Will get clear and focused before catching up. Are you okay? X

Mouse: Yes, My Lovely Friend. I'm fine—busy too. Just ended another fab meeting with Sammy; things looking so exciting; can't wait to tell you all. Glad you are okay. Keep focused for school. I'll try not to be a distracting Mousewife! Loving you—X

Sammy and I worked on our mission statements for The Star Dome Project this morning; we are so excited by the potential. We could even set up business alongside the enterprise; money is a constant problem in all our lives. Perhaps we could solve it. The first board meeting of 'The Next Steps Group' is looming and we need to be prepared with our presentation. Sammy's husband Bruce joined our conversation today. I wish The Laird was inspired; he thinks the whole scheme comes from Cloud Cuckoo Land.

What else did I do today? Oh yes—I delivered the fir tree back to a farm; the farm that lent us one for the Mid-Winter Feast. The Laird is out at a College meeting tonight and The Go-Getter has his friend, Stephen, staying. I am tired, but I have logged all our recent text messages. Goodness knows if I will ever get around to typing them up. I imagine any reader might get bored with our Lovers' endless struggle.

P.m. Mouse {Unsent}: My goodness me, Sir—was that you kissing me so sensually at around 5p.m. this afternoon? I was in the car, driving the entire family home when I found myself awash with your being in mine—our lips as one—my breath as yours in the sweetest of nectar kisses. Dear Heavens above! The tangible essence that sweeps through me—the exquisite force of it—the physical call to carry your seed within my womb; this fertile time of the month when I am pulled towards you with such magnetism. Mmm—perhaps The Small One is trying his luck again—

Goodnight, My Love. As the sleepy blanket closes over our day I find myself wrapped in you; in every inch of you. I know you are busy—I know the strength of us can be distracting—I know you are there even when you cannot turn your head to be with me. Go gently into the world of slumber. Let's hold each other in a gentle spoon and familiar caress as we drift off—X

Part Six Salute

The tide is high and the open water beckons like a longing bride. Lord Swallow is already at the Marina when his Lady arrives in the hush of dawn. Wearing extra layers and sailing jackets they hold hands and wander down to the shoreline to welcome the morning and check the winds. It is a long time since they have allowed themselves the pleasure of a day's sailing. They are excited—and aroused. Sweeping her off her feet The Captain carries his First Mate up the gang plank before placing her triumphantly on the deck of their precious vessel.

The Celestial Sea is waiting—has been poised for action on the cold concrete for months. This is her permitted Angel-outbreath and her crew is full of anticipation. They busy themselves sweeping the deck and removing the sail covers. They rig the sails and oil the cleats and pulleys. Lady Thumbelina airs the cabins and stores the day's provisions while Lord Swallow prepares the day's log; his morning prayer should be recorded. And then they are ready——

"Keep her steady while I untie the line from the stanchion," The Captain bounds down the gang plank, so eager to free their Boat and let her taste the briny sea once more. A couple of pushes, aided by The Craftsman, and The Celestial Sea is away; the final yards of concrete are waved goodbye and she splashes into the water, her Captain leaping for the rope ladder as she goes, soaking his trousers in the process.

The Lovers take the wheel together-boldly, as if they haven't been away for long. They are rash; throwing all to the wind they sail swiftly and expertly out into the harbour. They let the currents take them today; they need to reach deep waters quickly. Perhaps they miss some of the spectacular land marks as they go, but it doesn't matter—they have plenty of time to readjust; to take a slow, calculated sail another time. They forget they have been away for so long, for if truth be told they have never been parted. The Captain leads his Lady to their cosy cabin where he quickly removes his salt-soaked clothes before peeling the layers off his first mate. His hunger matches hers as The Boat catches the perfect breeze and takes them right away—

Chapter 1 Shoreline

Wednesday 27th June 2012

A.m. Mouse {Unsent}: Biting cold—fully dressed in bed—your presence in me electric this morn. The Laird is much easier, complaining of the cold though—unusual for him. "You are changing—growing your gossamer wings," I say; "do you really think so?" He replies, disbelievingly.

Good morning, My Love—and how do you fare in this cold weather? Can you feel me with you strongly right now? Or is it my hormones? My desire for you is—mmm

Adrian: Morning—cold feet all night. A stolen, dream planning session snuggled with the cat, ignoring the alarm. He apologizes for withdrawing; initially due to school focus and later his wrestle with a dollop of news and warning that some parents in Petal's Kindergarten were talking about us; Adrian and The Laird's wife. That's all the info received, but cause a spin it did—a shudder through The Boat—wooden dollies rickety and insecure for a while. This morning's thinking: this news and warning from Little J.—Petal reports that several parents from Kindergarten have been talking about us— that's it, but it's enough to alert the siren into a frenzy. Another parent, Fergus, {Lois' husband}, complained about the lack of fire safety awareness during The Festival, {he's a fireman} —my responsibility as the Health and safety Officer. Life-shocks indeed, but in my evening bed mode some of that tension has lifted. How interesting—those caged sparks flare a tiny bit, attempting to plot a new position and course. We may need to take soundings; establish what is actually under this—maybe. Perhaps best course may be to rig sail and enter the choppy water boldly, trusting that there will be no major obstructions, just surface ripples. There could so easily be something there though, and—CLANG! RIP!

Did you hear about Freya and Justin's boat being torn from its mooring in the storm and ending up beached beyond Whakatane?

Mouse: My Friend—what news! How could there be rumours about us when we have been so strict with ourselves for so long? Does our powerful connection produce waves to this extent? The watery swell about our bond seems to have become larger since our 'no go' agreement—have you noticed? But perhaps it is past gossip that has only just caught up with the outer edges. I wonder where it came from? We have not been seen together.

Anyway—I shall still send you my loving, morning message. No—on

283

second thoughts perhaps I won't—it might inflame things too much. I am far too hot to handle right now—desire acute—fertility alive and hungry. I shall go and jump in a cold bath. Mmm—good morning—X

P.s. The force of it—so strong—I cannot fight its pull for much longer, can you? Perhaps we should just catch the current and sail into choppy waters, hoping we don't end up wrecked and beached beyond Whakatane! X

It is freezing cold today—we had to scrape the frost off the windscreen before driving down The Mountain this morning, all the family on board as we remain reliant on the van. The Ute is still at the garage; the gear-box is the problem. Sean, the chief garage mechanic, is away and his female business partner is waiting for his verdict; terminal or worth repairing? So, it is an early departure for the family. I am the regular chauffeur and everything else these days, except for the most important thing—a faithful wife.

A.m. Adrian: *So—the story goes that once our friendship crossed boundaries and was exposed. An agreement was made and we had no contact for three months—at which time a request was made that we meet to clarify positions. Our friendship was tentatively restarted and has since continued, grazing with self-imposed limits.*

Mouse: *—Just sitting—in Tui Park. Today I walked directly in the Angel Sunlight Path on the water, seeing a blaze of yellow/green light all around— a meditation—stopping to offer myself to His Will; a vision of the circle of fire surrounding the whole—beautiful. And then your message arrived. Yes, my thoughts too. The way ahead is ours. Our journey so far is exposed, and that is where we are at. If we step beyond—even if only slightly—then that is our business. It is our life, after all. Have you time to be creative over The Boat passages before you leave for Wellington on Friday? I would like to get the chapters off to Mizzie next week if possible. The regular script is shaping up nicely. Loving you—X*

I have a normal day; home to continue writing, make a few phone calls, organize supper and then I drive down The Mountain to collect the family from both School and College.

P.m. Adrian: *Feeling free tonight—maybe have a go on The Boat passages myself; some creative juices available. How is The Laird? I lost my ring of fire around him in the week's scramble—*

Mouse: *My Fine Friend—thank you for your message. Had the feeling that I might not hear from you for a few days, but perhaps you **are** still feeling the need to stand back? Sorry it is so complicated. Perhaps your meeting with Jules will be positive, and then your Mousewife will become a redundant rodent. Ha, ha—wish it was funny. Fantastic that you feel creative juices flowing—would love to share them with you.*

The Laird is much steadier, although still not warm. Not fair on him really, knowing that I am in love with another man. Lying doesn't work either—you can't pretend to be in love with your spouse when you aren't. Hmm—I sense we will come to some sort of decision at the start of next term. We need to get Cedric off—the houses sold; both The Mountain and The U.K property. We have an 'Open Home' up here this Sunday; three people want to view the property. Your meeting with Jules, and Mizzie's verdict on The Book, might help clear the air; the path ahead more easily read.

Let's hope—

Adrian: *Want me to come up and take a load away tomorrow afternoon before your Open Home? Might help, eh? Would love to really work on it with you—*

Mouse: *Thanks, My Darling—that would be grand. Lunch and work. I shall be here from 12 noon onwards—X*

I work late into the evening. The Laird makes love to me when he comes to bed—but he isn't really interested, and neither am I.

Thursday 28th June 2007
A.m. Mouse:

Moments held in quiet question,
Minutes ticking by—nice—slow.
Frost and ice have left The Mountain,
To fur and feather, care she'll show.
Lord Swallow in his Forest chamber,
Quick to wake, and touch, and pray,
Fully present—things to say.
In the stillness of the dawn hush,
Taking him inside her soul,
Sharing every private secret,
She knows so well—he makes her whole—X

There is no message from Adrian this morning. It is very cold, although the frost has gone. I deliver the family to the relevant destinations before exercising The Bog-Brush in Tui Park. The sky is grey, tinted with apricot streaks. **7** ducks rise off the still water, skimming the surface when they land. Their ripples punctuate the bay, underlining the biting chill. I am wearing a woolly hat today; it doesn't really suit me. I complete a large supermarket shop before driving back home. I am excited about seeing Adrian, although I imagine he might cancel. I sense that he will. The shopping bags are piled up in the kitchen; the bill was high. Food is expensive in New Zealand. It will take me ages to store everything.

Midday, Adrian: *My Friend, I overlooked the fact that School is having a sharing assembly this afternoon. I also want to work on the pig-sty for Lara's farewell tomorrow. Don't think I'll make it today; sorry.*

Of course I am disappointed. I sit by the fire, staring into the flames. I sense my Swallow Man drifting away from the shore—alone in The Boat without me. Does he think about Jules? Wondering if she will be there for him? Perhaps. Restoking the fire, I find a strange shape on the glass window of the stove door; a magical creature with spidery, coral tentacles has appeared at the top of the glass. "Look at this," I show the dog the peculiar pattern, created by the flames and sooty residue. "It looks like a Coral Dragon," I say out loud. "I like that; perhaps it is watching us—'*The Coral Dragon Spy*'. I reckon it's friendly; perhaps it has come to keep me company while Lord Swallow is away this weekend." I fetch some paper and coloured pencils, sketching the unusual shape before it disappears. I sense it is important.

Sammy and I meet at two-thirty for the Next Steps Meeting, presenting our grand 'Star Dome Enterprise' scheme. The School Committee loves the idea; even the High School concept. Yes! How exciting is that? I catch up with Adrian after the meeting, working alone on the almost completed pig-sty. "I'm feeling out of the loop—gloomy I'm afraid," he admits. I am my usual, bubbly self. "It takes a lot to quell my bounce," I say. I leave him to his task; the Porcine Palace is spectacular. I hand over a copy of the completed Star Dome Enterprise missive and he gives me a copy of his recent work on The Boat; another draft of a Craftsman's passage.

P.m. Mouse: *She sends him blessings—and uplifting spirits—the pig-sty is a triumph. She loves her Farmer Friend and places a kiss upon his brow.*
P.s The Go-Getter is worried that he couldn't find Martini to return the games cupboard key—he has left it in the lock. Go gently, My Love. I am here if you need me. X

Cedric and The Laird have been mowing lawns for Bernard and Felicia this afternoon, so I swing by to collect them before driving home. Of course I chat about The Star Dome Project—Bernard is enthusiastic about the ideas; "I have a friend who is looking for a venue as a Teacher Training centre; might that be included?"

Adrian: *Thank you. Hit a gloomy spot just then—still stuck on the concrete. Tell The Go-Getter that I will put the key on Martini's desk. I'll surface again soon—X*

Mouse: *She reads his crafted script about The Boat, a wave of excitement gripping her as she senses his live presence within their story. She loves his seeing eye—his turn of phrase and magical input. But of course she does— they are Artemis and Apollo after all. It is wonderful. She has a few* suggestions she would like to share: his arrival on board *The Boat*—earlier than hers? His take on their tale—Artemis and Apollo mentioned? Yes or no? And the photograph of *The Celestial Sea* that was pinned to her family's kitchen wall in England? She imagines they may need to go through the index, earmarking key events that could be mirrored in *The Boat's* journey. Some creative 'together time' would be perfect—if they could keep their focus! She thanks him for working on it; she is delighted by his words and hopes he feels the same—X

Friday 29th June 2007

A.m. Mouse: He works alone—the man she loves. He has withdrawn—she supposes she should too; be the good wife and all that. But—the pull to perfect union—the life-giving call to be together, in whatever form, is still the greater force. They belong together. This land needs their connection. They both acknowledge the doors that fly open around their togetherness. A mighty rich harvest after their sacrifice of ploughing the potential fruit back into the soil. Hmm—she needs to see him—needs to talk to him about the farm; all the ideas have been met with such enthusiasm. Big J. even added to the positivity by asking for a wetland project alongside the outlined scheme. 'I have several single friends,' she added—'ladies of a certain age with money behind them who would love to be involved with something like this.'

Your biodynamic course has come at just the right time—a permaculture angle would be important too. The next job is to sketch out a rough idea of the plan; buildings, pasture, livestock, orchards, market gardens, compost etc. What say you, My Fine Sir? Can we work on these ideas together?

Go safely today—safely and gently, the brush of velvet against your thigh—a loving hand in yours—M—X

Adrian is quiet. I miss his regular catch-up texts. I see him briefly at school instead. "Wonderful plan," he comments. Others arrive on the scene and he turns away, not wanting us to be seen together.

Early P.m. Mouse: Hi Friend—thought to dive into Kitty's Leaving Lunch briefly. Wise or unwise? What do you think?

Still no response; Adrian must be busy. Perhaps it is the right and only thing to move away. I feel rather dead inside. I have been roped into cleaning the windows in Class 2 and spend a happy half-hour with a handful of parents. Then I visit the office, photocopying more pages of The Star Dome Project. One of the music teachers has a husband who is very keen on the idea of a Star Gazing observatory on our site; he has already worked out a two-year forecast and set-up cost; how keen is that? I incorporate his blurb in the project missive and hand out several copies to interested parties. I can't believe the positive openings that keep appearing.

The Laird is very wobbly when I collect him and Cedric from College. I don't know how to help him—or what he needs. I cannot give him the one thing he asks for, although I know that my undying adoration won't fix his depression. How I loathe the dark beast that hovers over him. Lucia arrives to play with Rinky—thank goodness for happy little girls. I manage to swim today, and work out a sensible timetable. The Heavens open later on when I take The Go-Getter to his hockey game. I wonder if Adrian is already on his way south for the conference? He probably feels bad that he didn't say goodbye properly. I don't like being so separate.

P.m. Adrian: *How did it go at Kitty's lunch? Saw your car there. I made it through the term—yay! Roof is on the pig palace and Lara is farewelled, staff goodbyed and I am en route. Nice trip—unwinding slowly in good company; Mandy and Rob. Fish and chips for tea—needed a break badly—stretched too thin. Quiet I feel—catching up time. Looking forward to chatting with you over the time away—freedom out-breath. Speak soon—*

Mouse: *My Friend—thank you for the message. Have been unsure how you are—where you are at—feeling you a long way off; not that I have any right to a claim on you. Ho hum. I'm sitting in the car, the comforting rain making patterns on the windscreen—listening to classical music as I wait for The Go-Getter's rep hockey game to finish. I shall watch the final fifteen minutes. I have had a snooze. The Laird is away for the night at a whisky 'do'. He was in a terrible state today—might have to get him signed off work if he doesn't improve over the holiday break. He is negative about the Star Dome Project and presentation; he sees me wanting to stay here with you, getting really stuck in. Hmm—I suggested that he should consider going home for a few months; take a sabbatical—get some counselling—undertake a feasibility study for his future school ideas. Could be a way to go; he was relatively keen on the idea. We shall see. I'm looking forward to chatting with you over the break. I've missed your balm.*

Kitty's lunch was lovely; I dived in to give her a goodbye hug—delicious slice of carrot cake as well—wicked, but I needed cheering up. Well done on the Pig Palace! You always master whatever creative project comes your way. So—you have survived the term—in better shape than The Laird, anyway. I wonder what is coming next? You'll never guess what else has jumped into the picture; Bernard has been trying for ages to get his neighbour to speak with School—all attempts via current channels have fallen flat thus far. He is a Dean from Waikato University, trying to link up with a school to establish some Teacher Training scheme. He would be interested in knowing more about our particular philosophy. He has been considering an offer from Bellevue College, but is unsure about the place. Can you believe that? We have organized a meeting for next week. Lois is hopping with glee over the potential. She says Big J. knows a lot about teacher training; she has been lecturing on the Auckland course. I look forward to telling her about it soon.

Well, My Fine Sir—I had better step out into the rain and support our Go-

Getter. He is so keen on the game! Take care—have a wonderful time. Keep me posted.

Saturday 30th June 2007

Adrian is quiet—keeping some distance again. I keep looking at my phone, hoping he might have sent a message, but it remains blank. The day is dire, in every way. The Laird's depression deepens and coats everything with a thick layer of foul tar. I swear to never undertake any risky project with him ever again. I will never own land or try to make a go of things with him ever again. I will never live away from community and family with him ever again. I want to be with Adrian—in all things—in all ways.

A.m. Mouse, {Unsent}: She realizes how important he has become to her; a day or two without their close bond and she is unhappy. Would he feel the same way if she withdrew as he has done? She has always been there for him—except perhaps for some days between January and April—days when she decided his silence meant he didn't want her in his life. But, these feelings were always over-ridden by the stronger sense that their love was beyond the earthier, petty games usually played between couples. There again—she keeps forgetting she is not free—should not even be speaking with her Lover in this way—should not have a lover at all. For in her mind this side of herself is free to give to another. It is virgin territory, waiting for decades to lie in the arms of its rightful partner. So—she asks him—how was it for him when she didn't contact him during those bleak months? What did he feel? Honestly— this is important. She supposes that what she is asking is this—'how important am I in your life?' How much do you want me, Sir? For if I am to disrupt our lives to this extent as a final conclusion in our favour I have to be absolutely certain that you want me beside you more than anything else in the world, for the price is high and this is no longer a game.

Later, Mouse, {Unsent}: Hi there, Silent Friend—hope you are having a grand time—meeting interesting people? Wooing the ladies? Mountain life is perfectly shitty—not sure how I will take 2 weeks of it without the school timetable to break the bleakness. Cooped up with a serious depressive and a morose adolescent who is adversely affected by his father's intolerable grimness is horrible. I reckon we should put Cedric on a plane sooner rather than later, and get medical help for The Laird. He won't make any decisions about Cedric's departure—for lots of reasons—the main one being that he wants to get on the plane too! I am trying to hold it all together, alone—tricky test. The Laird needs me at College these holidays to help him get organized. He's panicking big-time over his upcoming work load. I would love a let-up from the mire—put them both on a plane for some respite. Sorry Darling, just need someone to talk to. Take care—X

We spend another day at home; The Laird's shocking mood continues. I am very worried about him. He lives in a tormented hell. I suppose I have blown his cover by stepping away. He cannot hide from himself any longer. It needed to happen, somehow. I couldn't have born anther twenty years of providing the support/disguise for his issues.

P.m. Adrian: *Hello, My Friend. I'm on my way to Jules' place to stay after an invitation. Funny isn't it—the other place I was going to stay was pleased I had an alternative invite because they had unexpected visitors with kids. Flow—rightness. The conference is rich and thought-provoking—a great speaker—*

I feel dulled—knowing he will be off and away; thinking it is probably for the best. I don't feel like replying.

Later, Adrian: *He knows she waits and pains—his Friend—his abandoned companion—for news of her place in his life. And he floats on the day's currents, steering little—helpless and weak. The need to be liked sends his gaze out—his words soothing but lacking conviction—delighted to belong—courage leaving him. He turns at last to his inner—to attend to his tender belly; wheat and forced conversation and rich but intense meetings. He lies alone, wondering if he missed an opportunity to connect with Jules. But confusion—and leaving himself. She is a warm friend, but he does not relax with her as he does with his accepting Mousewife. There is an element of cautiousness with him that though he strives to quell it, the residue remains and sends him into confusion—too much. He looks for the relaxation that comes when he releases attachment to an outcome, or listens hard enough to the demands and accusations that he levels at himself.*
And so he lies flat out, tired, but awake—seeking to penetrate to the place he can reach with his mate—where the truth shines so clear that the shadows of guilt and doubt can no longer dwell. Can he find it tonight, or will sleep overtake him? Where does he find it? So wound up is he—nervous and excited. He imagines her beside him—maybe stroking his brow—listening to him struggling for words—accepting and tolerant—helping to steady their rocking Boat.

Mouse: *My Friend—I am here—yes—wondering—wishing you well—feeling flat—empty—stuck on the concrete—not minding—yet minding. I turn to face you, partly prepared to see you go; finding the truth of us refusing to leave our side. I run my fingers through your hair—My Prince—My Lord Swallow—always. Some things won't fade. Come to me; stay a while with me here—now—quiet and still together, as we know how—blue velvet night—gentle touch that says all—X*

Sunday 1ˢᵗ July 2007

A.m. Mouse: the bleak cold has left The Mountain, except for the persistent bleakness of The Laird's mind that has intensified with the end of term—his out-breath bringing with it a massive black cloud from which she cannot escape. And her Lord Swallow, fellow warrior, is away. She battles on, her positivity undaunted—The Laird's inability to move beyond, a living hell. The Light she placed around them, all three, late last night was silvery-white. She wonders at its different tone; a more intense heat, offering more protection perhaps.

Today they make the arrangements for Cedric's departure. The Laird is reluctant—does not feel it is the right decision to send him away. They all know he has to escape the constant negativity. Hmm—sorry, My Love, life on The Mountain is pretty grim at the moment. I have to fight to keep things afloat. Church, then lunch at Sharron and Warwick's house as a 'get together' after the mid-winter feast should help. Then I have the rest of the holidays to get The Laird straight for two College inspections and the European trip in September, although I have real concerns he may lose it before then.

So, My Darling Heart—your prayers for us today—your Lady has voiced her desire to 'come and go' in a more freed up way should they return to The U.K. The suggestion was not turned down. She needs to get him home. Wish I was in your arms; hope you are feeling more relaxed this morning. It always takes a while to feel comfortable in a new situation. I notice that in you especially, with your issues over being accepted. I love you—go gently—learn lots—make connections—send me some balm if you have time—M—X

Adrian: Been conversing with an old architect from Wellington—retired and keen to do some anthroposophical design. Talked with others about this system called C.S.A; Community Supported Agriculture, where people pay a yearly pledge to a farmer, or group of farmers—like shareholders; the farmers get a salary and present a budget each year.

Later, teatime: Busy time—a bit scrambly but stimulating. Hope you're holding up—strength to you—blessings around your family. My apologies for going so far away, My Friend. But it has been refreshing to get such a complete break and to meet new people. Still a little flat though—half speed— could do with a nice, comforting curl up. Not sure where things are with Jules; may see her tonight, or may not. With Aunty Bee and my cousin right now. Sounds like you need—

We have fun with Sharon and Warwick today—but the rain—my goodness, does it rain! We sit by the fire, eating far too much. The children have a great time, out in all weathers. We discuss the Mid-Winter Feast and how it could be improved next year. Sharon shows me an article in the local newspaper about the Yellow Pages takeover; "that's your brother's name, eh?" Well— fancy that! Most of the Mid-Winter Feast Committee is present. I enjoy chatting to Rory and his wife Kim. The Laird joins in a little, but he is unusually quiet. I like Sharon and Warwick's colonial villa. Warwick is a clever carpenter;

the wooden bathroom is a masterpiece. We are home by four o'clock. For some reason there is no mobile phone coverage on The Mountain. Shute. Perhaps the rain is interfering, or is my mobile phone broken? I telephone Adrian on the landline to let him know about the problem. He sounds well; "nice to hear your voice," he tells me. I write a text message which I store in the phone's memory. Perhaps I'll send it later:

P.m. Mouse: Tipping torrents—more rain than I have ever seen. Two days of it—awash! Lovely lunch gathering at Sharon and Warwick's. Too much cake, but good feedback after the Mid-Winter 'do'. Church today—calming—simple—felt you there beside me on my left, our fingers linked, speaking silently to each other.
'If you are truly being led by The Holy Spirit, then you stand beyond the common law,' the Priest's words made me sit up! 'Those who step out to follow Christ do not look back.' We finished with a hymn: 'Longing for Light we wait in the darkness, longing for truth we turn to you. Make us your own; your Holy People, Light for the World to see. Christ be our Light, shine in our hearts, shine through the darkness.'
Thank you for your messages, My Friend. Lovely to keep in touch through these wild storms. Is it rough where you are? I'm not sure about your exact whereabouts—shows how little catch-up time we have managed recently. Take care—M—X

Adrian: Urgent help with The Laird—any support around—the chrysalis must go through chaos to become a butterfly—as does the egg—out of destruction arises the new—

Monday 2nd July 2007
A.m. Mouse, {my phone is still dodgy, but I manage to send this message later on}: *It is mild this early holiday morning—and they are cut off. The local network is down. She finds a clear moment to telephone on the land line to let him know that she is still here. Perhaps it is a test for their telepathic skills. Hmm—she will try and send this message when she ventures out later on. How is he, she wonders? Making any progress with friend Jules? His Mountain Lady wishes the best for him. Today we begin a new routine—diet—swimming—working in The Laird's office at College. I like to set myself disciplined timetables; they usually inspire me to achieve greater things. But The Laird is never particularly positive or interested in domestic or personal endeavour; not nearly enough people involved, or physical, manly challenge! Too feminine just with her; his annoying wife; to be endured rather than enjoyed. I sigh—wishing for my Man—knowing how inspired he and I would be in planning and implementing such trivia! Have a lovely day, My Friend—M—X*

Adrian doesn't contact me. We achieve parts of the new regime. I discover that my phone is indeed broken, so I quickly purchase a replacement. I don't like it as much as my old friend though—and guess what? My original one has just started working again! What? I send Adrian one message on the new phone:

Mouse: *Had to get a new phone—old one died; wonder why? Perhaps it got wet, or dusty. Don't like the new one as much. Don't know my way around it; don't like the yellow screen; might need another lesson. Hope you are having fun?*

Later: managed to get my old friend/phone working, thank goodness; needn't have bought a new one after all—bother. Oh well, one of us might need it soon, I'm sure. This one must have got wet; I don't know. Sorry to bombard you with my text backlog—you might not want to hear from me if you are being sociable with other damsels. Anyway, My Friend, we had a better day—The Laird a little easier—swim and office work. And how do you fare? X

My phone screen remains blank. Adrian will be enjoying a new environment, yet finding it difficult not to spin out and lose himself. I can't imagine feeling so unsure of myself—all the time.

Chapter 2 Screen

Tuesday 3ʳᵈ July 2007

A.m. Adrian: Here in bed he lies, the wind surging and rushing outside— carrying the salty air over the coastal land. He is thinking about relationships—about Jules—about his Mousewife—about himself. Is there anything between Jules and him? There is the common ground of age, single status, anthroposophy and education—but it seems unlikely that she would be willing. He looks at himself—what could he offer her? No security; neither physical nor emotional; his fickle heart that abandons others and himself so readily would cause problems. His courage fails him around strong people— his words are lost—his opinion dropped—an agreeable fool who stands on the edge trying to be invisible; just like at school. Would she still be interested in him when she was rescuing him so often? Having to watch his sensitivity; she herself is bold. Hmm—he struggles already—it seems unlikely—and then there is softness too. He thinks he disappoints her with his weakness. She looks for a man he thinks, but is often disappointed by him. Perhaps he should be more enigmatic—more mysterious—rather than wearing his heart on his sleeve as he does.

He looks now for the place where he does not have an attachment to any outcome—where he is satisfied with his enoughness—needing nothing—no striving after connection—trust in the rightful weaving of the guides in his life. So, he smiles and relaxes—soon he will venture back to the house from his little sleep-out. Jules is just a friend with a soft possibility of some potential, and to be honest, there are aspects of her that he is unsure about. But trust, 'The Peace be with you,' as the Christian Community Priest says in church, touching each communicant's cheek. Yes—trust. It has been a fruitful trip; new information, connections and intentions; several new thrusts. Better to accept these gifts with thanks, allowing the energy to rise rather than letting the worry and confusion cloud and devitalize him. He heads home today with his Aunty—always a good talk to be had there. She travels as far as Hastings, then he will probably hitch-hike, maybe with a young German girl from the conference.

Home—how will it be—picking up the pieces? He feels lighter—but The Laird's collapse is concerning. He adds his Light to hers. Perhaps rest is all they need—lots of it.

Mouse: Familiar routine—dog already in place, awaiting her mistress's quiet writing time with a cup of tea and Lord Swallow. She knows he is present, even though he may be occupied elsewhere. They both know there is a part of them that is ever joined. The Castle Hound knows it too—her comfortable position and shaggy eye-brows glancing sideways says that she knows. And so—another day of similar task and routine—nothing interesting to tell her Man. He will be getting bored of all this by now; no wonder he needed to escape for a while. She must remember not to load him with her quandary, besides, they have other exciting things to talk about. The Book—yes—The Book. A final session on the original Craftsman's piece—might she suggest another paragraph on The Boat's building? The raising of the masts, the laying of the deck, perhaps? And his arrival on board; his voice in union with their beautiful vessel? An introduction to himself—his background—his recent, single status—his work etc? Then we can send the first Parts off to our editor.

Thank you for your message, My Friend. I miss you when you are silent. I can hear more of your balm arriving as I write, a welcome beeping from the computer because my mobile phone lies beside the screen; a live chapter creation, even though these texts are destined for Book 3. Take care, My Love—M—X

Adrian: Here is a text from two nights ago that got sent in my sleep to my friend Amy in Auckland—twice!! Strange—must have rolled on my phone after dropping it as I nodded off. Funny, eh? Go well in strength and hope, My Friend. Know that you can make a difference—penetrate the damp gloom around The Laird to ignite and rekindle his spark. Pile him high with bundles of dry twigs—get a merry blaze going—warm his cold heart—have a look at his wounds in this new light.

'Her reassurance—does her Swallow Man lean on this—mother? Or partner of ease? Partner where his maturity can find its place—his truth be easily spoken—his fears laid to rest. He contrasts this to Jules—who walks past to go to the bathroom—there he waits for an invitation, a sign—uncertain—hopeful—waiting—unsure of the waters around him—alert and watchful—heart on his sleeve. He knows this, but the impulse so strong and habitual'—

Mouse: My Darling Friend—you know I wish the very best for you, so—the only questions I will ask are these: 'does Jules see The King in you? And is there instant, strong chemistry on many levels between you both?'

Adrian: The Lord is my shepherd I shall not want. He leadeth me beside still waters. He maketh me lie down in green pastures. He leadeth me on paths of righteousness for his name's sake. He resoreth my Soul. He preparest a table in the presence of mine enemy. Yeah, though I walk through the valley of the shadow of death, I shall fear no evil, for thy rod and thy staff they comfort me. Thou annointest my head with oil; my cup runneth over. Surely goodness and mercy shall follow me all the days of my life and I shall dwell in the house of The Lord for evermore.

Mouse: *Thank you for the psalm, My Friend; I know it well—a favourite hymn in church. Thank you for reminding me of it—remember you spoke it to me in your car at Vonny's house when your Ma was staying and had just anointed you with oil? We were interrupted by Sasha—urgent calls for you to unlock the farm gates for her horses when they first arrived at the farm. Travel well today—keep me posted. See you soon—in care and trust—M—X*

P.s Was it the psalm that you sent to Amy? Or the one before?

Adrian: *It wasn't the psalm—it was the one about 'mother'. Did you get that? I was clearing some draft messages and thought I'd send the psalm before deleting it—X*

Mouse: *Yes—got the question of 'mother or lover of ease?' Nice, but what was your 'impulse so strong and habitual' as you waited for Jules' invitation? Were you referring to your skilful wooing tactics, or your habit of wearing your heart on your sleeve? I can certainly vouch for the wooing tactics, Fine Sir, even without our deeper bonding; they are fluent and very seductive! —! —X*

P.s. I'm cleaning out the grate in my old blue jumper—a Cinderella day—waiting for My Prince—considering the fascinating article on Quantum Physics and The Soul that I have been reading. I am trying to begin The Laird's day with a spiritual reading—prayer with a candle and a cup of tea. It worked well yesterday; he was definitely brighter, although he still can't make the final decision about Cedric's future.

Ho hum—on with the ash pile—big love—X

We have a regular day. The Laird goes to College, taking the boys and returning with another load of logs. Rinky and I stay put on The Mountain, reading and sewing. I manage to write. Cedric spends the morning with his best friend, Stephen Leighter; he enjoys that. Stephan's father teaches at College and his mother is lovely. A positive household for a change.

Midday, Adrian: *A trip north with my Aunty Bee. Now arrived in blustery Palmerston North. Just read her my texts of the morning—"great," she said; "So good that you are recording them. Your honest appraisal of yourself—could be a real solace to someone else." She sees us as Soul-Mates that can offer each other something in the moment—the nautical theme suggests the bond isn't incarnating; a past life connection that will eventually fade once it is finished.*

Mouse: *Interesting—not incarnating? Perhaps. Past life a definite. Let the present tides take us—help us to understand the questions we tentatively ask—in blustery Palmerston North—in wind-swept Twealm Realm—through whispered intention and silent waiting—I am with you. X*

P.s I have just settled down to the daily text logging. I like the routine; it suits my need for inward time. 35 messages since Friday! 19 to go. I am developing a small callous on the side of my right-hand, little finger—and a swollen top knuckle of my writing digit. My, my—these Soul-Mates have a history to record. The 3rd Book must be nearing completion by now. I wonder what the grand dénouement will be? A graceful fade into the Elvish Ether or a telepathic relationship across hemispheres?

Ambitious, My Lord Swallow—X

Late P.m. Adrian: *Well, well, a most interesting day. I have now seen all my Aunty Bee's children living in N.Z—and heard her unbelievable life story; incredible destructiveness of the father—fearful abuse of the children—and then to see them all and track the damage. Amazing. Staying the night— hitching tomorrow. Someone is milking the cows, bless them. Hope all is well all round—X*

Mouse: *Sounds like an interesting time. Just woken to find your message. Sleep well, My Friend. Travel safe—X*

Wednesday 4th July 2007

A.m. Adrian: *He is lying awake—thinking—early morning. Soon to rise with his cousin Anthea's preparations for work. He is going to be dropped off early on the road. Strong thoughts this morning for all his cousins—their Spiritual Light so, so dulled—stolen by spirits of hate, confusion, fear, rage and resentment. Squashed into uncomfortable forms; Nick into intellectualism —Sam into incredible stubbornness and total lack of reverence—Benny into extraordinary anger and red-hot, mental whirlwind, spitting sparks of fury, driven by rage—Jo, who appears most normal, nice even, is selfish—a womaniser; hard-working but hedonistic—all of them bearing the terrible scarring from a father who welcomed evil—possibly practising black magic. Benny was suffocated by him as a baby, possibly many times. Nick was picked up and thrown into bed if he ever cried at night; the façade of a nice guy but black with pain and hatred.*

This morning a thought to come against these beings with Christ's might, commanding them to loose their hold on these fine, young, intelligent members of his family. Then the thought came that I want to cultivate God's Love in me, blazing through my own shadows—the ones that have blocked my nose right now; these areas where I have withdrawn through doubt, where self-loathing has crept in. Yes—Oh Lord—I review my day now, seeing anew the sights where your creation shone—where the flower or the child, the cloud or the river, the sun's touch or the land's fall, the plain's march or the river's sweep, the human grace, courage and laughter all played—where God's loving hand was evidenced—where the finger of Love touched this wrestling heart; the moment that when expanded revealed the Love that all with eyes to see could witness. So to let this sweep through me—healing—

Mouse, sent later because of network failure: *Healing and trust— sweet nectar of Unconditional Love, where fear flees in the face of a child's*

298

bright smile—where comforting kitchen table and waiting meal say 'all is well and I am here for you'—where a hand is taken and brow kissed in strong holding.

*My Friend is up and writing before me today. I am about, but the waiting computer screen with the next chapter has distracted me for 15 minutes. Part Two—tearful goodbyes—taxi to the airport—arrival in a new hemisphere. I'm finding it interesting looking back; my acute memory taking me there instantly; the small details flooding in. I can't wait to work on it some more with you. Can you be free this Saturday? Thought I would ask for the whole day off, to complete the first draft of The Book, {except for Part Three}, and despatch it across the oceans. It will be the **7.7.2007** on Saturday! Something I hadn't realized until just now. What do you think? I couldn't tell The Laird that we would meet—but he would allow The Book work.*

So, My Love—your Priestly role is being challenged with the exposure of your Aunt's shocking family troubles. What a heavy load for her to bear. She must be one of those highly advanced Angels. Your prayer is beautiful—as always. The mobile phone network is dodgy again today, although your messages are getting through okay. Mine I am storing until the air waves clear. Perhaps your powerful prayer cuts through network blockages, undeterred while the intention is carried to help and heal all family members battling with darkness. I will try and send this message later. Travel safe and well. I wonder whom destiny will send your way today. Come home to me soon—X

I have a difficult morning trying to send text messages. My happiness has become dependent upon modern technology. Who would have ever imagined that?

Late A.m. Mouse: *Hi Friend—this is a tester message. Having problems.*

Cedric and Stephen are cleaning windows at College to earn some money today. I drive Cedric down The Mountain for his day's work. The Laird comes too—he might tackle some more desk work. I bump into the College Principal, asking if he would consider giving our alternative school some advice on starting a senior school initiative. Having established College, Brenan is the perfect person to ask. "Of course," he offers. Kiwis are always generous and accommodating. School will be pleased; Big J. suggested I ask him. I continue to battle with my mobile phone; it will send short messages, but nothing of any substance. Perhaps it needs a new Sim card. I shall get one in town when Rinky and I go shopping later on today.

Late A.m. Mouse: *Me again—testing—think my Sim card may be at fault. My phone will only send short messages, although I received yours okay. How are you? Thanks for lovely texts; just off to town for a new Sim card. Still testing—X*

Rinky loves sushi, so I buy her a treat as well as something from the bakery, making sure we include The Laird who always appreciates surprise, edible gifts.

Early P.m. Mouse: *Been to Vodaphone shop—problems with network apparently. My long messages might have to be for The Book only, not surprised my phone has lost its strength! Are you on your way home? Hope to see you soon—X*

Adrian hasn't sent any more messages—unless he has, but they haven't reached me.

P.m. Mouse: *Network seems to be okay now. I'll send the morning missives. Hope you are all right? Just taken the children to see a lovely film called 'The Bridge to Terabithia'—a young boy meets a girl in a forest—where their imaginations take off—M—X*

My thoughts turn to the long conversation that I had with Sharron yesterday—about the Mid-Winter Feast. From an Anthroposophical point of view we shouldn't bring any Christmas element into the event. We have had interesting debates about this; some strong community voices pushing their opinions on others: "We should be celebrating seasonally, not religiously." Few families are rooted in the school philosophy, so they are uninformed on a deeper level. "Cosmically, the globe is thrown off-kilter if the four major festivals aren't celebrated at the same time across the world;" Big J. gave us her Anthroposophical opinion after the event, even though she thoroughly enjoyed the successful fundraising party. "I suppose that makes sense," Sharron and I agreed. "There's no problem with the Mid-Winter bit— just leave out the overtly Christmas element." The four major festivals affecting the globe every quarter are: Christmas, Easter, St. John's and Michaelmas.

Our conversation turned to marriage—and men facing mid-life crises. Like most couples, Sharron and Warwick have their issues. Did Sharron purposefully steer the conversation that way? I mentioned The Laird's difficulties; "yes—I realize there are problems," she said. Sharron is good friends with Felicia and with Simon's wife, Dauncy. I imagine they have told her about Adrian and me. I almost brought it up, but decided against doing so. I could have confided in her and found a lovely friend but I hesitated and the moment passed.

The Go-Getter was playing with a school friend today. The two boys have come home together. Our boy makes us laugh at supper tonight: "did you know that the canary increases its brain size every year by learning a new tune? And if you burn all your eyebrows off they won't grow back, but if you burn just a bit off they *will* regrow!" He is amusing; our little ray of sunshine within a gloomy, black cloud. The boys rush back upstairs after the meal, keen to complete a Lego creation. Cedric is staying the night with Stephen. They have more College windows to clean tomorrow. Perfect. I like seeing my children busy and productive—and happy. I can't stand unhappiness. Who needs it? I go to bed early. The Laird doesn't join me.

Chapter 3 Steer

Thursday 5th July 2007

A.m. Mouse, {unsent}: *No word from him? She hopes he is alright. Home? Tired? Resting, she imagines. She dreamt of him last night. He had lost a front tooth—a cracked rib too. Strange. The Laird did not come to bed last night, although she felt him stroke her face before he left for the top cabin; "what am I to do with you, My Little One? You look just like a small mouse tonight." She wishes it could be different. The gentle, honest moments are fleeting. He might not have said those words if he had known she was awake. His dull, blotto state continues—lots of hiding in front of the T.V—and his piles of books—and the eternal sports commentary on the Internet. Better than the hand-wringing, head-bashing of a few days ago, she supposes. A doctor's visit is next up; some medication might be important, although she suspects the only thing that will really lighten his mood is a new horizon; a new future; a job offer in The U.K. Hmm, he does not turn to her any more—as a man should turn to his wife. He hasn't done so properly for a long time now—for years before they came to N.Z. Why else would she have needed another man?*

*She has lain in Lord Swallow's passionate and warm embrace all night—feeling his manhood enter her many times. She is ripe for him, but what does it mean? And if they are not incarnating and are to fade away what do these continuous, strong feelings demand? Perhaps nothing will change until she lets him go. She wrestles with The Laird—helping him to allow Cedric his freedom. Cedric has written a lovely note, explaining why he has decided to leave New Zealand. It makes sense. "But **I** want to go back to England," The Laird cries. "**I** want to have new shoes and a new adventure." He is so wrapped up in himself; she can't believe it. What is wrong with him? He is cross—and then he finds more to fuel his anger—her writing upon the screen—a hot passage. "Yes, it is passionate," she admits. "I will tell your School Principal," he threatens. "I don't know what I want any more."*

He is in such a mess—and it isn't just because of her. This would have flared up eventually. He has little faith—no personal sense of any deeper impulse—strange because it is what he teaches. Perhaps everything is her fault, as he so often tells her. He wants his wife to be truly sorry. But she cannot be. Meeting Lord Swallow is the best thing that has ever happened to her. She won't lie. X

Adrian: *Hi Friend—I'm back and readjusting. Feeling into how people are; a bit sensitive actually. How are you?*

Mouse: Hello there, Sir—lost you since yesterday. Glad you are home safely; expect it will take a while to adjust. Wish I was with you in a friendly, catch-up cuddle. Would you like a visit if I can escape? Am in the process of trying to get The Laird to make the final decision about Cedric. Hmm—not easy—I could send you stored text messages if you felt like them. Just let me know. Good to have you back—X

Adrian: Hi Friend—nice to hear from you. Quiet time for me. Would love a visit, but think it better that I restore myself under my own steam first. Back in bed right now—really low on energy. Might just relax and read—or plan my time. Not really excited by anything—just snuggling.

Mouse: My Lovely Friend—feeling just the same as you—'no-man's-landish,' if you know what I mean? The Laird is at College—trying to get on. I've been reading and crafting with the tinks. Could feel myself tucked up with you by the fire earlier, if that is allowed? Hound and I are now strolling. Then we must sort out the mess under the house—shocking state! Nice to have you close—X

Midday, Adrian: But now slight lift of energy and off to town I go. Working in little surges. Will be heading up your road sometime soon to collect hay for the animals. Almost feel like slipping away tonight—going feral somewhere. Maybe I will—dancing in the night.

Mouse: Let me know if you are passing—if you want a feral companion. Could do with some star magic with my Swallow Man; just text me. Laird not present to me at all—he even slept in the top cabin last night. I could easily slip away—on foot—in the moonlight—Dance of the Elves; they steal home for an hour or two, rekindling the truth they know is theirs—to sail in familiar waters once again upon their Wave Slicer; their Watery Dancer taking them far away from the shore.

The Laird left for College early this morning. He is making *some* headway in his office. He telephones me at eleven o'clock. I apologize for hurting him, although saying sorry isn't really enough, especially when I continue to upset him by writing a book about my illicit adventure. He is soft and kind for a change—I have missed that side of him in recent months. "I just need to express myself," I try to explain. "I know," he replies. "Far better to make a positive of it with my writing," I offer. "Hmm—I suppose so," he grudgingly agrees.

This afternoon the children and I get stuck in under the house, sorting out the clobber and making 'keeping' or 'going' piles. Goodness, we have a lot of junk—extraordinary considering we have only been in the country for two years. "Let's put up the basketball net," The Go-Getter enthuses. "Can we hammer it into this beam?"

P.m. Adrian: *Really must see you—so many exciting things on my mind. Off on a new venture already. Sanguine man to the rescue. So, I am keen to join you in writing The Book this weekend—the date you mentioned as being important earlier in the year; the **7.7.2007**—might be a turning point. I am definitely ready for a change, and wonder if it will be to farming. I've lost some confidence in myself, to be honest. Could I actually do it? Am I steady enough? Will it just be a whim?*

Mouse: *I'm in—can feel the potential in the new breeze. Need to see you too. I will ask to be away this Saturday; might get a free moment before. Text me if you are off for a midnight amble and I could meet you at the end of the drive. Can't wait to be creative with you—lots of ideas for The Book I would like to share. Go well, oh partner of mine—X*

Adrian: *Major room change about to take place. How about I come up your road about 6a.m. or so tomorrow—en route to collect hay further up The Mountain? It will be an early start, but. Feeling more connected after talking with Vonny, so the feral romp has lost its urgency. Tomorrow is okay now—risky though, eh? A bit furtive; I don't really like it—be better out in the open. Still, looking forward to sharing—bit of news, so thermos of warm tea and a chat. What say you?*

Mouse: *Love to, My Fine Sir. Just text me when you leave home. I tend to be up by then anyway. I'll bring the tea. Meet at the end of the drive? Special Love—M—X*

The little lady appears from under the house, covered in mud from top to toe; her cherub face is as muddy as her pink jeans. She is very excited; "I have a new routine," she announces; "basketball and then four laps around the house, more basketball and then five laps." I smile, delighted to see her so animated. "I might get dirty, but I don't care!" well—I am certainly very grubby after scrabbling about in the dirt for hours, so I am going to run a bath. Cedric and The Laird arrive home just as I am undressing; time to jump in the water.

P.m. Adrian: *Room nearly done—big change. Hope you're well?*

I don't return Adrian's message; the timing isn't right and I am tired. The Laird comes to bed but doesn't turn to me. I have told him that I am not interested in lovemaking if it isn't rooted in the spiritual. He doesn't understand what I am talking about—and that, coupled with his terrible depression—is the cause of our trouble.

Friday 6th July 2007

Early A.m. Adrian: Good morning. I'm hitched up and leaving now. Could you bring a sheet of paper and a hand-saw? Thanks—see you soon.

Mouse: Okay, My Friend—all set—X

I leave the dog inside. The fire is stoked. I pray for a clear hour to meet with my Lover and head out, into the dark. The moonlight behind the clouds makes a dramatic backdrop to my wild outing. A sudden wind gets up and plays chase with my hair, blowing it across my face and into my eyes. My feet crunching on the gravel sound especially loud this morning.

Adrian: Bright moonlight highlights clouds—gleams on the roof of the stationary car. Chill wind seeks the cracks between the layers of clothing.

Adrian has already arrived by the time I reach the end of the drive. I approach his parked car, but he is walking down the road from higher up, ready to meet me after an early forage, I suspect. We hug each other tentatively—this is unfamiliar territory; the clandestine nature of this prohibited meeting feels dangerous. We are excited and uncomfortable, both. Adrian takes my hand and we walk into the dawn, admiring the stunning sky scene as the light arrives overhead. "Let's drive further up—there's a great view from the pull-in a couple of bends up the road." Adrian is uneasy about lingering so near our Mountain driveway and to be honest, so am I.

Ah—this feels easier. The volcanic view is indeed spectacular. I produce the thermos of tea along with two pottery mugs. A warm beverage will soon restore us. Adrian kisses me gently—indicating that he hasn't moved away. We chat about his weekend; how he has decided that he belongs on the land more than he does in the classroom. "I have discovered a paddock and small orchard right next door to Vonny's house; I have spoken to the neighbour—he is happy for us to incorporate the land into the Community Farm; how cool is that? I'm really excited about the Community Shareholder's scheme too." Eventually we move on to the most pressing subject—our relationship. Adrian admits to his frustration over our situation; "sometimes I feel bold, but I am often scared. It must come to a head soon, surely? Vonny sees it all too clearly. *'Just get on with it,'* she advises. Hmm—I want to be present to The Laird—to his plight; his hurt." "I keep upsetting him," I say. "We still share family warmth. I feel calm about you and me though, even though I have no idea where we are being led. Something is unfolding. Yesterday I told him that I didn't feel he respected and honoured me in our marriage, so it wasn't just me breaking vows. He agreed that I had a point there; his bullying tone and derogatory remarks about female ways appear jokey but they are too regular and pointed to be superficial. He is rude about the alternative world I embrace too; *'all that mumbo jumbo you believe,'* he often snarls."

Adrian takes my hand again and we turn the conversation to our writing and the emerging storyline with The Boat as a central subject. Should we introduce Pirates? Or Monsters—or a Quest? "We need a cohesive plan," we agree. No author sets out without some idea of the storyline—or do they? "Perhaps Big J. and The Laird could become involved," we joke; "they could threaten The Boat's passage—or something."

Our perfect hour is over. Adrian drops me at the end of the drive before reversing and continuing to the farm at the very top of the road. The farmer is loading his trailer with hay at **7**.30. I crunch my way home. The Bog-Brush is overjoyed to see me! The Laird wakes up and comes downstairs in his underpants; his pale skin at odds with the wooden interior. "I'll try ringing Hampshire again," he announces. "I need to have one more conversation with the Headmaster before we send Cedric back there to school." Unfortunately he doesn't make contact. The time difference is always a problem.

A.m. Mouse: *The Angels' gifted time—short but lovely, despite their slight unease with the furtive nature of the meeting. How blessed to hold hands in the moonlight—his gentle lips brushing hers—their attention alert to the possible presence of eyes in the surrounding Bush. "Let's be bold, My Lady," he declared with confidence. "Better face them with loaded cannons and flag flying, our swords to the ready."*

Returning to the Marina all is well. The Harbour Master just awake and awaiting his cup of tea; all smiles and loving warmth. She cares for him— they are Earth Mates—very different to the Soul Mate connection shared by Lord Swallow and his Lady Thumbelina who dare to sail the wild seas. And now the presence of Pirates and Monsters! Whatever next? Those beings who serve the darkness. They lurk in unexpected places, hungry—climbing into the minds of the innocent. The crew takes up its warrior stance, realizing the force of that darkness that would corrupt them and their loved ones; those who travel this Earthly Path with them. They were ever fellow-folk-at-arms. They follow the banner of St. Michael; his is the flag they fly. The new course is set. They must re-launch The Boat, their quest becoming clear. Loving you—

Adrian: *Talked farming with a lovely guy called Gerry; laughter—tractor ride up ridiculously step hills—biodynamics—soil fertility—pasture management— cow horns.*

Oho—here we go. Such a blessing; a step of courage without trouble—a sign of approval? Tentative steps becoming stronger. Just made a quick stop to our Guardian Angel, Cordelia—checking if it was her who gave me the lovely, organic thank you gift that I found on the doorstep when I got home. And no—it was not from her. Sore belly—the price of baking indulgence yesterday.

Mouse: *Hello there, Oh Farming Prince of mine. How are you doing? I am heading back home from town. Rinky has Lucia with her. Just left The Laird at College. Time to cook and craft and write. The Go-Getter is busy making felted animals at the moment—lovely enthusiasm. Contagious? With you—X*

Adrian: Hay stored away. Off to see an orange pack-house with samples of the neighbour's mandarin crop. A bit weary now. Late night, early morning. Better pay attention to my driving—X

P.m. Mouse: Bay number **7** at Pillans Beach Holiday Resort all booked, for the whole of Saturday. I'll get there at 6.30 tomorrow morning. I have only paid for one, so it might be best for you to park at the beach and walk along the shore; same place as last time. Nice to be by the water at **7.07**a.m if possible. Join me there, My Friend. Can you bring your laptop? I'll bring food and cosy duvet etc. How did the mandarins measure up? Hope you get a kip, and an early night. Lots of love—your Little Mousewife—X

It pours with rain all day; tipping torrents. The children and I craft, cook, clean and generally mooch about. Things seem to be happening. We have people coming to view The Mountain section tomorrow. Let's hope they are interested and put in an offer.

P.m. Mouse: Goodness me—if it's as wet as this tomorrow we will have to stay in bed all day, writing! Yum. Hmm—yum—X

Adrian: For the fields he heads once more—encased in plastic—awkward strides hindered by the unfamiliar weight—a full belly of slow-cooked lamb chops. Blessings to you, little one who gave your life for our pleasure and comfort. And how will his girls be? No shelter in this field. They are waiting by the gate, glad for a break in their day. He will give them some hay soaked in molasses; they like that.

Mouse: Go gently amongst the soggy fields and rain-battering weather, My Friend. We are full of craft and contentment, although the piggy is shouting at the door for food and attention. I don't blame her really, 'tis wild on The Mountain this evening. Your Lady is tired; time for an evening kip—

I sleep early. The Laird is cross about me leaving the family tomorrow, although he has given his permission. "You will have to take the dog if you are taking the van," he decrees. He was positive about me having some space; why the change of tone?

Chapter 4 Space

Saturday 7th July 2007

The Laird has reverted to the kinder man I know this morning. He comes to kiss me goodbye in the bathroom. "Have a good time," he says. "You deserve all the pleasure you can get. We'll keep the dog here," he adds, holding me close. I am touched, especially as he suspects I might see Adrian.

*Early A.m. Adrian: Awake before the 5a.m. alarm. Listing the tasks that lie before him—the paving stones to lay a sound pathway for the coming term—he feels the mounting pressure already; almost impossible to attend to all. Judicious pruning may be needed—clearing ballast from The Boat; enlightening her. What will he realistically be able to achieve? Laying this aside he looks to the day; this day put aside for work of a different nature. A day at the forge—the anvil of creativity, or perhaps the sculptor's table—the painter's easel—the jeweler's desk—the writer's laptop. A day of crafting and connection, beating and working the copper into the finest filigree, carving and shaping the wood into smooth and satisfying form, searching the heart and the eyes and the ear for beauty, truth and goodness. Time marches steadily on, the potent hour of **7** drawing near. What will be held in this 12 hour block? What ferment will occur——?*

Mouse: She has been up since 4.30 a.m, The Laird rising a few minutes later, kissing her goodbye and saying; 'have fun—whatever you are going to do—have a lovely day. You deserve some pleasure.' She held him close; no need to say more. Prospective buyers are looking at the property this afternoon. He has a house full of busy children. She blesses him.

So—My Lord Swallow, the day is ours and I am shortly to leave The Mountain.

I drive carefully to Pillans Beach, anxious to savour every minute of this precious day. The Holiday Park gates are open; tall pines mark the turning like a group of expectant friends. The office assured me that they would be open early. It is dark and I take an incorrect turning, having to reverse between some holiday cabins at 6.30 a.m; not what I had planned, my reverse bleeper so noisy. Eventually I locate the beach front. My Swallow Man is already here and together we find Bay number **7**. He helps me park up and then takes my hand and leads me onto the dusky beach. "Let's have a walk and a prayer to bless our day; it's beautiful on the sand. I've already been paddling—the water's not too cold, but I underestimated a wave and soaked the bottom of my trousers."

We stroll away from the approaching dawn and then turn to walk back down the shore, facing the pink and purple streaks that are chasing away the night in a dramatic sunrise tableau. I smile wistfully, remembering the last sky show laid on for us as we made love on the private beach at Maketu last December—a sunset rather than a sunrise. I pray the omen is one of beginning rather than ending this time around.

Adrian recites a special prayer for the occasion; his own, I am sure:

Saturday 7th Day of the 7th Month in the 2007th Year After The Birth of The World's Saviour—Christ.

Oh Mighty Father, we stand mindful of Christ, mindful of the balance point between the forces of materialism that would chain us to the earth, and temptation that would lead us into the passions.

Strengthen us that we may stand strong, steady and steadfast between these pulls, honouring this gift of time that has been granted us. Before us stands the day; a day of healing and rejuvenation, creativity and sharing. May we be inspired to use this time honourably, producing something of value that adds to the light and love so strongly needed on The Earth, and for her Peoples. May this be a turning point; this potent day, from which we re-enter The World with renewed strength, clarity and hope.

Awe, reverence and gratitude be fostered within us so that our work flourishes. Blaze oh Sun, to kindle our fire of sacrifice; the inner flame that consumes not, but holds us to selfless service. Warm us, oh Sun, to awaken the slumbering compassion, the flickering hope and the tender joy into conviction and courage. Shine oh Sun, to enlighten our clear thinking. Ray it through with spiritual seeing; shaft it with inspiration, intuition and imagination.

Amen.

We watch the sunrise from the shelter of a cosy sand dune, close and together at last. I find a shell—and a feather—and him. This is perfect. "Look what I found stuck to my jumper just before you arrived;" Adrian puts his hand in his pocket, pulling out a small piece of copper wrapped carefully in a handkerchief. "I laughed out loud when I saw it. I held a class in the woodwork shed at the end of term, bashing pieces of copper into shape; funny that this piece attached itself to me." I take the tiny piece realizing that it looks just like—"a SEAHORSE!" Adrian exclaims, laughing again; "yes—it really is a tiny seahorse. How strange is that? I can't believe all the wonderful things that keep happening. *'Basher the Seahorse'* symbolizing The Earth, as well as Fire and Water; an advanced being. Definitely one for The Book," he adds; "better include him in the story. Copper seems to be our metal; seahorse a nice link

310

with the ocean. Angel blessed moments—how I adore our quiet times too. Do you know how much I admire you? Your intelligence, your efficiency and your steady standing. I like the way you dress; natural but sexy. Come on, let's go back to your van; I need to get out of these wet clothes." Adrian pulls me to my feet, adding; "I have to tell you that I'm feeling very aroused."

The camp ground is quiet; we don't see anyone and slide open the door quietly, climbing into the vehicle unseen. "Can you write down the prayer while I make up the bed?" I ask, wrestling with the awkward but adequate double bed arrangement. I have brought a couple of cardboard boxes to fill the unavoidable gaps, although I should have brought three. Never mind—I don't think we are going to be thinking about the bed's comfort. Adrian sits on the van's step, writing, while I play the role of Mrs Mousewife. Pillows and duvet complete the scene and I close the curtains before inviting my Swallow Man to join me. I bend to kiss him as he climbs into our boudoir and he returns the favour, loving me for a lingering, beautiful moment.

As Lovers reunited he is quick to strip off his clothes, surprising me with an urgency I haven't seen before. He is indeed aroused, removing my garments with the same speed and pulling me close in our cosy nest. And then he caresses every inch of me as we make love at long last. Words fail me at this point—kissing—loving—tenderness and passion combined as we bite into the forbidden fruit and allow the sweet juice to run down our chins. He enters my soft secret like a master returning home after a voyage at sea; relieved, hungry and—mine. We make love twice in a row, not minding the slight risk of the already present potency as he enters me a second time. I am protected. He is insatiably aroused and moves with deep, penetrating thrusts, arching high above me and gasping passionately as he releases again and again. My Angel Man is magnificent; his impressive virility takes my breath away and I am held entranced—pierced and spellbound as the Rainbows shatter and reform in tumultuous tumble. This is a new side to Lord Swallow. He claims me as his; powerful, undeniable and utterly glorious.

'What on earth have I done to deserve him?' I ask myself the familiar question; 'here I am again—under yet another stunning sky—on a beach one only ever dreams about—with my Soul Mate; the most beautiful Angel Man who claims me with mighty strength, coupling with me like I have never been coupled with before.'

"I love you—so much," Adrian fixes me with his kind eyes, smiling his entrancing smile that I can never resist. "I stand ready to accept any result of my actions. Oh, My Darling—My Little One." Our passion is instantly reignited as we admire and stroke the bare limbs that are curled about each other, laughing when we can't tell what belongs to whom, so happy to be properly together at last. And then he is inside me again, although he withdraws after a while, regretting his lustful energy. We haven't stopped to be silent and sacred. "I miss that; I'm sorry," he apologizes. "I can't find the words for the grace I want to say. Perhaps I should go and milk the cows, and come back when I am more centred." "Why don't you go for a run along the beach instead?" I suggest, anxious to keep him beside me for as long as possible.

So he takes my advice and leaves the van for a while, coming back after fifteen minutes feeling clearer.

"Let's vow to find the sacred first—next time, eh?" I am happy to agree, although our hungry lovemaking was fabulous and different. Variety is the spice of life, and all that, but I don't confuse the intention by saying so. Having an aroused, bare-chested Angel bearing down on me time and again is more than this struggling housewife can possibly hope for—especially as I have been starved of physical company and happiness for such a long time. And to be so deeply in love—well—

"How long is it since we last made love?" We aren't sure, but counting on our fingers we reach the answer at the same time; December to July; **7** months—of course. I reckon The Angels are having the best game ever. These repeating coincidences are bizarre and so exciting. "Better make sure we are making love at **7.07** p.m. as well as **7.07** a.m." I laugh. And then we are serious—what is our strong connection all about? The birth of Little Arthur? Or the birth of The Book? Are they one and the same? And if so, why?

I open my laptop and read aloud the now complete ending of our first story; 'The Celestial Sea'. "I adore it," Adrian announces, amazed that anyone can love him that much. "Oh, My Darling, moving with you is so easy—and natural." He closes his eyes to fully appreciate the moment. "Our very own love story, eh? One that we are still writing. I shall have to make love to you again—right now—for the next chapter!" He rolls over, pulling me under him once more. We are in Heaven, moving in our personal Rhythmic Dance that has a fluent grace all of its own, something I can't find words to describe as we lie entwined, eating each other by the spoonful—lips and fingers, Rainbows and velvet. He enters me again and again until the sun is high in the sky and we hear children playing outside the camp ground washrooms. And then we sleep, exhausted and blessed, most definitely.

* * * * * * *

After a basic picnic we wander down to the shore at midday, happy to pretend we have our lives ahead of us rather than a handful of hours at most. I collect some driftwood and a number of shells that are similar to the milk-white Pipi, but with a blue line around the outer rim. They remind me of the veils worn by Mother Theresa's Nuns in Calcutta. We lie in the sand dunes, looking up at the sky and talking about our story and the possible Quest. Are we writing a tale of Light over darkness—perhaps as the story progresses? We have no idea what is coming, but to maintain the record appears important. Does the story have karmic echoes with Arthur, Guinevere and Lancelot? Arthur returns to the modern world through a current medium; a mystical story heralding the birth of a new order. Perhaps the four elements will be brought into perfect harmony by the end. The Boat embraces air and water; the Coral Dragon Spy and the Copper Seahorse could represent the Fire and the Earth.

"Let's bring both newcomers into the plot," I suggest; "strange that they have appeared recently. The Seahorse is considered a type of Sea Dragon by the Chinese. Dragons are synonymous with Saint Michael and his mighty fight. Perhaps the friendly element of our story Dragons is important; a contradiction to the regular tale of evil—or do they deceive us? Perhaps The Celestial Sea heralds the cutting edge of a new era, where the present moral code is replaced by a higher form of Unconditional Love and bonding; where our Love is accepted." Adrian is thoughtful as he considers my words, adding quietly; "Little Arthur isn't so present in this Book, is he? We know he is there, but will the reader? Should we go back and add him in—or is it better that he comes and goes naturally; sometimes present, sometimes dormant?" "Let's record it as it is," I suggest. "That's what we have been doing so far."

I stroke my Lover's brow and run my fingers through his hair. "I love you so much," I tell him. "I admire your noble bearing and your powerful Spirit that dominates mine, no matter how many times you fall off your throne." We lie quietly together, savouring every moment of our precious bond. The **7** month wait has been a trial, and this day-trip only a small window of respite. We wonder if we would be compatible in real life; "I might become grouchy and horrid," Adrian sighs. "I wouldn't want that." We consider the pressures of a regular life; money, marriage, children, careers etc. Just talking about it makes Adrian gloomy; "there mightn't be any way forward for us," he says. "I can lose the magic at times."

We saunter back to the van for a spell of writing before our precious day ends. The mythology of The Boat begins to take shape, but we are slow with our creativity. Adrian is anxious that the mystical element sounds contrived beside the regular. "I don't feel the flow right now." We only spend an hour with our laptops. We don't make love again, but the kissing? That is our favourite magic and we lie together for ages, just being with each other. "Lovemaking without the sacred unbalances me," he admits.

It is dark by the time we leave the camp ground, delivering back the electric cable we borrowed. We kiss goodbye and climb into our separate vehicles. "I wish it didn't have to be this way," My Swallow Man vents his frustration. "Argg————-"

* * * * * * *

P.m. Mouse: She steers The Boat safely back into her new mooring— judging the angles correctly, the gentle purr of the motor helping the tricky manoeuvres; slow, deliberate and successful. She wishes her Lover was beside her, to take the helm and secure her safely, but he had to disembark further up the coast. The cows need milking. Anyway, she is expected back at The Castle. All is calm on her arrival; The Laird easy and accepting. "What did you do today?" He asks. "Did you see anyone?" She tells him of their creative work together—"yes, Adrian came over for a while, to work on the passages he has written." Her generous husband appears accepting, commenting later; "well, I suppose I am both sad and happy at the same time; happy that you have found some pleasure today, but sad that I cannot give you that *enjoyment."* She blesses him and gives him a lovely hug. *"We can have a day out next,"* she mollifies him. *"We can learn to enjoy ourselves too."* *"Hmm— maybe,"* he replies, unsure. The tranquil home atmosphere is lovely, and so different. Or perhaps it is the glorious warmth filling her every cell after such intimacy with the man she loves. Just thinking of him arouses her relentless passion; he is so strong inside her. She feels him deep in her secret still, the memory of his wrapping inside and outside her person intoxicating and fluent. Exquisite.

She sends him deep blessing—hoping he is restored and refuelled after their long wait—X

Adrian: *Hello Friend, nice to hear that all is well—indeed, blessed. I'm now tucked up, reading up on Biodynamics. Cows were already in their stalls; easy milking. Feeling very warm; fulfilled and easy after our connection— lovely—rich memories—thank you. Sleep well—Angel Woman—X*

Late P.m. Mouse: *He lays his head upon her breast—she encircles him with loving limbs—they kiss—and kiss—and smile—and smile, hardly enough of themselves to share between each other. Their time in Berth no.**7** on this **7**th of the **7**th **2007**—they knew this day would be important—'and how many months since we last sailed?' They have lost count. '**7**—of course the answer is **7**. No need to ask why.' She loves him. They are perfecting the art of achieving 'The Knife-Edged Keel.'*

Calm Waters lie ahead—My Angel Man. X

And therein lies the truth; we are each other's Angel. Is it too much to meet one's Angel on Earth? And if so, how can one ever move on from such a powerful and glorious bonding? I sigh, closing the chapter. Lord Swallow and I are reunited, my family is peaceful and I am complete. I suppose this Book is done.

* * * * * * *
* * * *

P.s. Adrian: {*For The Book*} *Part Two; The Craftsman finishes his inspection of the emerging vessel and leans back, satisfied——*

'Take the helm, The Truth is hidden, Scattered **7**'s; knots to Heaven. Why the mystery? Strange affair; peculiar font change, secret flare. Copper symbol, orange pick, clues in letters; Angel trick. Rig the sails and make a note, The Treasure can be found afloat.'

Lightning Source UK Ltd.
Milton Keynes UK
UKOW03f0048070117

291531UK00004B/101/P